SCOTTISH MYTHS AND LEGENDS

SCOTTISH MYTHS AND LEGENDS

Selected by
ROSEMARY GRAY

Of brownyis and of bogillis full is this buke.
GAWIN DOUGLAS

LOMOND BOOKS
Broxburn

This edition published by Lomond Books Ltd
Broxburn EH52 5NF, Scotland 2016
www.lomondbooks.com

ISBN 978 1 84204 253 3

Typeset in Great Britain by Antony Gray

Printed and bound in Great Britain by Clays Ltd, Elcograf S.p.A.

Contents

SCOTTISH MYTHS AND LEGENDS

Beira, Queen of Winter

Dark Beira was the mother of all the gods and goddesses in Scotland. She was of great height and very old, and everyone feared her. When roused to anger she was as fierce as the biting north wind and harsh as the tempest-stricken sea. Each winter she reigned as Queen of the Four Red Divisions of the World, and none disputed her sway. But when the sweet spring season drew nigh, her subjects began to rebel against her and to long for the coming of the Summer King, Angus of the White Steed, and Bride, his beautiful queen, who were loved by all, for they were the bringers of plenty and of bright and happy days. It enraged Beira greatly to find her power passing away, and she tried her utmost to prolong the winter season by raising spring storms and sending blighting frost to kill early flowers and keep the grass from growing.

Beira lived for hundreds and hundreds of years. The reason she did not die of old age was because, at the beginning of every spring, she drank the magic waters of the Well of Youth which bubbles up in the Green Island of the West. This was a floating island where summer was the only season, and the trees were always bright with blossom and laden with fruit. It drifted about on the silver tides of the blue Atlantic, and sometimes appeared off the western coasts of Ireland and sometimes close to the Hebrides. Many bold mariners have steered their galleys up and down the ocean, searching for Green Island in vain. On a calm morning they might sail past its shores and yet never know it was near at hand, for oft-times it lay hidden in a twinkling mist. Men have caught glimpses of it from the shore, but while they gazed on its beauties with eyes of wonder, it vanished suddenly from sight by sinking beneath the waves like the setting sun. Beira, however, always knew where to find Green Island when the time came for her to visit it.

The waters of the Well of Youth are most potent when the days begin to grow longer, and most potent of all on the first of the lengthening days of spring. Beira always visited the island on the night before the first lengthening day – that is, on the last night of her reign as Queen of Winter. All alone in the darkness she sat beside the Well of Youth, waiting for the dawn. When the first faint beam of light appeared in the eastern sky, she drank the water as it bubbled fresh from a crevice in the rock. It was necessary that she should drink of this magic water before any bird visited the well and before any dog barked. If a bird drank first, or a dog barked ere she began to drink, dark old Beira would crumble into dust.

As soon as Beira tasted the magic water, in silence and alone, she began to grow young again. She left the island and, returning to Scotland, fell into a magic sleep. When, at length, she awoke, in bright sunshine, she rose up as a beautiful girl with long hair yellow as buds of broom, cheeks red as rowan berries and blue eyes that sparkled like the summer sea in sunshine. Then she went to and fro through Scotland, clad in a robe of green and crowned with a chaplet of bright flowers of many hues. No fairer goddess was to be found in all the land, save Bride, the peerless Queen of Summer.

As each month went past, however, Beira aged quickly. She reached full womanhood in midsummer, and when autumn came on her brows wrinkled and her beauty began to fade. When the season of winter returned once again, she became an old and withered hag, and began to reign as the fierce Queen Beira.

Often on stormy nights in early winter she wandered about, singing this sorrowful song:

'O life that ebbs like the sea!
    I am weary and old, I am weary and old –
Oh! how can I happy be
    All alone in the dark and the cold.

I'm the old Beira again,
    My mantle no longer is green,
I think of my beauty with pain
    And the days when another was queen.

My arms are withered and thin,
    My hair once golden is grey;
'Tis winter – my reign doth begin –
    Youth's summer has faded away.

> Youth's summer and autumn have fled –
>   I am weary and old, I am weary and old.
> Every flower must fade and fall dead
>   When the winds blow cold, when the winds blow cold.'

The aged Beira was fearsome to look upon. She had only one eye, but the sight of it was keen and sharp as ice and as swift as the mackerel of the ocean. Her complexion was a dull, dark blue, and this is how she sang about it:

> 'Why is my face so dark, so dark?
>   So dark, oho! so dark, ohee!
> Out in all weathers I wander alone
>   In the mire, in the cold, ah me!'

Her teeth were red as rust, and her locks, which lay heavily on her shoulders, were white as an aspen covered with hoar frost. On her head she wore a spotted mutch [a woman's cap]. All her clothing was grey, and she was never seen without her great dun-coloured shawl, which was drawn closely round her shoulders.

It is told that in the days when the world was young Beira saw land where there is now water and water where there is now land.

Once a wizard spoke to her and said: 'Tell me your age, O sharp old woman.'

Beira answered: 'I have long ceased to count the years. But I shall tell you what I have seen. Yonder is the seal-haunted rock of Skerryvore in the midst of the sea. I remember when it was a mountain surrounded by fields. I saw the fields ploughed, and the barley that grew upon them was sharp and juicy. Yonder is a loch. I remember when it was a small round well. In those days I was a fair young girl, and now I am very old and frail and dark and miserable.'

It is told also that Beira let loose many rivers and formed many lochs, sometimes willingly and sometimes against her will, and that she also shaped many bens and glens. All the hills in Ross-shire are said to have been made by Beira.

There was once a well on Ben Cruachan, in Argyll, from which Beira drew water daily. Each morning at sunrise she lifted off the slab that covered it, and each evening at sunset she laid it over the well again. It happened that one evening she forgot to cover the well. Then the proper order of things was disturbed. As soon as the sun went down the water rose in great volume and streamed down the mountainside, roaring like a tempest-swollen sea. When day dawned, Beira found that the valley beneath was filled with water. It was in this way that Loch Awe came to be.

Beira had another well in Inverness-shire which had to be kept covered in like manner from sunset till sunrise. One of her maids, whose name was Nessa, had charge of the well. It happened that one evening the maid was late in going to the well to cover it. When she drew near she beheld the water flowing so fast from it that she turned away and ran for her life. Beira watched her from the top of Ben Nevis, which was her mountain throne, and cried: 'You have neglected your duty. Now you will run for ever and never leave water.'

The maiden was at once changed into a river, and the loch and the river which runs from it towards the sea were named after her. That is why the loch is called Loch Ness and the river the River Ness.

Once a year, when the night on which she was transformed comes round, Ness (Nessa) arises out of the river in her girl form, and sings a sad sweet song in the pale moonlight. It is said that her voice is clearer and more beautiful than that of any bird, and her music more melodious than the golden harps and silvern pipes of fairyland.

In the days when rivers broke loose and lochs were made, Beira set herself to build the mountains of Scotland. When at work she carried on her back a great creel filled with rocks and earth. Sometimes as she leapt from hill to hill her creel tilted sideways, and rocks and earth fell from it into lochs and formed islands. Many islands are spoken of as 'spillings from the creel of the big old woman'.

Beira had eight hags who were her servants. They also carried creels, and one after the other they emptied out their creels until a mountain was piled up nigh to the clouds.

One of the reasons why Beira made the mountains was to use them as stepping stones; another was to provide houses for her giant sons. Many of her sons were very quarrelsome; they fought continually one against another. To punish those of them who disobeyed her, Beira shut the offenders up in mountain houses, and from these they could not escape without her permission. But this did not keep them from fighting. Every morning they climbed to the tops of their mountain houses and threw great boulders at one another. That is why so many big grey boulders now lie on steep slopes and are scattered through the valleys. Other giant sons of Beira dwelt in deep caves. Some were horned like deer, and others had many heads. So strong were they that they could pick up cattle and, throwing them over their shoulders, carry them away to roast them for their meals. Each giant son of Beira was called a Fooar.

It was Beira who built Ben Wyvis. She found it a hard task, for she had to do all the work alone, her hag servants being busy elsewhere. One day, when she had grown very weary, she stumbled and upset her creel. All the rocks and earth it contained fell out in a heap, and formed the mountain which is called Little Wyvis.

The only tool that Beira used was a magic hammer. When she struck it lightly on the ground the soil became as hard as iron; when she struck it heavily on the ground a valley was formed. After she had built up a mountain, she gave it its special form by splintering the rocks with her hammer. If she had made all the hills of the same shape, she would not have been able to recognise one from another.

After the mountains were all formed, Beira took great delight in wandering between them and over them. She was always followed by wild animals. The foxes barked with delight when they beheld her, wolves howled to greet her and eagles shrieked with joy in mid-air. Beira had great herds and flocks to which she gave her protection – nimble-footed deer, high-horned cattle, shaggy grey goats, black swine and sheep that had snow-white fleeces. She charmed her deer against the huntsmen, and when she visited a deer forest she helped them to escape from the hunters. During early winter she milked the hinds on the tops of mountains, but when the winds rose so high that the froth was blown from the milking pails, she drove the hinds down to the valleys. The froth was frozen on the crests of high hills, and lay there snow-white and beautiful. When the winter torrents began to pour down the mountainsides, leaping from ledge to ledge, the people said: 'Beira is milking her shaggy goats, and streams of milk are pouring down over high rocks.'

Beira washed her great shawl in the sea, for there was no lake big enough for the purpose. The part she chose for her washing is the strait between the western islands of Jura and Scarba. Beira's 'washing-pot' is the whirlpool, there called Corrybreckan. It was so named because the son of a Scottish king, named Breckan, was drowned in it, his boat having been upset by the waves raised by Beira.

Three days before the Queen of Winter began her work, her hag servants made ready the water for her, and the Corry could then be heard snorting and fuming for twenty miles around. On the fourth day Beira threw her shawl into the whirlpool, and tramped it with her feet until the edge of the Corry overflowed with foam. When she had finished her washing she laid her shawl on the mountains to dry, and as soon as she lifted it up, all the mountains of Scotland were white with snow to signify that the great Queen had begun her reign.

Now, the meaning of this story is that Beira is the spirit of winter. She grows older and fiercer as the weeks go past, until at length her strength is spent. Then she renews her youth, so that she may live through the summer and autumn and begin to reign once again. The ancient people of Scotland saw that during early winter torrents poured down from the hills, and in this Beira fable they expressed their belief that the torrents were let loose by the Winter Queen, and that the lochs were, at the beginning, formed by the torrents that sprang from magic wells. They saw great boulders lying on hillsides and in valleys, and accounted for their presence in these places by telling how they were flung from mountain tops by the giant sons of Beira.

In the next chapter the story will be told of the coming of Angus and Bride, the King and Queen of Summer and Plenty, and of the stormy conflicts waged during the closing weeks of winter and the early weeks of spring between Beira and Angus-the-Ever-Young, who comes from the fabled Green Isle of the West the land of eternal summer and perpetual youth.

The Coming of Angus and Bride

All the long winter Beira kept captive a beautiful young princess named Bride. She was jealous of Bride's beauty, and gave her ragged clothing to wear, and put her to work among the servants in the kitchen of her mountain castle, where the girl had to perform the meanest tasks. Beira scolded her continually, finding fault with everything she did, and Bride's life was made very wretched.

One day Beira gave the princess a brown fleece and said: 'You must wash this fleece in the running stream until it is pure white.'

Bride took the fleece and went outside the castle, and began to wash it in a pool below a waterfall. All day long she laboured at the work, but to no purpose. She found it impossible to wash the brown colour out of the wool.

When evening came on, Beira scolded the girl, and said: 'You are a useless hussy. The fleece is as brown as when I gave it to you.'

Bride protested: 'All day long have I washed it in the pool below the waterfall of the Red Rock.'

'Tomorrow you shall wash it again,' Beira said; 'and if you do not wash it white, you will go on washing on the next day, and on every day after that. Now, begone! and do as I bid you.'

It was a sorrowful time for Bride. Day after day she washed the fleece, and it seemed to her that if she went on washing until the world came to an end, the brown wool would never become white.

One morning as she went on with her washing a grey-bearded old man came near. He took pity on the princess, who wept bitter tears over her work, and spoke to her, saying: 'Who are you, and why do you sorrow?'

The princess replied: 'My name is Bride. I am the captive of Queen Beira, and she has ordered me to wash this brown fleece until it is white. Alas! it cannot be done.'

'I am sorry for you,' the old man said.

'Who are you, and where do you come from?' asked Bride.

'My name is Father Winter,' the old man told her. 'Give me the fleece, and I shall make it white for you.'

Bride gave Father Winter the brown fleece, and when he had shaken it three times it turned white as snow.

The heart of Bride was immediately filled with joy, and she exclaimed: 'Dear Father Winter, you are very kind. You have saved me much labour and taken away my sorrow.'

Father Winter handed back the fleece to Princess Bride with one hand, and she took it. Then he said: 'Take also what I hold in my other hand.' As he spoke he gave her a bunch of pure white snowdrops. The eyes of Bride sparkled with joy to behold them.

Said Father Winter: 'If Beira scolds you, give her these flowers, and if she asks where you found them, tell her that they came from the green rustling fir woods. Tell her also that the cress is springing up on the banks of streams, and that the new grass has begun to shoot up in the fields.'

Having spoken thus, Father Winter bade the princess farewell and turned away.

Bride returned to the mountain castle and laid the white fleece at Beira's feet. But the old queen scarcely looked at it. Her gaze was fixed on the snowdrops that Bride carried.

'Where did you find these flowers?' Beira asked with sudden anger.

Said Bride: 'The snowdrops are now growing in the green rustling fir woods, the cress is springing up on the banks of streams, and the new grass is beginning to shoot up in the fields.'

'Evil are the tidings you bring me!' Beira cried. 'Begone from my sight!'

Bride turned away, but not in sorrow. A new joy had entered her heart, for she knew that the wild winter season was going past, and that the reign of Queen Beira would soon come to an end.

Meanwhile Beira summoned her eight hag servants, and spoke to them, saying: 'Ride to the north and ride to the south, ride to the east and ride to the west, and I will ride forth also. Smite the world with frost and tempest, so that no flower may bloom and no grass blade survive. I am waging war against all growth.'

When she had spoken thus, the eight hags mounted on the backs of shaggy goats and rode forth to do her bidding. Beira went forth also, grasping in her right hand her black magic hammer. On the night of that very day a great tempest lashed the ocean to fury and brought terror to every corner of the land.

Now the reason why Beira kept Bride a prisoner was because her fairest and dearest son, whose name was Angus-the-Ever-Young, had fallen in love with her. He was called 'the Ever Young' because age never came near him, and all winter long he lived on the Green Isle of the West, which is also called the 'Land of Youth'.

Angus first beheld Bride in a dream, and when he awoke he spoke to the King of the Green Isle, saying: 'Last night I dreamed a dream and saw a beautiful princess whom I love. Tears fell from her eyes, and I spoke to an old man who stood near her, and said: "Why does the maiden weep?" Said the old man: "She weeps because she is kept captive by Beira, who treats her with great cruelty." I looked again at the princess and said: "Fain would I set her free." Then I awoke. Tell me, sire, who is this princess, and where shall I find her?'

The King of the Green Isle answered Angus, saying: 'The fair princess whom you saw is Bride, and in the days when you will be King of Summer she will be your queen. Of this your mother, Queen Beira, has full knowledge, and it is her wish to keep you away from Bride, so that her own reign may be prolonged. Tarry here, O Angus, until the flowers begin to bloom and the grass begins to grow, and then you shall set free the beautiful Princess Bride.'

Said Angus: 'Fain would I go forth at once to search for her.'

'February, the wolf-month, has now come,' the king said. 'Uncertain is the temper of the wolf.'

Said Angus: 'I shall cast a spell on the sea and a spell on the land, and borrow for February three days from August.'

He did as he said he would do. He borrowed three days from August, and the ocean slumbered peacefully while the sun shone brightly over mountain and glen. Then Angus mounted his white steed and rode eastward to Scotland over the Isles and over the Minch, and he reached the Grampians when dawn was breaking. He was clad in raiment of shining gold, and from his shoulders hung his royal robe of crimson which the wind uplifted and spread out in gleaming splendour athwart the sky.

An aged bard looked eastward, and when he beheld the fair Angus he lifted up his harp and sang a song of welcome, and the birds of the forest sang with him. And this is how he sang:

'Angus hath come – the young, the fair,
The blue-eyed god with golden hair –
The god who to the world doth bring
This morn the promise of the spring;
Who moves the birds to song ere yet
He hath awaked the violet,
Or the soft primrose on the steep,
While buds are laid in lidded sleep,
And white snows wrap the hills serene,
Ere glows the larch's vivid green
Through the brown woods and bare. All hail,
Angus! and may thy will prevail . . .
He comes . . . he goes . . . And far and wide
He searches for the Princess Bride.'

Up and down the land went Angus, but he could not find Bride anywhere. The fair princess beheld him in a dream, however, and knew that he longed to set her free. When she awoke she shed tears of joy, and on the place where her tears fell there sprang up violets, and they were blue as her beautiful eyes.

Beira was angry when she came to know that Angus was searching for Bride, and on the third evening of his visit she raised a great tempest which drove him back to Green Isle. But he returned again and again, and at length he discovered the castle in which the princess was kept a prisoner.

Then came a day when Angus met Bride in a forest near the castle. The violets were blooming and soft yellow primroses opened their eyes of wonder to gaze on the prince and the princess. When they spoke one to another the birds raised their sweet voices in song and the sun shone fair and bright.

Said Angus: 'Beautiful princess, I beheld you in a dream weeping tears of sorrow.'

Bride said: 'Mighty prince, I beheld you in a dream riding over bens and through glens in beauty and power.'

Said Angus: 'I have come to rescue you from Queen Beira, who has kept you all winter long in captivity.'

Bride said: 'To me this is a day of great joy.'

Said Angus: 'It will be a day of great joy to all mankind ever after!'

That is why the first day of spring – the day on which Angus found the princess – is called 'Bride's Day'.

Through the forest came a fair company of fairy ladies, who hailed Bride as queen and bade welcome to Angus. Then the Fairy Queen waved her wand, and Bride was transformed. As swiftly as the bright sun springs out from behind a dark cloud, shedding beauty all round, so swiftly did Bride appear in new splendour. Instead of ragged clothing, she now wore a white robe adorned with spangles of shining silver. Over her heart gleamed a starlike crystal, pure as her thoughts and bright as the joy that Angus brought her. This gem is called 'the guiding star of Bride'. Her golden-brown hair, which hung down to her waist in gleaming curls, was decked with fair spring flowers – snowdrops and daisies and primroses and violets. Blue were her eyes, and her face had the redness and whiteness of the wild rose of peerless beauty and tender grace. In her right hand she carried a white wand entwined with golden cornstalks, and in her left a golden horn which is called the 'Horn of Plenty'.

The linnet was the first forest bird that hailed Bride in her beauty, and the Fairy Queen said: 'Ever after this you shall be called the "Bird of Bride".' On the seashore the first bird that chirped with joy was the oystercatcher, and the Fairy Queen said: 'Ever after this you shall be called the "Page of Bride".'

Then the Fairy Queen led Angus and Bride to her green-roofed underground palace in the midst of the forest. As they went forward they came to a river which was covered with ice. Bride put her fingers on the ice, and the Ice Hag shrieked and fled.

A great feast was held in the palace of the Fairy Queen, and it was the marriage feast of Bride, for Angus and she were wed. The fairies danced and sang with joy, and all the world was moved to dance and sing with them. This was how the first 'Festival of Bride' came to be.

'Spring has come!' the shepherds cried; and they drove their flocks on to the moors, where they were counted and blessed.

'Spring has come!' chattered the raven, and flew off to find moss for her nest. The rook heard and followed after, and the wild duck rose from amidst the reeds, crying: 'Spring has come!'

Bride came forth from the fairy palace with Angus and waved her hand, while Angus repeated magic spells. Then greater growth was given to the grass, and all the world hailed Angus and Bride as king and queen. Although they were not beheld by mankind, yet their presence was everywhere felt throughout Scotland.

Beira was wroth when she came to know that Angus had found Bride. She seized her magic hammer and smote the ground unceasingly until it was frozen hard as iron again so hard that no herb or blade of grass could continue to live upon its surface. Terrible was her wrath when she beheld the grass growing. She knew well that when the grass flourished and Angus and Bride were married, her authority would pass away. It was her desire to keep her throne as long as possible.

'Bride is married, hail to Bride!' sang the birds. 'Angus is married, hail to Angus!'

Beira heard the songs of the birds, and called to her hag servants: 'Ride north and ride south, ride east and ride west, and wage war against Angus. I shall ride forth also.'

Her servants mounted their shaggy goats and rode forth to do her bidding. Beira mounted a black steed and set out in pursuit of Angus. She rode fast and she rode hard. Black clouds swept over the sky as she rode on, until at length she came to the forest in which the Fairy Queen had her dwelling. All the fairies fled in terror into their green mound and the doors were shut. Angus looked up and beheld Beira drawing nigh. He leapt on the back of his white steed, and lifted his young bride into the saddle in front of him and fled away with her.

Aneus rode westward over the hills and over the valleys and over the sea, and Beira pursued him.

There is a rocky ravine on the island of Tiree, and Beira's black steed jumped across it while pursuing the white steed of Angus. The hoofs of the black steed made a gash on the rocks. To this day the ravine is called 'The Horse's Leap'.

Angus escaped to the Green Isle of the West, and there he passed happy days with Bride. But he longed to return to Scotland and reign as King of Summer. Again and again he crossed the sea; and each time he reached the land of glens and bens, the sun broke forth in brightness and the birds sang merrily to welcome him.

Beira raised storm after storm to drive him away. First she called on the wind named 'The Whistle', which blew high and shrill, and brought down rapid showers of cold hailstones. It lasted for three days, and there was much sorrow and bitterness throughout the length and breadth of Scotland. Sheep and lambs were killed on the moors, and horses and cows perished also.

Angus fled, but he returned soon again. The next wind that Beira raised to prolong her winter reign was the 'Sharp-Billed Wind' which is called 'Gobag'. It lasted for nine days, and all the land was pierced by it, for it pecked and bit in every nook and cranny like a sharp-billed bird.

Angus returned, and Beira raised the eddy wind which is called 'The Sweeper'. Its whirling gusts tore branches from the budding trees and bright flowers from their stalks. All the time it blew, Beira kept beating the ground with her magic hammer so as to keep the grass from growing. But her efforts were in vain. Spring smiled in beauty all around, and each time she turned away, wearied by her efforts, the sun sprang forth in splendour. The small modest primroses opened their petals in the sunshine, looking forth from cosy nooks that the wind, called 'Sweeper', was unable to reach. Angus fled, but he soon returned again.

Beira was not yet, however, entirely without hope. Her efforts had brought disaster to mankind, and the 'Weeks of Leanness' came on. Food became scarce. The fishermen were unable to venture to sea on account of Beira's tempests, and could get no fish. In the night-time Beira and her hags entered the dwellings of mankind, and stole away their stores of food. It was, indeed, a sorrowful time.

Angus was moved with pity for mankind, and tried to fight the hags of Beira. But the fierce queen raised the 'Gales of Complaint' to keep him away, and they raged in fury until the first week of March. Horses and cattle died for want of food, because the fierce winds blew down stacks of fodder and scattered them over the lochs and the ocean.

Angus, however, waged a fierce struggle against the hag servants, and at length he drove them away to the north, where they fumed and fretted furiously.

Beira was greatly alarmed, and she made her last great effort to subdue the Powers of Spring. She waved her magic hammer, and smote the clouds with it. Northward she rode on her black steed, and gathered her servants together, and called to them, saying: 'Ride southward with me, all of you, and scatter our enemies before us.'

Out of the bleak dark north they rode in a single pack. With them came the Big Black Tempest. It seemed as if winter had returned in full strength and would abide for ever. But even Beira and her hags had to take rest. On a dusky evening they crouched down together on the side of a bare mountain, and, when they did so, a sudden calm fell upon the land and the sea.

'Ha! ha!' laughed the wild duck who hated the hag. 'Ha! ha! I am still alive, and so are my six ducklings.'

'Have patience! idle chatterer,' answered the Hag. 'I am not yet done.'

That night she borrowed three days from Winter which had not been used, for Angus had previously borrowed for Winter three days from August. The three spirits of the borrowed days were tempest spirits, and came towards Beira mounted on black hogs. She spoke to them, saying: 'Long have you been bound! Now I set you at liberty.'

One after another, on each of the three days that followed, the spirits went forth riding the black hogs. They brought snow and hail and fierce blasts of wind. Snow whitened the moors and filled the furrows of ploughed land, rivers rose in flood, and great trees were shattered and uprooted. The duck was killed, and so were her six ducklings; sheep and cattle perished, and many human beings were killed on land and drowned at sea. The days on which these things happened are called the 'Three Hog Days'.

Beira's reign was now drawing to a close. She found herself unable to resist any longer the power of the new life that was rising in every vein of the land. The weakness of extreme old age crept upon her, and she longed once again to drink of the waters of the Well of Youth. When, on a bright March morning, she beheld Angus riding over the hills on his white steed, scattering her fierce hag servants before him, she fled away in despair. Ere she went she threw her magic hammer beneath a holly tree, and that is the reason why no grass grows under holly trees.

Beira's black steed went northward with her in flight. As it leapt over Loch Etive it left the marks of its hoofs on the side of a rocky mountain, and the spot is named to this day 'Horseshoes'. She did not rein in her steed until she reached the island of Skye, where she found rest on the summit of the 'Old Wife's Ben' (Ben-e-Cail-lich) at Broadford. There she sat, gazing steadfastly across the sea, waiting until the day and night would be of equal length. All that equal day she wept tears of sorrow for her lost power, and when night came on she went westward over the sea to Green Island. At the dawn of the day that followed she drank the magic waters of the Well of Youth.

On that day which is of equal length with the night, Angus came to Scotland with Bride, and they were hailed as king and queen of the unseen beings. They rode from south to north in the morning and forenoon, and from north to south in the afternoon and evening. A gentle wind went with them, blowing towards the north from dawn till midday, and towards the south from midday till sunset.

It was on that day that Bride dipped her fair white hands in the high rivers and lochs which still retained ice. When she did so, the Ice Hag fell into a deep sleep from which she could not awake until summer and autumn were over and past.

The grass grew quickly after Angus began to reign as king. Seeds were sown, and the people called on Bride to grant them a good harvest. Ere long the whole land was made beautiful with spring flowers of every hue.

Angus had a harp of gold with silver strings, and when he played on it, youths and maidens followed the sound of the music through the woods. Bards sang his praises and told that he kissed lovers, and that when they parted one from another to return to their homes, the kisses became invisible birds that hovered round their heads and sang sweet songs of love, and whispered memories dear. It was thus that one bard sang of him:

> 'When softly blew the south wind o'er the sea,
> Lisping of springtime hope and summer pride,
> And the rough reign of Beira ceased to be,
>   Angus the Ever-Young,
> The beauteous god of love, the golden-haired,
>   The blue mysterious-eyed,
> Shone like the star of morning high among
>   The stars that shrank afraid
> When dawn proclaimed the triumph that he shared
>   With Bride the peerless maid.
> Then winds of violet sweetness rose and sighed,
>   "No conquest is compared
> To love's transcendent joys that never fade." '

In the old days, when there was no calendar in Scotland, the people named the various periods of winter and spring, storm and calm. The story of the struggle between Angus and Beira is the story of the struggle between spring and winter, growth and decay, light and darkness, warmth and cold.

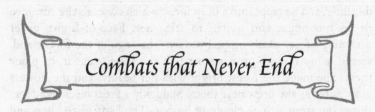

Combats that Never End

There are two mountains that overlook the Spey Valley, one to the east and one to the west, and a fairy king dwells on each of them. They are both sons of Beira. One fairy king is white, and has great fame as an archer; he has a silver bow and arrows of gold, and once a day he shoots an arrow across the strath. The other fairy king is black as the raven, and on his left breast there is a red spot. He has no weapon, but is yet terrible in battle, because he can make himself invisible at will. When he does so, nothing remains in sight except the red spot. He has great strength, and when he goes against his enemies he seizes them unawares and throws them to the ground. No matter how well they are armed, his enemies tremble when the invisible fairy comes against them. All they see is a red spot moving about in the air.

Now, the white fairy has a fair bride whose name is Face-of-Light. It is a great joy to her to wander among the mountains where herds of deer crop the green herbage, and through the strath where cornfields rustle in soft winds and fragrant flowers bloom fair to see. The black fairy has no bride, and is jealous of the white fairy because his days are filled with joy by the beauty of Face-of-Light. These two fairies have ever been enemies. The black fairy keeps out of sight of the famous archer, fearing his arrows of gold.

One summer evening when the twilight shadows were lengthening and deepening across the strath, Face of Light tripped merrily over the grassy banks, gathering wild flowers. Silence had fallen on the world; no bird sang and no wind whispered, the lochs were asleep, and the shrunken river made scarcely a sound louder than the sigh of a sleeping babe; it was no longer bright when Face-of-Light turned away from it.

The black fairy looked out from his mountain home. He knew that the white fairy had lain down to rest, and he watched Face-of-Light gathering wild flowers. Nearer and nearer she came to his dwelling, and he crept into a deep forest which conceals the entrance to his mountain, and waited to seize her. Face-of-Light, never dreaming of her peril, tripped towards the edge of the forest; and, seeing many flowers growing beneath the trees, went in to pluck them. She made the forest bright with her beauty, and the flowers grew fairer as she drew near them. Suddenly a great black hand was thrust out from a thick clump of bushes. The hand seized her, and she shrieked in terror and struggled to escape. The white fairy heard her cries, which pierced the air like the keen long whistle of the curlew, leapt up, and looked forth from his mountain top. In a moment he knew what had happened. Face-of-Light had been seized by his enemy, the black fairy, who was dragging her to a dark dungeon in the middle of his mountain. The white fairy was unable to come to her rescue for two reasons. Like his dark enemy, he could not pass the utmost limits of his mountain house, and having already shot a golden arrow that day, he could not shoot another until a new day had dawned.

Night came on, and the black fairy climbed to the top of his mountain, where he danced with joy because he had taken captive the bride of his enemy. The white fairy was stricken with sorrow, and when he heard the cries of Face-of-Light coming from the dungeon, he fell down in a swoon.

All night long Face-of-Light sobbed and wept, while the black fairy danced on the mountain top and sang songs of triumph. He danced so fast that he raised a wind which swept down the strath and shook the trees from sleep, so that they moaned and sighed all night long. The cries of Face-of-Light were heard by human beings, and those who were awakened said one to another: 'Listen to the hag of night. How terrible are her cries!'

Not until the dawn began to break did the white fairy recover from his swoon. Just when the first shaft of grey light pierced the eastern sky, he opened his eyes. Then he remembered his sorrow and wept softly. His tears fell as dew on the flowers and the grass.

Weeping, he climbed his mountain, and then wandered round about the crest of it. His heart was heavy for the loss of Face-of-Light, and when he listened he heard her moaning in her dark prison. The black fairy had ceased to dance. He stood upright on the highest point of his mountain fastness, and shouted to his enemy:

'Ha! Face-of-Light is my prisoner.' Then suddenly he was silent. He saw the white fairy stringing his silver bow and then drawing from his shining quiver a bright golden arrow.

'Ha!' cried the black fairy, 'would you dare shoot at me?'

'Set free Face-of-Light, or I shall shoot,' the white fairy made answer. His face was white as snow and hard as ice.

The black fairy laughed, and willed himself to become invisible, and then, just as the white fairy raised his bow to take aim, his enemy vanished from sight. No part of him could be seen but the great red spot on his left breast, which seemed to float in the air.

For a moment the white fairy, gazing eastward, looked with wonder at the red spot which grew brighter and brighter. His bow was bent, and his golden arrow was held ready for flight.

The sound of defiant laughter came down the wind as the black fairy, now invisible, danced with joy on his mountain top.

To and fro swayed the red spot, and the white fairy thought he would shoot at it. His aim was true and his arm was strong. Straight from the bow flew the bright golden arrow. It darted through the air with lightning speed and struck the red spot, which, be it known, was the heart of the black fairy. A shriek rang out across the strath. It was the death shriek of the black fairy, who fell down on the bare rock and died. His lifeblood streamed forth, and the whole eastern sky was covered with it. In the midst of the redness gleamed the bright golden arrow of the white fairy.

No sooner was the black fairy slain than Face-of-Light was set free. The doors of her dungeon flew open, and she came forth in all her beauty. When she did so, the mountains and the strath were made bright, the river sparkled in the light, and the lochs flashed like burnished silver. All the land was made glad when Face-of-Light was set free from her dark prison. The slumbering flowers opened their eyes to gaze upon her, and the birds broke forth in merry song, while the white fairy smiled and danced with joy.

The black fairy lay dead and invisible on his mountain top until evening. Then Beira came to visit him. When she found that her son had been slain, she took from her wallet a pot of healing balsam and rubbed it on his wound. Then she rubbed the balsam on his eyes and on his lips. When she did this, he came to life, and began once again to plot evil against the white fairy and his beautiful bride.

This story, which used to be told in Strathspey, is the story of the struggle between darkness and light. The black fairy is night, which begins to make itself invisible at dawn, and the red spot on his left breast is the red light of morning. The golden arrow of the white fairy is the golden shaft of sunlight that darts across the eastern heaven as the sun rises in morning splendour. Face-of-Light is the spirit of the River Spey, which is bright in daytime and lost to sight in the darkness of night. When the storyteller says that Face-of-Light leaves the river, he means that its brightness leaves it when the shadows of night are falling.

A different story is told in the Ness Valley. There are two mountains on either side of Loch Ness, and on each is a Fooar, or giant. These sons of Beira are rivals. One loves the daylight and the other loves darkness.

Every morning at dawn one Fooar flings across Loch Ness a white boulder. When the boulder goes through the air the sky becomes bright. Every evening the other Fooar flings across Loch Ness a black boulder, and the sky grows dark.

The rivals can throw their boulders only once in every twenty-four hours. When the white boulder is flung, it strikes the night Fooar, and he falls down in a swoon. He does not recover until evening, and then he rises and, in turn, flings his black boulder, and strikes down his rival, who then lies unconscious until the dawn. When the giant of day grasps his white boulder and raises it on high, his red hand can be seen in the sky, and the red hand of the giant of night is often seen at evening. Sometimes the giants turn round the boulders to adjust them for throwing. Then the gold rings on their fingers and the golden armlets on their arms flash athwart the sky in bright splendour.

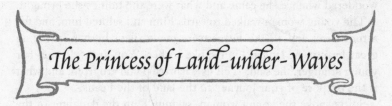

When no wind blows and the surface of the sea is clear as crystal, the beauties of Land-under-Waves are revealed to human eyes. It is a fair country with green vales through which flow silvern streams, and the pebbles in the beds of the streams are flashing gems of varied hues. There are deep forests that glitter in eternal sunshine, and bright flowers that never fade. Rocks are of gold, and the sand is dust of silver.

On a calm morning in May, the Feans, who were great warriors in ancient Scotland, being the offspring of gods and goddesses, were sitting beside the Red Cataract, below which salmon moved slowly, resting themselves ere they began to leap towards the higher waters of the stream. The sun was shining bright, and the sea was without a ripple. With eyes of wonder the Feans gazed on the beauties of Land-under-Waves. None spoke, so deeply were they absorbed. They saw the silver sands, the rocks of gold, the gleaming forests, the beautiful flowers, and the bright streams that flow over beds covered with flashing gems.

As they gazed a boat was seen on the sea, and for a time the Feans were not sure whether it moved above the surface or below it. In time, however, as it drew near they saw that it was on the surface. The boat came towards the place where they sat, and they saw that a woman pulled the oars.

All the Feans rose to their feet. Finn, the King of the Feans, and Goll, his chief warrior, had keen sight, and when the boat was still afar off they saw that the woman had great beauty. She pulled two oars, which parted the sea, and the ripples seemed to set in motion all the trees and flowers of Land-under-Waves.

The boat came quickly, and when it grounded on the beach, the loveliest woman that ever eyes gazed upon rose out of it. Her face was mild and touched with a soft sadness. She was a stranger to the Feans, who knew well that she had come from afar, and they wondered whence she came and what were the tidings she brought.

The young woman walked towards Finn and saluted him, and for a time Finn and all the Feans were made silent by her exceeding great beauty. At length Finn spoke to her. 'You are welcome, fair young stranger,' he said. 'Tell us what tribe you are from, and what is the purpose of your journey to the land of the Feans.'

Softly spoke the young woman, saying: 'I am the daughter of the King Under-Waves, and I shall tell you why I have come here. There is not a land beneath the sun which I have not searched for Finn and his brave warriors.'

'Beautiful maiden,' Finn said, 'will you not tell us why you have searched through the lands that are far and near, seeking to find us?'

'Then you are Finn and no other,' spoke the maiden.

'I am indeed Finn, and these who stand near me are my warriors.' It was thus that Finn made answer, speaking modestly, and yet not without pride.

'I have come to ask for your help,' said the maiden, 'and I shall have need of it very soon. My enemy pursues me even now.'

'I promise to help you, fair princess,' Finn assured her. 'Tell me who it is that pursues you.'

Said the maiden: 'He who pursues me over the ocean is a mighty and fearless warrior. His name is Dark Prince-of-Storm, and he is the son of the White King of Red-Shields. He means to seize the kingdom of my father and make me his bride. I have defied him, saying: "Finn shall take me to my home; he shall be my saviour. Great as is your prowess, you cannot fight and beat Finn and his heroic band." '

Oscar, the young hero and the grandson of Finn, spoke forth and said: 'Even if Finn were not here, the Dark Prince would not dare to seize you.'

As he spoke a shadow fell athwart the sea, blotting out the vision of Land-under-Waves. The Feans looked up, and they saw on the skyline a mighty warrior mounted on a blue-grey steed of ocean; white was its mane and white its tail, and white the foam that was driven from its nostrils and its mouth.

The warrior came swiftly towards the shore, and as his steed rode forward with great fury, waves rose and broke around it. The breath from its panting nostrils came over the sea like gusts of tempest.

On the warrior's head was a flashing helmet, and on his left arm a ridged shield. In his right hand he grasped a large heavy sword, and when he waved it on high it flashed bright like lightning.

Faster than a mountain torrent galloped his horse. The Feans admired the Dark Prince. He was a great and mighty warrior who bore himself like a king.

The steed came to land, and when it did so, the Dark Prince leapt from its back and strode up the beach.

Finn spoke to the fair daughter of the King Under-Waves and said: 'Is this the prince of whom you have spoken?'

Said the princess: 'It is he and no other. Oh, protect me now, for great is his power!'

Goll, the old warrior, and Oscar, the youthful hero, sprang forward and placed themselves between the Dark Prince and the fair princess. But the Dark Prince scorned to combat with them. He went towards Finn, who was unarmed. Goll was made angry at once. He seized a spear and flung it at the stranger. It did not touch his body, but it split the ridged shield right through the middle. Then Oscar raised his spear and flung it from his left hand. It struck the warrior's steed and slew it. This was accounted a mighty deed, and Ossian, the bard of the Feans, and father of Oscar, celebrated it in a song which is still sung in Scotland.

When the steed perished, the Dark Prince turned round with rage and fury, and called for fifty heroes to combat against him. Then he said that he would overcome all the Feans and take away the fair princess.

A great battle was waged on the beach. The Dark Prince sprang upon the Feans, and fought with fierceness and great strength.

At length Goll went against him. Both fought with their swords alone, and never was seen before such a furious combat. Strong was the arm of Goll, and cunning the thrusts he gave. As he fought on, his battle power increased, and at length he struck down and slew the Dark Prince. Nor was ever such a hero overcome since the day when the Ocean Giant was slain.

When the Dark Prince was slain, the wind fell and the sea was hushed, and the sun at evening shone over the waters. Once again Land-under-Waves was revealed in all its beauty.

The princess bade farewell to all the Feans, and Finn went into a boat and went with her across the sea until they reached the gates of Land-under-Waves. The entrance to this wonderful land is a sea-cave on the Far Blue Isle of Ocean. When Finn took leave of the princess, she made him promise that if ever she had need of his help again, he would give it to her freely and quickly.

A year and a day went past, and then came a calm and beautiful morning. Once again the Feans sat on the shore below the Red Cataract, gazing on the beauties of Land-under-Waves. As they gazed, a boat came over the sea, and there was but one person in it.

Said Oscar: 'Who comes hither? Is it the princess of Land-under-Waves once more?'

Finn looked seaward and said: 'No, it is not the princess who comes hither, but a young man.'

The boat drew swiftly towards the shore, and when the man was within call he hailed Finn with words of greeting and praise.

'Who are you, and whence come you?' Finn asked.

Said the man: 'I am the messenger of the princess of Land-under-Waves. She is ill, and seems ready to die.'

There was great sorrow among the Feans when they heard the sad tidings.

'What is your message from the fair princess?' Finn asked.

Said the man: 'She bids you to remember your promise to help her in time of need.'

'I have never forgotten my promise,' Finn told him, 'and am ready now to fulfil it.'

Said the man: 'Then ask Jeermit, the healer, to come with me so that he may give healing to the Princess Under-Waves.'

Finn made a sign to Jeermit, and he rose up and went down the beach and entered the boat. Then the boat went out over the sea towards the Far Blue Isle, and it went swiftly until it reached the sea-cave through which one must pass to enter Land-under-Waves.

Now Jeermit was the fairest of all the members of the Fean band. His father was Angus-the-Ever-Young, who conferred upon him the power to give healing for wounds and sickness. Jeermit had knowledge of curative herbs and life-giving waters, and he had the power, by touching a sufferer, to prolong life until he found the means to cure.

Jeermit was taken through the sea-cave of the Far Blue Isle, and for a time he saw naught, so thick was the darkness; but he heard the splashing of waves against the rocks. At length light broke forth, and the boat grounded. Jeermit stepped out, and found himself on a broad level plain. The boatman walked in front, and Jeermit followed him. They went on and on, and it seemed that their journey would never end. Jeermit saw a clump of red sphagnum moss, and plucked some and went on. Ere long he saw another clump, and plucked some more. A third time he came to a red moss clump, and from it too he plucked a portion. The boatman still led on and on, yet Jeermit never felt weary.

At length Jeermit saw before him a golden castle. He spoke to the boatman, saying: 'Whose castle is that?'

Said the boatman: 'It is the castle of the King Under-Waves, and the princess lies within.'

Jeermit entered the castle. He saw many courtiers with pale faces. None spoke: all were hushed to silence with grief. The queen came towards him, and she seized his right hand and led him towards the chamber in which the dying princess lay.

Jeermit knelt beside her, and when he touched her the power of his healing entered her veins, and she opened her eyes. As soon as she beheld Jeermit of the Feans she smiled a sweet smile, and all who were in the chamber smiled too.

'I feel stronger already,' the princess told Jeermit. 'Great is the joy I feel to behold you. But the sickness has not yet left me, and I fear I shall die.'

'I have three portions of red moss,' said Jeermit. 'If you will take them in a drink they will heal you, because they are the three life drops of your heart.'

'Alas!' the princess exclaimed, 'I cannot drink of any water now except from the cup of the King of the Plain-of-Wonder.'

Now, great as was Jeermit's knowledge, he had never heard before of this magic cup.

'A wise woman has foretold that if I get three draughts from this cup I shall be cured,' said the princess. 'She said also that when I drink I must swallow the three portions of red moss from the Wide-Bare-Plain. The moss of healing you have already found, O Jeermit. But no man shall ever gain possession of the magic cup of the King of the Plain-of-Wonder, and I shall not therefore get it, and must die.'

Said Jeermit: 'There is not in the world above the sea, or the world below the sea, a single man who will keep the cup from me. Tell me where dwells the King of the Plain-of-Wonder. Is his palace far distant from here?'

'No, it is not far distant,' the princess told him. 'Plain-of-Wonder is the next kingdom to that of my father. The two kingdoms are divided by a river. You may reach that river, O Jeermit, but you may never be able to cross it.'

Said Jeermit: 'I now lay healing spells upon you, and you shall live until I return with the magic cup.'

When he had spoken thus, he rose up and walked out of the castle. The courtiers who had been sad when he entered were merry as he went away, and those who had been silent spoke one to another words of comfort and hope, because Jeermit had laid healing spells upon the princess.

The King and the Queen of Land-under-Waves bade the healer of the Feans farewell, and wished him a safe and speedy journey.

Jeermit went on alone in the direction of the Plain-of-Wonder. He went on and on until he reached the river of which the princess had spoken. Then he walked up and down the river bank searching for a ford, but he could not find one.

'I cannot cross over,' he said aloud. 'The princess has spoken truly.'

As he spoke a little brown man rose up out of the river. 'Jeermit,' he said, 'you are now in sore straits.'

Said Jeermit: 'Indeed I am. You have spoken wisely.'

'What would you give to one who would help you in your trouble?'

'Whatever he may ask of me.'

'All I ask for,' said the brown man, 'is your good will.'

'That you get freely,' said Jeermit to him.

'I shall carry you across the river,' said the little man.

'You cannot do that.'

'Yes, indeed I can.'

He stretched forth his hands and took Jeermit on his back, and walked across the river with him, treading the surface as if it were hard ground.

As they crossed the river they passed an island over which hovered a dark mist.

'What island is that?' asked Jeermit.

'Its name,' the brown man told him, 'is Cold-Isle-of-the-Dead. There is a well on the island, and the water of it is healing water.'

They reached the opposite bank, and the brown man said: 'You are going to the palace of King Ian of Wonder-Plain?'

'I am.'

'You desire to obtain the Cup of Healing?'

'That is true.'

'May you get it,' said the brown man, who thereupon entered the river.

Ere he disappeared he spoke again and said: 'Know you where you now are?'

'In the Kingdom of Plain-of-Wonder,' Jeermit said.

'That is true,' said the little brown man. 'It is also Land-under-Mountains. This river divides Land-under-Mountains from Land-under-Waves.'

Jeermit was about to ask a question, but ere he could speak the little brown man vanished from before his eyes.

Jeermit went on and on. There was no sun above him and yet all the land was bright. No darkness ever comes to Land-under-Mountains, and there is no morning there and no evening, but always endless day.

Jeermit went on and on until he saw a silver castle with a roof of gleaming crystal. The doors were shut, and guarded by armed warriors.

Jeermit blew a blast on his horn, and called out, 'Open and let me in.'

A warrior went towards him with drawn sword. Jeermit flung his spear and slew the warrior.

Then the doors of the castle were opened and King Ian came forth.

'Who are you, and whence come you?' he asked sternly.

'I am Jeermit,' was the answer he received.

'Son of Angus-the-Ever-Young, you are welcome,' exclaimed the king. 'Why did you not send a message that you were coming? It is sorrowful to think you have slain my greatest warrior.'

Said Jeermit: 'Give him to drink of the water in the Cup of Healing.'

'Bring forth the cup!' the king called.

The cup was brought forth, and the king gave it to Jeermit, saying: 'There is no virtue in the cup unless it is placed in hands of either Angus or his son.'

Jeermit touched the slain warrior's lips with the cup. He poured drops of the water into the man's mouth, and he sat up. Then he drank all the water in the cup, and rose to his feet strong and well again, for his wound had been healed.

Said Jeermit to the king: 'I have come hither to obtain this cup, and will now take it with me and go away.'

'So be it,' answered the king. 'I give you the cup freely. But remember that there is no longer any healing in it, for my mighty warrior has drunk the magic water.'

Jeermit was not too well pleased when the King of Wonder-Plain spoke thus. 'No matter,' said he; 'I shall take the cup with me.'

'I will send a boat to take you across the river and past the Cold-Isle-of-the-Dead,' the king said.

Said Jeermit: 'I thank you, but I have no need of a boat.'

'May you return soon,' the king said with a smile, for he believed that Jeermit would never be able to cross the river or pass the Cold-Isle-of-the-Dead.

Jeermit bade the king farewell and went away, as he had come, all alone. He went on and on until he reached the river. Then he sat down, and gloomy thoughts entered his mind. He had obtained the cup, but it was empty; he had returned to the river and could not cross it.

'Alas!' he exclaimed aloud, 'my errand is fruitless. The cup is of no use to me, and I cannot cross the river, and must needs return in shame to the King of Wonder-Plain.'

As he spoke the little brown man rose out of the river.

'You are again in sore straits, Jeermit,' he said.

'Indeed, I am,' answered the son of Angus. 'I got what I went for, but it is useless, and I cannot cross the river.'

'I shall carry you,' said the little brown man.

'So be it,' Jeermit answered.

The little brown man walked over the river with Jeermit on his shoulders, and went towards the Cold-Isle-of-the-Dead.

'Whither are you carrying me now?' asked Jeermit with fear in his heart.

Said the little brown man: 'You desire to heal the daughter of the King Under-Waves.'

'That is true.'

'Your cup is empty, and you must fill it at the Well of Healing, on the Cold-Isle-of-the-Dead. That is why I am carrying you towards the isle. You must not get off my back or set foot on the shore, else you will never be able to leave it. But have no fear. I shall kneel down beside the well, and you can dip the cup in it, and carry off enough water to heal the princess.'

Jeermit was well pleased to hear these words, for he knew that the little brown man was indeed his friend. He obtained the healing water in the manner that was promised. Then the little brown man carried him to the opposite bank of the river, and set him down on the border of Land-under-Waves.

'Now you are happy-hearted,' said the little brown man.

'Happy-hearted indeed,' Jeermit answered.

'Ere I bid you farewell I shall give you good advice,' said the little brown man.

'Why have you helped me as you have done?' Jeermit asked.

'Because your heart is warm, and you desire to do good to others,' said the little brown man. 'Men who do good to others will ever find friends in the Land of the Living, in the Land of the Dead, in Land-under-Waves and in Land-under-Mountains.'

'I thank you,' Jeermit said. 'Now I am ready for your good advice, knowing that your friendship is true and lasting.'

Said the little brown man: 'You may give the princess water from the Cup of Healing, but she will not be cured unless you drop into the water three portions of sphagnum moss.'

'I have already found these portions on the broad level plain.'

'That is well,' said the other. 'Now I have more advice to offer you. When the princess is healed the king will offer you choice of reward. Take nothing he offers, but ask for a boat to convey you home again.'

'I will follow your advice,' Jeermit promised.

Then the two parted, and Jeermit went on and on until he came to the golden palace of the King Under-Waves. The princess welcomed him when he was brought into her room, and said: 'No man ever before was given the cup you now carry.'

Said Jeermit: 'For your sake I should have got it, even if I had to fight an army.'

'I feared greatly that you would never return,' sighed the princess.

Jeermit put into the Cup of Healing the three portions of blood-red moss which he had found, and bade the princess to drink.

Thrice she drank, and each time she swallowed a portion of red moss. When she drank the last drop, having swallowed the third portion of red moss, she said: 'Now I am healed. Let a feast be made ready, and I shall sit at the board with you.'

There was great joy and merriment in the castle when the feast was held. Sorrow was put away, and music was sounded. When the feast was over, the king spoke to Jeermit and said: 'I would fain reward you for healing my daughter, the princess. I shall give you as much silver and gold as you desire, and you shall marry my daughter and become the heir to my throne.'

Said Jeermit: 'If I marry your daughter I cannot again return to my own land.'

'No, you cannot again return, except on rare and short visits. But here you will spend happy days, and everyone shall honour you.'

Said Jeermit: 'The only reward I ask for, sire, is a small one indeed.'

'I promise to give you whatever you ask for.'

Said Jeermit: 'Give me a boat, so that I may return again to my own land, which is very dear to me, and to my friends and kinsmen, the Feans, whom I love, and to Finn MacCool, the great chief of men.'

'Your wish is granted,' the king said.

Then Jeermit bade farewell to all who were in the castle, and when he parted with the princess she said: 'I shall never forget you, Jeermit. You found me in suffering and gave me relief; you found me dying and gave me back my life again. When you return to your own land remember me, for I shall never pass an hour of life without thinking of you with joy and thankfulness.'

Jeermit crossed the level plain once again, and reached the place where the boat in which he had come lay safely moored. The boat-man went into it and seized the oars, and Jeermit went in after him. Then the boat sped through the deep dark tunnel, where the waves splash unseen against the rocks, and passed out of the cave on the shore of the Far Blue Isle. The boat then went speedily over the sea, and while it was yet afar off, Finn saw it coming. All the Feans gathered on the shore to bid Jeermit welcome.

'Long have we waited for you, son of Angus,' Finn said.

'What time has passed since I went away?' asked Jeermit, for it seemed to him that he had been absent for no more than a day and a night.

'Seven long years have passed since we bade you farewell,' Finn told him, 'and we feared greatly that you would never again come back to us.

Said Jeermit: 'In the lands I visited there is no night, and no change in the year. Glad am I to return home once again.'

Then they all went to Finn's house, and a great feast was held in honour of Jeermit, who brought back with him the Cup of Healing which he had received from the King of Wonder-Plain.

Nimble Men, Blue Men and Green Ladies

Among the children and descendants of Beira are the Nimble Men, or Merry Dancers of the Aurora Borealis, the Blue Men of the Minch and the Green Ladies.

The Nimble Men are divided into two clans. The heroes of one clan are clad in garments white as hoarfrost, and the heroes of the other clan in garments of pale yellow. Brighter and more varied colours are worn by the maidens. Some are gowned in green, some in red, and some in silvery white and a few wear royal purple.

On winter nights when there is peace on land and sea the Nimble Men and Merry Maidens come forth to dance in the northern sky. They are all of giant stature but comely of form, and their dances are very graceful. The men bow to the maids and the maids curtsey to the men, and when the dance is at its height some of the men leap high and whirl round about, so merry are they. Fairy pipers play enchanting music while the couples dance across the northern sky.

There was once a prince of the White Clan of Nimble Men, and his name was Light Foot. He loved the Princess Comely, who was the fairest of all the Merry Maidens, but he had a rival named Green Eyes, the chief of the Yellow Clan. Princess Comely liked best to dance with Light Foot, because among the Nimble Men he was without an equal as a dancer.

One dark night when the mountains were white with new-fallen snow and the valleys glistened with hoarfrost, all the northern sky was lit up in splendour by the Nimble Men and Merry Maidens, who came out to dance in honour of Queen Beira. It was the first great gathering of the winter season, and all the dancers were clad in new and dazzling garments. They began to dance soon after darkness set in, and it was nigh to midnight ere they sank down to rest.

Princess Comely had danced all the time with Light Foot, and when she sat down he knelt before her, whispering softly: 'Fairest of the fair, O be my bride!'

Said Princess Comely, 'Your bride I shall be.'

The words were heard by Green Eyes, who was crouching near at hand. His heart was filled with anger, and leaping up, he called upon the members of his clan to draw their swords and fight Light Foot and his followers. Then all was confusion. The warriors of both clans sprang at one another, brandishing their gleaming weapons. Up leapt Light Foot to fight against Green Eyes. Rising to full stature he darted across the sky to smite him down. Up leapt the Princess Comely and all the maidens, and they ran away shrieking. Then a battle royal began to rage between the rival clans. The sound of swords striking swords reached the earth, and seemed like the rustling of frosty twigs when the wind rises suddenly and scampers through the forest.

For hours the fearsome fight was waged with fury, and men and women came forth to watch it with wonder and in silence. They saw the warriors leaping white with anger. Hard and swift were the blows, and many were slain. At length below the feet of the Nimble Men there appeared a cloud which was red with the blood that flowed from many wounds received in the battle royal. From the sky the blood drops fell like dew on the green stones of the mountain, which were thus for ever stained with red spots. That is why the red-speckled green stones are called 'blood stones'.

When the night was almost spent, Princess Comely returned to the battleground, and found that the conflict had come to an end. As she drew near, a few wounded warriors rose up and staggered away. She began to search among the fallen warriors for Light Foot, and at length she found him lying cold and dead. A cry of sorrow broke from her lips, and was wafted towards the earth on the first breath of dawn. Those who heard it knew then that the prophecy of the Seer was being fulfilled, and they sang the song he had made:

> 'When yon lady seeks her lover
>   In the cold and pearly morn,
> She will find that he has fallen
>   By the hand that she did scorn.
> She will clasp her arms about him
>   And in her anguish die –
> On, never again will trip the twain across the northern sky!'

The Blue Men are found only in the Minch, and chiefly in the strait which lies between the Island of Lewis and the Shant Isles (the charmed islands) and is called the 'Sea-stream of the Blue Men'. They are not giants, like the Nimble Men, but of human size, and they have great strength. By day and by night they swim round and between the Shant Isles, and the sea there is never at rest. The Blue Men wear blue caps and have grey faces which appear above the waves that they raise with their long restless arms. In summer weather they skim lightly below the surface, but when the wind is high they revel in the storm and swim with heads erect, splashing the waters with mad delight. Sometimes they are seen floating from above the waist out of the sea, and sometimes turning round like porpoises as they dive.

Here is a boatman's song about the Blue Men:

When the tide is at the turning and the wind is fast asleep,
And not a wave is curling on the wide, blue deep,
Oh, the waters will be churning in the stream that
                                        never smiles,
Where the Blue Men are splashing round the charmèd isles.

As the summer wind goes droning o'er the sun-bright seas,
And the Minch is all a-dazzle to the Hebrides,
They will skim along like salmon – you can see their
                                        shoulders gleam,
And the flashing of their fingers in the Blue Men's Stream.

But when the blast is raving and the wild tide races,
The Blue Men are breast-high with foam-grey faces;
They'll plunge along with fury while they sweep the
                                        spray behind,
Oh, they'll bellow o'er the billows and wail upon the wind.

And if my boat be storm-toss'd and beating for the bay,
They'll be howling and be growling as they drench it
                                        with the spray –
For they'd like to heel it over to their laughter when it lists,
Or crack the keel between them, or stave it with their fists.

Oh, weary on the Blue Men, their anger and their wiles!
The whole day long, the whole night long, they're splashing
round the isles;
They'll follow every fisher – ah! they'll haunt the fisher's
dream –
When billows toss, oh! who would cross the Blue Men's Stream?

In days of old, the 'Blue Men's Stream' was sometimes called 'The Current of Destruction', because so many ships were swamped in it. The people blamed the Blue Men, who dwelt in caves, they said, at the bottom of the sea. Their sentinels were always on the lookout, and when a vessel came in sight, word was sent to the men in the caves to come up. Sailors were afraid of them, and many sailed round the Shant Islands instead of taking the short cut between these and the big Island of Lewis.

When the chief of the Blue Men had all his men gathered about him, ready to attack a ship, he rose high in the water and shouted to the skipper two lines of poetry, and if the skipper did not reply at once by adding two lines to complete the verse, the Blue Men seized the ship and upset it. Many a ship was lost in days of old because the skipper had no skill at verse.

True is the Gaelic saying, however: 'There comes with time what comes not with weather.'

One day, when the wind was high and the billows rough and angry, the Blue Men saw a stately ship coming towards their sea-stream under white sails. Royally she cleft her way through the waves. The sentinels called to the blue fellows who were on the sea floor, and as they rose they wondered to see the keel pass overhead so swiftly. Some seized it and shook it as if to try their strength, and were astonished to find it so steady and heavy. It carried on straight as a spear in flight.

The chief of the Blue Men bobbed up in front of the ship, and when waist-high among the tumbling waves, shouted to the skipper:

'Man of the black cap, what do you say
As your proud ship cleaves the brine?'

No sooner were the words spoken than the skipper answered:

> 'My speedy ship takes the shortest way,
> And I'll follow you line by line.'

This was at once an answer and a challenge, and the chief of the Blue Men cried angrily:

> 'My men are eager, my men are ready
> To drag you below the waves – '

The skipper answered defiantly in a loud voice:

> 'My ship is speedy, my ship is steady,
> If it sank it would wreck your caves.'

The chief of the Blue Men was worsted. Never before had a seaman answered him so promptly and so well. He had no power to injure the ship, because the skipper was as good a bard as he was himself, and he knew that if he went on shouting half-verses until the storm spent itself the skipper would always complete them. He signalled to his followers to dive; and down below the wave ridges they all vanished, like birds that dive for fish. The big ship went on proudly and safely under snow-white, wind-tight sails while:

> The sea-wind through the cordage sang
> With high and wintry merriment.

Once upon a time some fishermen who were crossing the 'Sea-stream of the Blue Men' in calm weather found one of the blue fellows sleeping on the surface. They seized him, and lifting him into the boat, bound him tightly with a rope. He slept so soundly that although the fishermen let him fall out of their hands he did not awake.

They resolved to take him to the shore, but they had not gone far when two Blue Men bobbed above the clear waters and shouted:

> 'Duncan will be one, Donald will be two,
> Will you need another ere you reach the shore?'

The skipper of the boat was about to shout two lines in reply, but, before he could speak, the Blue Man in the boat opened his eyes, and with a quick movement he snapped the rope that bound him as easily as if it had been only an oat straw and answered:

> 'Duncan's voice I hear, Donald too is near,
>   But no need of helpers has strong Ian More.'

As he spoke he leapt out of the boat into the sea. That was how the fishermen came to know that all the Blue Men have names of their own.

The Green Ladies are different from the fairies, who are called 'Wee Folk', for, like the Blue Men, they are of human size. Some of them are withered old hags, resembling Beira in the winter season, and some of them are as fair as Beira in her summer girlhood. They have power to change their forms at will. A Green Lady may sometimes deceive a traveller by appearing before him in the form of his lady-love, and after speaking to him for a time, turn away with mocking laughter and vanish from sight. Perhaps, too, she may appear as a dog, and torment shepherds by driving their sheep hither and thither in wild confusion.

Each Green Lady lives alone in a solitary place, either below a river or waterfall or in a green knoll, a forest or a deep ravine. One is rarely seen in daytime. The Green Lady wanders about in the dusk of late evening, in moonlight or in darkness. She is ever a deceiver, and woe to the traveller who has not the knowledge how to overcome her spells, for she may drown him at a river ford or lead him over the edge of a precipice. It is difficult to fight against her, for if she asks a man what weapon he has, and he names it, she can, by working magic, make the weapon quite harmless.

One evening a smith was riding homeward from battle on his horse, and when it was growing dusk he reached a ford. Suddenly a Green Lady rose out of the water in front of him.

'Stop!' she cried; 'you cannot ride across.'

Said the man: 'Begone, O evil one; or I shall smite you!'

'What have you to fight with?' she asked.

Said the man: 'I have my sword.'

Immediately he named his sword it lost its power to do her injury.

The Green Lady laughed mockingly, and then asked: 'What else have you to fight with?'

Said the man: 'I have my spear.'

When he named the spear it became as useless as the sword.

The Green Lady laughed again, a shrill mocking laugh. 'Have you room for a rider behind you?' she asked.

Said the man: 'Yes, and there is room also for a rider in front.'

As he spoke he seized the Green Lady, lifted her up in front of him, threw the reins over her head, and said: 'Now I have you in my power.'

'You will never leave the ford,' she answered, 'because your sword and spear have been made useless to you.'

Said the man: 'I have still one weapon left.'

'Which one is that?' she asked.

Said the smith: 'The sharp bright weapon against my leg.'

He meant the dirk in his right stocking, but as he did not mention its name, the Green Lady could not make it useless.

'Then I will leave you,' cried the lady in alarm.

Said the smith: 'You cannot leave me until I choose to let you go. The reins are about you, and you cannot move beyond them, for the magic power has now been taken from you and has passed to me.'

The Green Lady knew well that this was so. She knew also that she would have to do whatever the man ordered her to do before he would set her free.

The horse was urged forward by the smith, and the ford was crossed in safety. Then the animal trotted across the moor as the moon rose over the hills, shining fair and bright.

'Let me go,' the Green Lady cried, 'and I shall give you a herd of speckled cattle.'

Said the man: 'You will have to give me a herd of cattle, but still I shall not let you go.'

The horse went on, and the Green Lady wept tears of sorrow and anger.

'Let me go,' she cried, 'and I shall build for you tonight a house which fire will not burn nor water or storm wind injure, and it shall be charmed against all evil beings.'

The man reined up his horse, and said: 'Fulfil your promise, and I shall set you free.'

He dismounted, and the Green Lady dismounted also. The smith tied the reins round her, and repeated his command.

'Your wish will be fulfilled,' she said.

Then the Green Lady uttered a loud cry, which was heard over

seven hills. The cry was repeated over and over again by Big Angus
of the Rock, aka Echo, a lonely spirit who is at everyone's service.
Big Angus is a son of Beira, and it is told he was wont to cause his
mother much trouble by contradicting her orders and giving orders
of his own, for he desired to be King of the Universe, although he
was weak-minded and light-headed. To punish him, Beira shut him
inside a rock, and compelled him ever after to repeat any words that
were said in his hearing. Ever since that day Big Angus has had to
repeat over and over again everything he hears in his lonely rocky
prison.

So Big Angus repeated the cry of the Green Lady, which was a
command to fairies and goblins to come to her aid. As these little
people fear all Green Ladies, they answered her cry without delay.
They came from the hilltops and from inside cliffs, from green
knolls in lonely moors and deep forests, and from every other haunt
they loved. Those that were dancing ceased to dance, and those that
were setting out on journeys turned back. They crossed the moors
jumping like crickets, and came through the air like birds and
gathered round the Green Lady, waiting to obey her.

She set them to work at once to hew wood and gather stones.
They cut down trees in the rowan wood, and quarried stones below
a waterfall. As they went on working, the Green Lady cried out:

> 'Two stones over one stone,
> One stone over two stones –
>   Work speedily, work speedily –
> Bring every timber from the wood
>   But mulberry, but mulberry.'

The house was built very quickly. Across the moor the fairies
stood in two rows – one row from the house to the waterfall and one
from the house to the rowan wood. The stones that were quarried
were passed along from hand to hand, and so were the pieces of
timber that were hewed down and sawed and dressed.

When the dawn was beginning to appear in the eastern sky the
house was ready, and all the fairies and goblins vanished from sight.

'Set me free,' cried the Green Lady.

The smith said: 'I shall set you free when you have promised not
to do me any injury.'

'I promise that readily,' said she.

Said the smith: 'Promise also that neither I nor my children will ever be drowned by you in the fords of the three rivers.'

He named the rivers he referred to. They all flowed near his home.

The Green Lady promised that also. Then the smith set her free, and she cried: 'You have not named the fourth river. Let you and your children beware!'

As she spoke she went past the smith like a green flame. He never again saw her, but seven years afterwards one of his sons was drowned in the ford of the fourth river he had not named, and then he knew that the Green Lady had taken her revenge.

Other Green Ladies have made friends with certain families, and have kept watch over their houses, shielding them from harm. Once a poor fisherman lost his boat, and sat down on the beach at a river mouth lamenting his fate. A Green Lady appeared before him, and said: 'If I give you a new boat will you divide your fish with me?'

Said the fisherman: 'I promise to do so.'

Next morning he found a new boat lying on the beach. He went out to sea and caught many fish. When he returned to the shore he left half of his catch on a green knoll on the river bank. The Green Lady was well pleased, and helped the man to prosper.

One evening, however, he left no fish for her. He went out to sea next day as usual, but did not catch anything. Sad was his heart when he returned home empty-handed, but it was even sadder next morning when he found that his boat had been smashed to pieces during the night in a storm which had risen suddenly and raged until daybreak. He never again saw the Green Lady, and he had reason to be sorry that he had not kept his bargain with her.

There was once a Green Lady who received favours from a bold pirate whose name was Mac Ean Yeer. She kept watch over him on sea and land, so that he was always able to escape from those who pursued him. The Green Lady advised him to paint one side of his boat black and the other side white, so that watchers on the shore would see a black boat passing to the north and a white boat passing to the south, and thus be deceived, thinking the boat which went out to attack a galley was not the same one they saw returning. In time, when the people came to know the trick, they said of deceitful persons: 'He's black on one side and white on the other, like the boat of Mac Ean Yeer.'

Mac Ean lived to be an old man, and when he died in Islay the Green Lady shrieked aloud and passed northward. The shriek was heard in Mull, and ere the echoes died away she had reached the Coolin Hills in Skye.

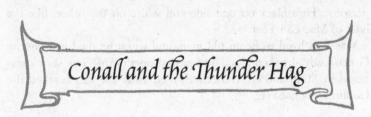

Conall and the Thunder Hag

Among the hags who served Beira was the Thunder Hag. When Angus began to reign she fled across the ocean to a lonely island, where she plotted to wreak vengeance by bringing disaster to man and beast, because they had rejoiced when Beira was overcome.

One day in midsummer, when all the land was bathed in warm, bright sunshine and the sea was lulled to sleep, the Thunder Hag rode over Scotland in a black chariot drawn by fierce red hounds and surrounded by heavy clouds. The sky was darkened, and as the hag drew near, the rattling of the chariot wheels and the baying of the hounds sounded loud and fearsome. She rode from sea to sea, over hill and moor, and threw fireballs at the deep forests, which set them ablaze. Terror spread through the land as the chariot passed in smoke and clouds.

On the next day the hag came back. She threw more fireballs on forests of fir and silver birch, and they burned fiercely. Dry heather on the moors and the sun-dried grass were also swept by flame.

The king was greatly troubled, and he sent forth his chief warriors to slay the hag; but they fled in terror when they saw her coming near.

On the third day she returned. Then the king called for Conall Curlew, the fearless hero, and spoke to him, saying: 'My kingdom will be destroyed if the hag is not slain. I need your help, O brave and noble one.'

Said Conall: 'I shall go out against the hag, sire, and if I do not slay her today, I may slay her on the morrow.'

Conall went forth, and when he saw and heard the chariot drawing near he went up to the summit of a high mountain and waited to attack her. But the hag kept herself hidden behind a cloud which surrounded the chariot. Conall had to return to the king without having done anything.

'I could not see the hag because of the dark cloud,' he said.

'If she comes again tomorrow,' the king said, 'you may fare better.'

Conall then made preparations for the next coming of the hag. He went out into the fields that were nigh to the royal castle, and separated all the lambs from the sheep, all the calves from the cows, and all the foals from the mares. When morning came on there was great tumult among the animals.

There never was heard before such a bleating of sheep, such a lowing of cattle or neighing of mares in the land of Alba, and it was piteous to hear the cries of the lambs, and the calves, and the foals which were taken from their mothers. The men were filled with wonder at the thing Conall had done, nor could they understand why he had done it, and the hearts of the women were touched by the cries of the young animals, and they wept to hear them.

It was indeed a morning of sorrow and wailing when the cloud in which the hag's chariot was hidden came nigh to the castle. The cloud darkened the heavens, and when it passed over the wooded hill the fireballs set the trees in flame, and all the people fled before the cloud and concealed themselves in caves and in holes in the ground; all except the warriors, who waited, trembling, with deep eyes and pale faces.

Conall stood alone on a green knoll, and his spear was in his hand.

When the cloud came over the valley of the castle, the hag heard the cries of the animals that assailed her ears, and so great was her curiosity that she peered over the edge of the black cloud.

Great fear fell on the hearts of the warriors when they saw the horrible face of the hoary-headed hag; but Conall was a man without fear, and he was waiting for the hag to reveal herself.

As soon as he saw her, he swung his right arm over his shoulder, and he cast the spear towards the cloud. The swallow does not dart swifter than the spear of Conall darted through the air.

The hag was wounded, and threw wide her grisly paws and sank down within the chariot. She called to the black hounds: 'Race quickly!' and they ran swiftly towards the west. The sound of the rattling of the chariot wheels grew fainter and fainter. The clouds which the hag passed over swiftly in her flight were rent in twain, and rain fell in torrents, quenching the fires that were in the woods and on the moors.

There was great rejoicing in the land because of the mighty deed done by Conall, and the king honoured that noble hero by placing a

gold ring on his finger, a gold armlet on his arm and a gold necklet
on his neck.

There was peace and prosperity in the land after that. The hag did
not return again, so greatly did she dread Conall Curlew, the hero
of heroes.

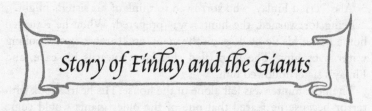

Story of Finlay and the Giants

Finlay the hunter lived with his sister in a lonely little house among the mountains, and near at hand there were giants who were descendants of Beira. This giant clan was ruled over by a hag-queen who was very old and fierce and cunning. She had great stores of silver and gold in her cave, and also a gold-hilted magic sword and a magic wand. When she struck a stone pillar with this wand it became a warrior, and if she put the gold-hilted sword into his hand, the greatest and strongest hero in the world would be unable to take up arms against him with success.

Every day that Finlay went out to hunt he warned his sister, saying: 'Do not open the windows on the north side of the house, or let the fire go out.'

His sister did not, however, heed his warning always. One day she shut the windows on the south side of the house, and opened those on the north side, and allowed the fire to go out.

She wondered what would happen, and she had not long to wait, for a young giant came towards the house and entered it. He had assumed a comely form, and spoke pleasantly to Finlay's sister. They became very friendly, and the giant came often, but made the foolish girl promise not to tell her brother of his visits. After that the girl began to quarrel with Finlay. This went on for a time.

One day when Finlay was returning to his home he saw a little shieling in a place where no shieling used to be. He wondered who dwelt in it, and walked towards the door and entered. He saw an old woman sitting on the floor, and she bade him welcome.

'Sit down,' she said. 'Your name is Finlay.'

'That is true,' answered he; 'who are you and whence come you?'

'I am called Wise Woman,' she answered. 'I have come here to protect and guide you. Alas! you do not know that you are in danger of your life. A young giant has bewitched your sister, and is waiting to kill you this very day with a sharp blue sword.'

'Alas!' cried Finlay, who sorrowed to think of his sister's plight.

Being forewarned, the hunter was prepared. When he returned home he set his fierce dogs on the giant, and threw a pot of boiling water over him. The giant fled shrieking towards his cave, and Finlay's sister followed him.

Then the hunter was left alone in the house. His heart shook with terror because he feared that one of the older giants would come against him to avenge the injury done to the young giant.

He had good reason to be afraid. As soon as the young giant reached the cave, his brother cried: 'I shall go forth and deal with the hunter.'

'I had better go myself,' his father said fiercely.

'It is I who should go,' growled the fierce grey hag.

'I spoke first,' urged the young giant's brother, and sprang towards the mouth of the cave in the gathering dusk.

Finlay waited alone in his little house. The door was shut and securely barred, and the peat fire glowed bright and warm, yet he shivered with the coldness of terror. He listened long and anxiously, and at length heard a growling noise like distant thunder. Stones rumbled down the hillside as the giant raced on, and when he entered a bog the mud splashed heavily against the cliffs. Finlay knew then that a giant was coming, and ere long he heard his voice roaring outside the door: 'Fith! foth! foogie! The door is shut against a stranger. Open and let me in.' He did not wait for Finlay to answer, but burst the door open with a blow. The hunter stood behind the fire which burned in the middle of the room, his bow in his hand and an arrow ready. He fired as the giant entered, but did not kill him. The giant shrieked and leapt towards Finlay, but the dogs made fierce attack. Then the hunter shot another arrow from his bow and killed the giant.

Next morning Finlay hastened to the shieling of Wise Woman, taking with him the giant's head.

'Well, valiant lad,' she exclaimed, 'how fared it with you last night?'

Finlay told her all that had taken place, and explained that it was owing to the help given him by the dogs he was able to slay the giant.

'There is need of the dogs,' Wise Woman said, 'but the day of their great need has yet to come.'

That evening Finlay again sat alone in his house, wondering what

would happen next. No sooner did night come on than he heard a
noise like distant thunder, but much louder than on the night before.
Great boulders rumbled down the hillside, and mud splashed on the
cliffs. Another and more terrible giant was coming, seeking to be
avenged.

'Thoth! Thoth! Foogie!' roared his heavy voice outside the house.
'I smell a man inside. Open the door that I may enter. Although you
killed my son last night, you shall not slay me.'

He burst the door open, and as he did so the house shook. Finlay
feared the roof was about to fall upon him, but he feared more when
he beheld the giant in the firelight, for the monster had five heads.

He drew his bow and shot an arrow. The giant paused. Finlay shot
a second arrow, which, like the first, wounded the monster, but did
not kill him. Then the hunter drew his sword and smote him heavily,
but his wounds were not mortal. The giant stretched out his grisly
hands to seize Finlay, but the dogs leapt at him, and a fierce struggle
took place; in the end Finlay triumphed, and the giant was slain.

Next morning the hunter went to the shieling of Wise Woman,
and told her of the night of terror and the long and deadly combat.
'The dogs,' he said, 'helped me. But for the dogs I should have been
overcome.'

Said Wise Woman: 'There is need for the dogs, but the day of
their greatest need has yet to come. Tonight the fierce grey hag will
seek to avenge the death of her husband and son. Beware of her, O
valiant lad! She will not come raging and roaring like the giants, but
gently and mannerly. She will call to you in a meek and mild voice,
asking you to let her in. But, remember, it is her intention to take
your life. Do as I instruct you and all will be well.'

Wise Woman then gave him instructions, and he went home.
When night came on there was silence all around. Finlay waited
alone, listening intently, and the silence terrified him more than the
noises like distant thunder he had heard on the two previous nights.
He shook and shivered beside the warm bright peat fire, waiting and
waiting and listening. At length he sprang up suddenly, for he heard
a rustling sound like the wind stirring dead leaves. A moment later a
weak patient voice outside the door called: 'I am old and weary. I
have need of food and of shelter for the night. Open and let me in.'

Finlay went to the door and made answer: 'I shall let you in, old woman, if you promise to be civil and mannerly, and not do me an injury.'

Said the hag: 'Oh! I shall give no trouble. I promise to be civil and mannerly. Let me enter your house.'

Finlay opened the door, and the hag walked in. She looked a poor frail old woman, and seemed to be very weary. When she had curtsied to Finlay, she sat down on one side of the fire. Finlay sat down on the opposite side.

The hag stretched out her hands to warm them, and began to look about her. Finlay's three dogs were prowling up and down the room, snarling angrily and showing their teeth.

'These are fierce dogs,' the widow said. 'Arise and tie them with thongs.'

'The dogs will not do any harm to a peaceable old woman,' said Finlay.

'Tie them up in any case, I pray you. I dislike angry dogs.'

'I cannot do that, old woman, because I have nothing to tie them with.'

Said the hag: 'I will give you three red ribbons from my cap. They are strong enough to hold a big ship at anchor.'

Finlay took the red ribbons from her and pretended to tie up the dogs. But he only made them lie down in a corner.

'Have you tied up the dogs?' asked the hag very softly.

'You can see for yourself that they are lying now with their necks close together,' Finlay answered. The hag looked at the dogs, and believing they had been secured with her magic ribbons, smiled to herself.

She sat beside the fire in silence for a time, and Finlay sat opposite her. After a time the hunter noticed that she was growing bigger and bigger.

'What means this?' cried Findlay. 'You seem to be growing bigger and bigger.'

'Oh, no, my darling!' she answered. 'The cold of the night made me shrink, and now I am feeling more comfortable beside your warm bright fire.'

There was silence again, and Finlay watched her for a time and then cried: 'You are growing bigger, without doubt. You may be pleased or displeased because I say so, but you cannot deny it.'

The hag frowned and answered angrily: 'I am growing bigger, as you say. What of that? You fear me now, and you have good reason to. You slew my husband last night, and you slew my son on the night before. I shall certainly kill you tonight.'

When she had spoken thus she sprang to her feet, and the house shook about her. Finlay sprang to his feet also, and as he did so the hag seized him by the hair of his head. Having promised not to injure him inside the house – a promise she could not break - she dragged him outside. The three dogs rose, and sprang through the door after her.

Finlay wrestled fiercely with the hag, and the two twisted and turned hither and thither. The mother of the young giant would have killed him without delay, but the dogs kept attacking her, and gave her much trouble. At length, with the help of the dogs, Finlay managed to throw her down. She lay upon one of her arms, and the dogs held the other.

'Oh! let me rise to my feet,' cried the hag, who had no power to struggle when she lay on the ground.

Said Finlay: 'I shall not allow you to rise up.'

'Allow me to ransom myself,' the hag pleaded.

Said Finlay: 'What ransom will you give?'

'I have a trunk of gold and a trunk of silver in my cave. You shall have both,' she answered.

Said Finlay: 'Having overcome you, these are mine already.'

'I will give you a gold-hilted sword which is in my cave,' the hag then promised. 'He who wields this magic sword will overcome any man or any beast in the world.'

Said Finlay: 'The sword is mine already.'

'I will give you a magic rod if you spare me,' the hag cried then. 'It is a matchless weapon. It can also work wonders. If you strike a stone pillar with it, the pillar will turn into a warrior, and if you will put the gold-hilted sword in this warrior's hand, he will conquer the world for you.'

Said Finlay: 'Your wand is mine already by right of conquest. What else have you to offer for ransom?'

'Alas!' the hag cried, 'I have naught else to give you.'

Said Finlay: 'Then you shall die. The world will be well rid of you.'

He slew the fierce hag, and then arose quickly and put red sphagnum moss on his wounds and sores, so that they might be healed speedily. Next morning he arose and went and informed Wise Woman of what had taken place, saying: 'It was chiefly owing to the dogs that the hag was overcome.'

Said Wise Woman: 'O valiant hero! the dogs have had their day.'

Then Finlay told about the treasure in the cave, and said: 'I know not how I can obtain the gold and silver, the gold-hilted sword and the magic wand.'

Said Wise Woman: 'Tonight my daughter and I will go with you to the giants' cave. I will take my own magic wand with me.'

When darkness came on, the three went to the cave. They set to work and gathered armfuls of dry heather, which they heaped up at the cave mouth and set on fire, so that the young giant within might be choked by the fumes and scorched by the flames. Soon the giant crawled to the mouth of the cave, panting heavily. He came through the smoke dazed and half blinded. Suddenly a warning light appeared on his forehead.

Finlay drew his bow and said: 'I will shoot.'

'Do not shoot,' Wise Woman warned him. 'A wound would only make him fiercer, and the dogs would be of no use to you among the flames. If he is allowed to escape out of the blaze, the dogs would not see him in the darkness. I shall strike him with my magic wand. I can strike once only, and if I fail he will strike the next blow with the gold-hilted sword which is in his hand.'

The giant scattered the fire to get out of the cave, but ere he could rise Wise Woman smote him on the head with her magic wand, and he fell back dead.

When they entered the cave they found that Finlay's sister was within. But she was dead; she had perished in her cave prison.

Finlay took out all the treasure that was in the cave, and carried it to the shieling of Wise Woman. Then he tested the magic wand. He struck a stone pillar with it, and the pillar became a warrior. Then he struck the warrior, and he became a stone pillar again.

'This is wonderful,' Finlay exclaimed.

'It is indeed,' said Wise Woman. Then she told him that he must visit the king next day and inform him of all that had taken place, and she made him take a vow not to enter the palace.

Next day, Finlay set out to the palace of the king. When he reached it he bade the royal servants inform the king that the great giants had been slain.

Said the king: 'Let the valiant hero come within.'

Finlay, however, declined to enter the palace, and sent him word, saying: 'I dare not enter your palace, as I have a vow to fulfil.'

The king came outside and spoke to Finlay, saying: 'Come within. I shall give you my daughter, the princess, in marriage. You shall also have half of my kingdom as long as I live, and the remainder shall be yours when I die.'

Said Finlay: 'I give you thanks, sire, but I cannot enter.'

When he had spoken thus, he walked towards a grey stone pillar and smote it with the magic wand. The pillar became a noble warrior. Then he smote the warrior, and he became a pillar again. The king was greatly astonished, and exclaimed: 'I have never seen anything like this before.'

He went into the palace to give orders about Finlay, whom he wished to detain, but when he came out again he found that the hunter had gone.

The king sent out foot-runners and horsemen to search throughout the kingdom for Finlay, but they returned without having found a trace of him.

Finlay married the daughter of Wise Woman, and he prospered. Years went past. Finlay had a family of three sons. He loved the boys very dearly, and spent happy days roaming with them among the mountains. All went well with him until Wise Woman died. Then misfortune overtook him. His wife died, and all his wealth was stolen from him by night robbers who were in league with the giants. He lost also the magic wand, but he kept possession of the gold-hilted sword. Nor did his troubles end when he became poor again, for a witch cast spells on his three young sons and smote them with a magic wand. Then the boys were transformed into three beautiful white dogs and fled away.

Finlay was stricken with sorrow and set out to search for his children. He crossed mountains and moors, following in the tracks of the three white dogs, but without avail. The day went past and evening came on, and still he hastened onward. When darkness had fallen he came to a small glen and saw a light. He walked towards the light, and found it shone from the window of a house. At this house he asked for a night's lodgings, and it was given to him. The old man of the house spoke to him, saying: 'You are sad and tearful, stranger. Are you searching for your three sons?'

Said Finlay: 'Oh, yes! Have you seen them?'

'They are travelling over mountain and moor,' said the old man. 'I cannot do anything to help you. Tomorrow night you will reach the house of a brother of mine, and if he will not help you, I do not know what you should do.'

Finlay resumed his journey next day, and when darkness came on he reached the house of the old man's brother, who said: 'Your sons are travelling over mountain and moor as three white dogs. They cannot rest or stay, for they must travel by day and by night. I cannot do anything for you. Tomorrow night you will reach the house of my elder brother, and he will give you advice.'

Next night Finlay reached the house of the elder brother, and he said: 'Your sons will remain under spells until doomsday unless you will do one thing.'

'What is that?' Finlay asked.

'You must have three garments made of bog-cotton, and leave them on a hill which your sons in dog form are now running round. When they see the white garments they will put them on. Each one of the garments will take you a year to make, unless you get a band of women to collect the bog-cotton, and a band of women to spin and weave.'

'Alas!' Finlay exclaimed, 'I cannot hire workers, because I have lost all I possessed.'

'You still have the gold-hilted sword,' the man said. 'It may be of service to you.'

Next morning Finlay resumed his journey with a heavy heart indeed. He went on until dusk. Then he heard cries of sorrow and despair. In another moment he beheld a great giant coming towards him, dragging a young man whom he had taken captive. Finlay drew his gold-hilted sword, and spoke boldly to the giant, saying: 'Let your captive go free, or I shall smite you.'

'Ho, ho!' laughed the giant. 'Your sword will bend like a grass blade when it strikes my body.'

As he spoke he stretched out his right hand to seize Finlay and take him captive also. But Finlay smote the giant with the gold-hilted magic sword and slew him.

The young man was overjoyed and thanked Finlay, praising him for his valour. 'Come with me to my father's house,' he said. 'He is the king of this country, and will reward you.'

The young prince had many sores and wounds, and Finlay put red sphagnum moss on them. Then the two went together to the palace and entered it. When the king heard his son's story, he said to Finlay: 'You shall stay here, brave wanderer, and I shall make you rich and prosperous.'

'Alas!' Finlay exclaimed. 'I cannot tarry here except for one night.'

The queen came forward and said: 'You are sad and unhappy, good stranger! What is the cause of your grief?'

Finlay told the queen about his lost sons and his weary and fruitless search for them.

Said the queen: 'One of the king's shepherds has told me that every morning when he goes out he sees three beautiful white dogs on the green hill nigh to the palace.'

'Ah! those are my sons,' Finlay cried. Then he told the queen what the elder of the three old men had said.

The queen listened intently, and then spoke, saying: 'I shall give you my help. Until I have had made the garments of bog-cotton, there will be no rest for me, good stranger, because you have rescued my son from death.'

Next morning the queen sent women to collect bog-cotton and women to spin and weave. The bog-cotton was collected speedily, for hundreds of women went out to obey the queen's command. Then the yarn was spun; it was put into the weaver's loom and woven. Then women sewed the garments, which were afterwards washed and bleached until they were as white and soft as new-fallen snow on a mountain top. The garments were laid on the green hill when the sun was setting.

Next morning Finlay went out early to look for his sons, and the prince whom he had rescued went with him. They found that the white agreements had been taken away, but the boys could not be seen anywhere. Finlay and the prince searched far and wide for them in vain, and then returned to the palace.

A week went past, and Finlay sorrowed greatly. Each morning he asked the shepherd if he had seen either the boys or the white dogs, and the shepherd answered saying: 'No, I have not seen the white dogs on the green hill.'

On the seventh day three youths appeared at the door of the palace and asked to see the stranger who resided there. Finlay came towards them with tears falling from his eyes.

'What ails you?' one of the youths asked.

Said Finlay: 'I am mourning for my three beloved sons whom I shall never behold again.'

'We are your sons, dear father!' the youths exclaimed together.

Finlay dried the tears which blinded him, and then recognised his lost sons. He embraced them and kissed them, and took them before the king and the queen, who bade them welcome.

After that Finlay dwelt in the palace of the king, and his three sons grew up and became mighty warriors.

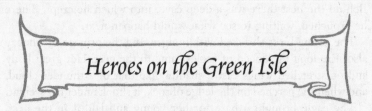

Heroes on the Green Isle

There was once a prince who found himself in the Green Isle of the West, and this is the story of how he came there.

The Prince of the Kingdom of Level-Plains set out on his travels to see the world, and he went northward and westward until he came to a red glen surrounded by mountains. There he met with a proud hero, who asked him: 'Whence come you, and whither are you going?'

Said the prince: 'I am searching for my equal,' and as he spoke he drew his sword. He was a bold and foolish young man.

'I have no desire to fight with you,' the proud hero answered. 'Go your way in peace.'

The prince was jealous of the hero who spoke thus so calmly and proudly, and he insolently replied: 'Draw your sword or die.'

Then he darted forward. The hero swerved aside to escape the sword-thrust, and next moment he leapt upon the prince, whom he overcame after a brief struggle, and bound with a rope. Then he carried him to the top of a cliff, and said: 'You are not fit to be among men. Go and dwell among the birds of prey.' So saying he flung him over the cliff.

The prince fell heavily into a large nest on a ledge of rock, the nest of the queen of eagles, a giant bird of great strength. For a time he lay stunned by his fall. When he came to himself he regretted his folly, and said: 'If ever I escape from this place I shall behave wisely, and challenge no man without cause.'

He found himself in the great nest with three young eagles. The birds were hungry, and when the prince held his wrists towards one, it pecked the rope that bound them until it was severed; so then he stretched his legs towards another bird, and it severed the rope about his ankles. He was thus set free. He rose up and looked about him. The ledge jutted out in mid-air on the cliffside, and the prince saw it was impossible either to ascend or descend the slippery rocks.

Behind the nest there was a deep cave, into which he crept. There he crouched, waiting to see what would happen next.

The young birds shrieked with hunger, and the prince was hungry also. Ere long the queen of eagles came to the nest. Her great body and outstretched wings cast a shadow like that of a thunder cloud, and when she perched on the ledge of rock, it shook under her weight.

The eagle brought a hare for her young and laid it in the nest. Then she flew away. The prince at once crept out of the cave and seized the hare. He gathered together a bundle of dry twigs from the side of the nest and kindled a fire in the cave, and cooked the hare and ate it. The smoke from the fire smothered the young birds, and when the queen of eagles returned she found that they were dead. She knew at once that an enemy must be near at hand, and looked into the cave. There she saw the prince, who at once drew his sword bravely and fought long and fiercely against her, inflicting many wounds to defend himself. But he was no good match for that fierce bird, and at length she seized him in her talons and, springing off the ledge of rock, flew through the air with him. His body was soon torn by the eagle's claws and sore with wounds. The eagle, also sorely wounded, rose up among the clouds, and turning westward flew hurriedly over the sea. Her shadow blotted out the sunshine on the waters as she passed in her flight and boatmen lowered their sails, thinking that a sudden gust of wind was sweeping down upon them.

The prince swooned, and regained consciousness, and swooned again. As the bird flew onwards the sun scorched him. Then she dropped him into the sea, and he found the waters cold as ice. 'Alas!' he thought, 'I shall be drowned.' He rose to the surface and began to swim towards an island near at hand, but the eagle pounced down, and seizing him again, rose high in the air. Once again she dropped him, and then he swooned and remembered no more, until he found himself lying on a green bank on a pleasant shore. The sun was shining, birds sang sweetly among blossoming trees of great beauty and the waves made music on the beach. Somewhere near he could hear a river fairy singing a summer song.

Next he heard behind him a splashing of water, and a shower of pearly drops fell upon his right arm as he lay there weak and helpless. But no sooner did the water touch his arm than it became strong again. The splashing continued, and he twisted himself this way and that until the pearly spray had drenched every part of his body. Then he felt strong and active again, and sprang to his feet. He looked round and saw that the showers of spray had come from a well in which the wounded queen of eagles was bathing herself. The prince knew then that this was a Well of Healing.

He remembered how fiercely the eagle had dealt with him, and wished he still had his sword. Having no sword, he drew his dirk and crept softly towards the well. He waited a moment, crouching behind a bush, and then, raising his dirk, struck off the eagle's head. But he found it was not easy to kill the monster in the Well of Healing. No sooner was the head struck off than it sprang on again. Thrice he beheaded the eagle, and thrice the head was restored. When, however, he struck off the head a fourth time, he held the blade of his dirk between the head and neck until the eagle was dead. Then he dragged the body out of the well, and buried the head in the ground. Having done so, he bathed in the well, and when he came out of it, all his wounds were healed, and he found himself as active and able as if he had just awakened from a long sleep. He looked about him, and saw fruit growing on a blossoming tree. He wondered at that, but being very hungry he plucked the fruit and ate it. Never before had he tasted fruit of such sweet flavour. Feeling refreshed, and at the same time happy and contented, he was about to walk through the forest of beautiful trees and singing birds when he saw three men coming towards him. He enquired of them, saying: 'Who are you, and whence come you?' They answered: 'There is no time to tell. If you are not a dweller on this island, come with us while there is yet time to escape.'

The prince wondered to hear them speak thus, but, having learned wisdom, he followed them in silence. They went down the beach and entered a boat. The prince stepped in also. Two of the men laid oars in the rowlocks, and one sat at the stern to steer. In another moment the boat darted forward, cleaving the waves; but not until it had gone half a league did the man at the helm speak to the prince. He said simply: 'Look behind and tell me what you see.'

The prince looked, and all he saw was a green speck on the horizon. A cry of wonder escaped his lips.

'The speck you see,' said the steersman, 'is the Green Isle. It is now floating westward to the edge of the ocean.'

Then the prince understood why the men had hurried to escape, and he realised that if he had not taken their advice, he would have been carried away beyond the reach of human aid.

Said the steersman: 'Now we can speak. Who are you, and whence come you?'

The prince told the story of his adventure with the queen of eagles, and the men in the boat listened intently. When he was done, the steersman said: 'Now listen, and hear what we have gone through.'

This was the story told by the steersman, whose name was Conall Curlew, the names of the rowers being Garna and Cooimer.

'Yesterday at dawn we beheld the Green Isle lying no farther distant from the shore than a league. The fourth man who was with us is named Mac-a-moir, and he spoke, saying: "Let us visit the Green Isle and explore it. I am told that the king has a daughter named Sunbeam, who is of peerless beauty, and that he will give her as a bride to the bravest hero who visits his castle. He who is bold enough will come with me."

'We all went down to the beach with Mac-a-moir and launched a boat to cross over to the Green Island. The tide favoured us, and we soon reached it. We moored the boat in a sheltered creek, and landed. The beauties of the forest tempted us to linger, and eat fruit and listen to the melodious songs of numerous birds, but Mac-a-moir pressed us to hasten on. Soon we came to a green valley in which there was a castle. I, Conall, knocked at the gate, and a sentinel asked what I sought, and I answered: "I have come to ask for Sunbeam, daughter of the King of Green Isle, to be the bride of Mac-a-moir."

'Word was sent to the king, who said: "He who seeks my daughter Sunbeam must first hold combat with my warriors."

' "I am ready for combat," Mac-a-moir declared.

'The gate was opened, and the heroes entered. Mac-a-moir drew his sword, and the first warrior came against him. Ere long Mac-a-moir struck him down. A second warrior, and then a third, fought and fell also in turn.

'Said the king, when the third warrior fell: "You have overcome the champion of the Green Isle."

' "Bring forth the next best," Mac-a-moir called.

'Said the king: "I fear, my hero, that you wish to slay all my warriors one by one. You have proved your worth. Now let us test you in another manner. My daughter dwells in a high tower on the summit of a steep hill. He who can take her out will have her for his bride. He will also receive two-thirds of my kingdom while I live, and the whole of my kingdom when I die."

'All who were present then went towards the tower, which stood on three high pillars.

' "Who will try first to take out the king's daughter?" I asked.

'Said Mac-a-moir: "I shall try first."

'He tried, but he failed. He could neither climb the pillars nor throw them down.

'Said the king: "Many a man has tried to take my daughter out of this tower, but each one has failed to do so. You had better all return home."

'The other two, Garna and Cooimer, made attempts to shake down the tower, but without success.

'Said the king: "It is no use trying. My daughter cannot be taken out."

'Then I, Conall, stepped forward. I seized one of the pillars and shook it until it broke. The tower toppled over, and as it came down I grasped the Princess Sunbeam in my arms, and placed her standing beside me.

' "Your daughter is now won," I called to the king.

'The Princess Sunbeam smiled sweetly, and the king said: "Yes, indeed, she has been won."

' "I have won her," I reminded him, "for Mac-a-moir."

'Said the king: "He who will marry Sunbeam must remain on the Green Isle."

' "So be it," Mac-a-moir answered him as he took Sunbeam's hand in his and walked towards the castle, following the king.

'A great feast was held in the castle, and Mac-a-moir and the princess were married.

'Said the king: "I am well pleased with Mac-a-moir. It is my desire that his three companions should remain with him and be my warriors."

'I, Conall, told him: "It is our desire to return to our own country."

'The king did not answer. He sat gloomily at the board, and when the wedding feast was ended he walked from the feasting hall.

'Mac-a-moir came and spoke to us soon afterwards, saying: "If it is your desire to go away, make haste and do so now, for the king is about to move the Green Isle far westward towards the realms of the setting sun."

'We bade him farewell, and took our departure. You met us as we hastened towards the boat, and it is as well that you came with us.'

The prince dwelt a time with Conall and his companions. Then he returned to his own land, and related all that had taken place to his father, the King of Level-Plains.

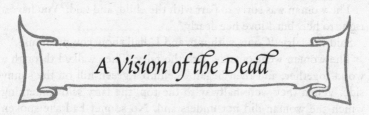

A Vision of the Dead

There once dwelt in Nithsdale a woman who was enabled by fairy aid to see the spirits of the dead in the Other World. This was how it came about. One day she sat spinning wool in her house. Her baby lay in a cradle beside her, listening to the soft humming sound of the spinning wheel and her mother's sweet song. Suddenly a rustling, like the rustling of dead leaves in the wind, was heard at the door. The woman looked up and saw a beautiful lady, clad in green and carrying a baby. She entered, and smiling sweetly, spoke and said: 'Will you nurse my bonnie baby until I return?'

The woman answered: 'Yes, I shall do that.' She took the baby in her arms, and the lady went away, promising to return. But the day went past and night came on, and still she did not come back for her child. The woman wondered greatly, but she wondered even more next morning when she awoke to find beside her bed beautiful new clothes for her children, and some delicious cakes. Being very poor she was glad to dress her children in the new clothes, and to find that they fitted well. The cakes were of wheaten bread and had a honey flavour. It was a great delight to the children to eat them.

The lady did not return that day or the next day. Weeks went past, and the woman nursed the strange child. Months went past, and still the lady stayed away. On many a morning wheaten cakes with honey flavour were found in the house, and when the children's clothes were nearly worn out, new clothing was provided for them as mysteriously as before.

Summer came on, and one evening the lady clad in green again entered the house. A child who was playing on the floor stretched forth his hands to grasp the shining silver spangles that adorned her gown, but to his surprise, his hands passed through them as if they were sunbeams. The woman saw this, and knew her visitor was a fairy.

Said the fairy lady: 'You have been kind to my bonnie baby; I will now take her away.'

The woman was sorry to part with the child, and said: 'You have a right to her, but I love her dearly.'

Said the fairy: 'Come with me, and I shall show you my house.'

The woman went outside with the fairy. They walked through a wood together, and then began to climb a green hill on the sunny side. When they were halfway to the top, the fairy said something which the woman did not understand. No sooner had she spoken than the turf on a bank in front of them lifted up and revealed a door. This door opened, and the two entered through the doorway. When they did so, the turf came down and the door was shut.

The woman found herself in a bare chamber which was dimly lighted.

'Now you shall see my home,' said the fairy woman, who took from her waist-belt a goblet containing a green liquid. She dropped three drops of this liquid in the woman's left eye, and said: 'Look now.'

The woman looked, and was filled with wonder. A beautiful country stretched out in front of her. There were green hills fringed by trees, crystal streams flashing in sunshine, and a lake that shone like burnished silver. Between the hills there lay a field of ripe barley.

The fairy then dropped three drops of the green liquid in the woman's right eye, and said: 'Look now.'

The woman looked, and she saw men and women she had known in times past, cutting the barley and gathering fruit from the trees.

She cried out: 'I see many who once lived on earth and have long been dead. What are they doing here?'

Said the fairy: 'These people are suffering punishment for their evil deeds.'

When she had spoken thus, the fairy woman passed her hand over the woman's eyes, and the vision of green hills and harvest fields and reapers vanished at once. She found herself standing once more in the bare, dimly-lighted chamber. Then the fairy gave her gifts of cloth and healing ointments, and, leading her to the door, bade her farewell. The door opened, the turf was lifted up, and the woman left the fairy's dwelling and returned to her own home.

For a time she kept the power of seeing the fairies as they went to and fro near her house. But one day she spoke to one of them, and the fairy asked: 'With which eye do you see me?'

Said the woman: 'I see you with both my eyes.'

The fairy breathed on her eyes, and then was lost to sight. Never again did the woman behold the fairies, for the power that had been given her was taken away from her eyes by this fairy to whom she had spoken.

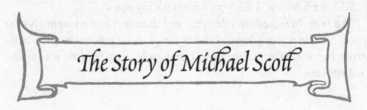

The Story of Michael Scott

Michael Scott, who lived during the thirteenth century, was known far and near as a great scholar, and it is told that he had dealings with the fairies and other spirits. When he wanted to erect a house or a bridge he called the 'wee folk' to his aid, and they did the work for him in a single night. He had great skill as a healer of wounds and curer of diseases, and the people called him a magician.

When Michael was a young man he set out on a journey to Edinburgh with two companions. They travelled on foot, and one day, when they were climbing a high hill, they sat down to rest. No sooner had they done so than they heard a loud hissing sound. They looked in the direction whence the sound came, and saw with horror a great white serpent, curved in wheel shape, rolling towards them at a rapid speed. It was evident that the monster was going to attack them, and when it began to roll up the hillside as swiftly as it had crossed the moor, Michael's two companions sprang to their feet and ran away, shouting with terror. Michael was a man who knew no fear, and he made up his mind to attack the serpent. He stood waiting for it, with his staff firmly grasped in his right hand.

When the serpent came close to Michael it uncurved its body and, throwing itself into a coil, raised its head to strike, its jaws gaping wide and its forked tongue thrust out like an arrow. Michael at once raised his staff, and struck the monster so fierce a blow that he cut its body into three parts. Then he turned away, and called upon his friends to wait for him. They heard his voice, stopped running, and gazed upon him with wonder as he walked towards them very calmly and at an easy pace. It was a great relief to them to learn from Michael that he had slain the fearsome monster.

They walked on together, and had not gone far when they came to a house in which lived a wise old woman. As the sun was beginning to set and it would soon be dark, they asked her for a night's lodging, and she invited them to enter the house. One of the men then told her of their adventure with the wheeling serpent which Michael had slain.

Said the Wise Woman: 'Are you sure the white serpent is dead?'

'It must be dead,' Michael answered, 'because I cut its body into three parts.'

Said the Wise Woman: 'This white serpent is no ordinary serpent. It has power to unite the severed parts of its body again. Once before it was attacked by a brave man, who cut it in two. The head part of its body, however, crawled to a stream. After bathing in the stream it crawled back and joined itself to the tail part. The serpent then became whole again, and once more it bathed in the healing waters of the stream. All serpents do this after attacking a human being. If a man who has been stung by a serpent should hasten to the stream before the serpent can reach it, he will be cured and the serpent will die.'

'You have great knowledge of the mysteries,' Michael exclaimed with wonder.

Said the Wise Woman: 'You have overcome the white serpent this time, but you may not be so fortunate when next it comes against you. Be assured of this: the serpent will, after it has been healed, lie in wait for you to take vengeance. When next it attacks, you will receive no warning that it is near.'

'I shall never cross the high mountain again,' Michael declared.

Said the Wise Woman: 'The serpent will search for you and find you, no matter where you may be.'

'Alas!' Michael exclaimed, 'evil is my fate. What can I do to protect myself against the serpent?'

Said the Wise Woman: 'Go back to the place where you smote the serpent, and carry away the middle part of its body. Make haste, lest you be too late.'

Michael took her advice, and asked his companions to go with him; but they were afraid to do so, and he set out alone.

He walked quickly, and soon came to the place where he had struck down the monster. He found the middle part and the tail part of the white serpent's body, but the head part was nowhere to be seen. He knew then that the woman had spoken truly, and, as darkness was coming on, he did not care to search for the stream to which the head part had gone. Lifting up the middle part of the body, which still quivered, he hastened back towards the house of the Wise Woman. The sky darkened, and the stars began to appear. Michael grew uneasy. He felt sure that something was following him at a distance, so he quickened his steps and never looked back. At length he reached the house in safety, and he was glad to find that there were charms above the door which prevented any evil spirit from entering.

The Wise Woman welcomed Michael, and asked him to give her the part of the serpent's body which he had brought with him. He did so willingly, and she thanked him, and said: 'Now I shall prepare a meal for you and your companions.'

The woman at once set to work and cooked an excellent meal. Michael began to wonder why she showed him and his friends so much kindness and why she was in such high spirits. She laughed and talked as merrily as a girl, and he suspected she had been made happy because he had brought her the middle part of the white serpent's body. He resolved to watch her and find out, if possible, what she was going to do with it.

After eating his supper Michael pretended that he suffered from pain, and went into the kitchen to sit beside the fire. He told the woman that the heat took away the pain, and asked her to allow him to sleep in a chair in front of the fire. She said, 'Very well,' so he sat down, while his weary companions went to bed. The woman put a pot on the fire, and placed in it the middle part of the serpent's body.

Michael took note of this, but said nothing. He pretended to sleep. The part of the serpent began to frizzle in the pot, and the woman came from another room, lifted off the lid, and looked in. Then she tested the juice of the serpent with her right finger. When she did so a cock crew on the roof of the house. Michael was startled. He opened his eyes and looked round.

Said the Wise Woman: 'I thought you were fast asleep.'

'I cannot sleep because of the pain I suffer,' Michael told her.

Said the Wise Woman: 'If you cannot sleep, you may be of service to me. I am very weary and wish to sleep. I am cooking the part of the serpent. Watch the pot for me, and see that the part does not burn. Call me when it is properly cooked, but be sure not to touch it before you do so.'

'I shall not sleep,' Michael said, 'so I may as well have something; to do.'

The Wise Woman smiled, and said: 'After you call me, I shall cure your trouble.' Then she went to her bed and lay down to sleep.

Michael sat watching the pot, and when he found that the portion of the serpent's body was fully cooked, he lifted the pot off the fire. Before calling the old woman, he thought he would first do what she had done when she lifted the lid off the pot. He dipped his finger into the juice of the serpent's body. The tip of his right finger was badly burned, so he thrust it into his mouth. The cock on the roof flapped its wings at once, and crowed so loudly that the old woman woke up in bed and screamed.

Michael felt that there must be magic in the juice of the serpent. New light and knowledge broke in upon him, and he discovered that he had the power to foretell events, to work magic cures, and to read the minds of other people.

The old woman came out of her room. 'You did not call me,' she said in a sad voice.

Michael knew what she meant. Had he called her, she would have been the first to taste the juice of the white serpent and receive from it the great power he now himself possessed.

'I slew the serpent,' he said, 'and had the first right to taste of its juice.'

Said the Wise Woman: 'I dare not scold you now. Nor need I tell you what powers you possess, for you have become wiser than I am. You can cure diseases, you can foretell and foresee what is to take place, you have power to make the fairies obey your commands, and you can obtain greater knowledge about the hidden mysteries than any other man alive. All that I ask of you is your friendship.'

'I give you my friendship willingly,' Michael said to her. Then the Wise Woman sat down beside him and asked him many questions about hidden things, and Michael found himself able to answer each one. They sat together talking until dawn. Then Michael woke his companions, and the woman cooked breakfast. When Michael bade her goodbye, she said: 'Do not forget me, for you owe much to me.'

'I shall never forget you,' he promised her.

Michael and his companions resumed their journey. They walked until sunset, but did not reach a house.

'Tonight,' one of the men said, 'we must sleep on the heather.'

Michael smiled. 'Tonight,' said he, 'we shall sleep in Edinburgh.'

'It is still a day's journey from here,' the man reminded him.

Michael laid his staff on the ground and said: 'Let us three sit on this staff and see how we fare.'

His companions laughed, and sat down as he asked them to do. They thought it a great joke.

'Hold tight!' Michael advised them. The men, still amused, grasped the staff in their hands and held it tightly.

'Staff of mine!' Michael cried, 'carry us to Edinburgh.'

No sooner did he speak than the staff rose high in the air. The men were terror-stricken as the staff flew towards the clouds and then went forward with the speed of lightning. They shivered with fear and with cold. Snowflakes fell on them as the staff flew across the sky, for they were higher up than the peak of Ben Nevis. When night was falling and the stars came out one by one, the staff began to descend. Happy were Michael's companions when they came down safely on the outskirts of Edinburgh.

They walked into the town in silence, and the first man they met stood and gazed with wonder upon them in the lamplight.

'Why do you stare at strangers?' Michael asked.

Said the man: 'There is snow on your caps and your shoulders.'

Having spoken thus, a sudden fear overcame him, and he turned and fled, believing that the three strangers were either wizards or fairies.

Michael shook the snow off his cap and shoulders, and his companions did the same. They then sought out a lodging, and having eaten their suppers, went to bed.

Next morning Michael found that his companions had risen early and gone away. He knew that they were afraid of him, so he smiled and said to himself: 'I bear them no ill-will. I prefer now to be alone.'

Michael soon became famous as a builder. When he was asked to build a house, he called the fairies to his aid, and they did the work in the night-time for him.

Once he was travelling towards Inverness, and came to a river which was in flood. The ford could not be crossed, and several men stood beside it looking across the deep turbid waters. 'It is a pity,' one said to Michael, 'there is no bridge here.'

Said Michael: 'I have come to build a bridge, and my workers will begin to erect it tonight.'

Those who heard him laughed and turned away, but great was their surprise next morning to find that a bridge had been built. They crossed over it with their horses and cattle, and as they went on their way they spread the fame of Michael far and wide.

As time went on Michael found that his fairy workers wished to do more than he required of them. They began to visit him every evening, crying out: 'Work! work! work!'

So Michael thought one day that he would set them to perform a task beyond their powers, and when next they came to him crying out: 'Work! work! work!' he told them to close up the Inverness firth and cut it off from the sea. The fairies at once hastened away to obey his command.

Michael thought of the swift tides and of the great volume of water flowing down from the rivers by night and by day, and was certain that the fairies would not be able to close the firth.

Next morning, however, he found that the river Ness was rising rapidly, and threatening to flood the town of Inverness. He climbed a hill and looked seaward. Then he found that the fairies had very nearly finished the work he had set them to do. They had made two long promontories which jutted across the firth, and there remained only a narrow space through which the water surged. The incoming tide kept back the waters flowing from the river, and that was why the Ness was rising in flood. Not until after the tide turned did the waters of the river begin to fall.

Michael summoned his fairy workers that evening, and ordered them to open up the firth again. They hastened away to obey him, and after darkness came on they began to destroy the promontories. The moon rose as they went on with their work. A holy man walking along the shore saw the fairies, and prayed for protection against them. When he did so the fairies fled away, and were unable again to visit the promontories, and so these still lie jutting across the firth like crab's toes. The one has been named Chanonry Point, and on the peninsula opposite it there now stands Fort George, which was placed there to prevent enemy ships from sailing up to Inverness.

When the fairies found they were unable to complete their task they returned to Michael, crying out again: 'Work! work! work!'

Michael then thought of an impossible task which would keep them busy. He said: 'Go and make rope-ladders that will reach to the back of the moon. They must be made of sea sand and white foam.'

The fairies hastened away to obey his command. They could not, however, make the ropes for Michael, try as they might.

Some say that Michael's workers are still attempting to carry out the work he last set them to do, and that is why wreaths of foam and ropes of twisted sand are sometimes found on the seashore to this day.

It is said that one weak-minded and clumsy old fairy man used to spend night after night trying to make ropes of sand and foam on the shore of Kirkcaldy Bay. When he grew weary he lay down to rest himself, and on cold nights he could be heard moaning: 'My toes are cold, my toes are cold.'

In the Kingdom of Seals

The sea fairies have grey skin-coverings and resemble seals. They dwell in cave houses on the borders of Land-under-Waves, where they have a kingdom of their own. They love music and the dance, like all fairies, and when harper or piper plays on the beach they come up to listen, their sloe-black eyes sparkling with joy. On moonlight nights they hear the mermaids singing on the rocks when human beings are fast asleep, and they call to them: 'Sing again the old sea croons; sing again!' All night long the sea fairies call thus when mermaids cease to sing, and the mermaids sing again and again to them. When the wind pipes loud and free, and the sea leaps and whirls and swings and cries aloud with wintry merriment, the sea fairies dance with the dancing waves, tossing white petals of foam over their heads and twining pearls of spray about their necks. They love to hunt the silvern salmon in the forests of sea-tangle and in the ocean's deep blue glens, and far up dark ravines through which flow rivers of sweet mountain waters gemmed with stars.

The sea fairies have a language of their own, and they are also skilled in human speech. When they come ashore they can take the forms of men or women and turn billows into dark horses with grey manes and long grey tails, and on these they ride over mountain and moor.

There was once a fisherman who visited the palace of the sea fairies, and told on his return all he had seen and all he had heard. He dwelt in a little township nigh to John-o'-Groat's House, and was wont to catch fish and seals. When he found that he could earn much money by hunting seals, whose skins make warm winter clothing, he troubled little about catching salmon or cod, and worked constantly as a seal-hunter. He crept among the rocks searching for his prey, and visited lonely seal-haunted islands across the Pentland Firth, where he often found the strange sea-prowlers lying on smooth flat ledges of rock fast asleep in the warm sunshine.

In his house he had great bundles of dried sealskins, and people came from a distance to purchase them from him. His fame as a seal-hunter went far and wide.

One evening a dark stranger rode up to his house, mounted on a spirited black mare with grey mane and grey tail. He called to the fisherman who came out: 'Make haste and ride with me towards the east. My master desires to do business with you.'

'I have no horse,' the fisherman answered, 'but I shall walk to your master's house tomorrow.'

Said the stranger: 'Come now. Ride with me. My good mare is fleet-footed and strong.'

'As you will,' answered the fisherman, who at once mounted the mare behind the stranger.

The mare turned round and right-about, and galloped eastward faster than the wind of March. Shingle rose in front of her like rock-strewn sea-spray and a sand-cloud gathered and swept out behind like mountain mists that are scattered before a gale. The fisherman gasped for breath, for although the wind was blowing against his back when he mounted the mare, it blew fiercely in his face as he rode on. The mare went fast and far until she drew nigh to a precipice. Near the edge of it she halted suddenly and the pair dismounted. The fishermen found then that the wind was still blowing seaward, although he had thought it had veered round as he rode. Never before had he sat on the back of so fleet-footed a mare.

Said the stranger: 'We have almost reached my master's dwelling.'

The fisherman looked round about him with surprise, and saw neither house nor the smoke of one. 'Where is your master?' he asked.

Said the stranger: 'You shall see him presently. Come with me.'

As he spoke he walked towards the edge of the precipice and looked over. The fisherman did the same, and saw nothing but the grey lonely sea heaving in a long slow swell, and sea-birds wheeling and sliding down the wind.

'Where is your master?' he asked once again.

With that the stranger suddenly clasped the seal-hunter in his arms, and crying, 'Come with me,' leapt over the edge of the precipice. The mare leapt with her master.

Down, down they fell through the air, scattering the startled sea-birds. Screaming and fluttering, the birds rose in clouds about and above them, and down ever down the men and the mare continued to fall till they plunged into the sea, and sank and sank, while the light around them faded into darkness deeper than night. The fisherman wondered to find himself still alive as he passed through the sea depths, seeing naught, hearing naught and still moving swiftly. At length he ceased to sink, and went forward. He suffered no pain or discomfort, nor was he afraid. His only feeling was of wonder, and in the thick, cool darkness he wondered greatly what would happen next. At length he saw a faint green light, and as he went onward the light grew brighter and brighter, until the glens and bens and forests of the sea kingdom arose before his eyes. Then he discovered that he was swimming beside the stranger and that they had both been changed into seals.

Said the stranger: 'Yonder is my master's house.'

The fisherman looked, and saw a township of foam-white houses on the edge of a great sea-forest and fronted by a bank of sea-moss which was green as grass but more beautiful, and very bright. There were crowds of seal-folk in the township. He saw them moving about to and fro, and heard their voices, but he could not understand their speech. Mothers nursed their babes, and young children played games on banks of green sea-moss, and from the brown and golden sea-forest came sounds of music and the shouts of dancers.

Said the stranger: 'Here is my master's house. Let us enter.'

He led the fisherman towards the door of a great foam-white palace with its many bright windows. It was thatched with red tangle and the door was of green stone. The door opened as smoothly as a summer wave that moves across a river mouth, and the fisherman entered with his guide. He found himself in a dimly-lighted room and saw an old grey seal stretched on a bed, and heard him moaning with pain. Beside the bed lay a bloodstained knife, and the fisherman knew at a glance that it was his own. Then he remembered that, not many hours before, he had stabbed a seal, and that it had escaped by plunging into the sea, carrying the knife in its back.

The fisherman was startled to realise that the old seal on the bed was the very one he had tried to kill, and his heart was filled with fear. He threw himself down and begged for forgiveness and mercy, for he feared that he would be put to death.

The guide lifted up the knife and asked: 'Have you ever seen this knife before?' He spoke in human language.

'That is my knife, alas!' exclaimed the fishermen.

Said the guide: 'The wounded seal is my father. Our doctors are unable to cure him. They can do naught without your help. That is why I visited your house and urged you to come with me. I ask your pardon for deceiving you, but as I love my father greatly, I had to do as I have done.'

'Do not ask my pardon,' the fisherman said; 'I have need of yours. I am sorry and ashamed for having stabbed your father.'

Said the guide: 'Lay your hand on the wound and wish it to be healed.'

The fisherman laid his hand on the wound, and the pain that the seal suffered passed into his hand, but did not remain long. As if by magic, the wound was healed at once. Then the old grey seal rose up strong and well again.

Said the guide: 'You have served us well this day!'

When the fisherman had entered the house, all the seals that were within were weeping tears of sorrow, but they ceased to weep as soon as he had laid his hand on the wound, and when the old seal rose up they all became merry and bright.

The fisherman wondered what would happen next. For a time the seals seemed to forget his presence, but at length his guide spoke to him and said: 'Now you can return to your own home where your wife and children await you. I shall lead you through the sea depths, and take you on my mare across the plain which we crossed when coming hither.'

'I give you thanks,' the fisherman exclaimed.

Said the guide: 'Before you leave there is one thing you must do; you must take a vow never again to hunt seals.'

The fisherman answered: 'Surely, I promise never again to hunt for seals.'

Said the guide: 'If ever you break your promise you shall die. I counsel you to keep it, and as long as you do so you will prosper. Every time you set lines, or cast a net, you will catch much fish. Our seal-servants will help you, and if you wish to reward them for their services, take with you in your boat a harp or pipe and play sweet music, for music is the delight of all seals.'

The fisherman vowed he would never break his promise, and the guide then led him back to dry land. As soon as he reached the shore he ceased to be a seal and became a man once again. The guide, who had also changed shape, breathed over a great wave and, immediately, it became a dark mare with grey mane and grey tail. He then mounted the mare, and bade the fisherman mount behind him. The mare rose in the air as lightly as wind-tossed spray, and passing through the clouds of startled sea-birds reached the top of the precipice. On she raced at once, raising the shingle in front and a cloud of sand behind. The night was falling and the stars began to appear, but it was not quite dark when the fisherman's house was reached.

The fisherman dismounted, and his guide spoke and said: 'Take this from me, and may you live happily.'

He handed the fisherman a small bag and crying: 'Farewell! Remember your vow,' he wheeled his mare right round and passed swiftly out of sight.

The fisherman entered his house, and found his wife still there. 'You have returned,' she said. 'How did you fare?'

'I know not yet,' he answered. Then he sat down and opened the bag, and to his surprise and delight found it was full of pearls.

His wife uttered a cry of wonder, and said: 'From whom did you receive this treasure?'

The fisherman then related all that had taken place, and his wife wondered to hear him.

'Never again will I hunt seals,' he exclaimed. And he kept his word and prospered, and lived happily until the day of his death.

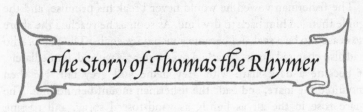

The Story of Thomas the Rhymer

At the beginning of each summer, when the milk-white hawthorn is in bloom, anointing the air with its sweet odour, and miles and miles of golden whin adorn the glens and hill-slopes, the fairies come forth in grand procession, headed by the Fairy Queen. They are mounted on little white horses, and when on a night of clear soft moonlight the people hear the clatter of many hoofs, the jingling of bridles and the sound of laughter and fairy music coming sweetly down the wind, they whisper one to another: ' 'Tis the Fairy Folks' Raid', or, 'Here come the Riders of the Shee.'

The Fairy Queen, who rides in front, is gowned in grass-green silk, and wears over her shoulders a mantle of green velvet adorned with silver spangles. She is of great beauty. Her eyes are like wood violets, her teeth like pearls, her brow and neck are swan-white and her cheeks bloom like ripe apples. Her long clustering hair of rich auburn gold, which falls over her shoulders and down her back, is bound round about with a snood that glints with starlike gems, and there is one great flashing jewel above her brow. On each lock of her horse's mane hang sweet-toned silver bells that tinkle merrily as she rides on.

The riders who follow her in couples are likewise clad in green, and wear little red caps bright as the flaming poppies in waving fields of yellow barley. Their horses' manes are hung with silver whistles upon which the soft winds play. Some fairies twang harps of gold, some make sweet music on oaten pipes and some sing with birdlike voices in the moonlight. When song and music cease, they chat and laugh merrily as they ride on their way. Over hills and down glens they go, but no hoof-mark is left by their horses. So lightly do the little white creatures trot that not a grass blade is broken by their tread, nor is the honeydew spilled from blue harebells and yellow buttercups. Sometimes the fairies ride over treetops or through the air on eddies of western wind. The Riders of the Shee always come from the west.

When the Summer Fairy Raid is coming, the people hang branches of rowan over their doors and round their rooms, and when the Winter Raid is coming they hang up holly and mistletoe as protection from attack; for sometimes the fairies steal pretty children while they lie fast asleep, and carry them off to Fairyland, and sometimes they lure away pipers and bards, and women who have sweet singing voices.

Once there was a great bard who was called Thomas the Rhymer. He lived at Ercildoune (Earlston), in Berwickshire, during the thirteenth century. It is told that he vanished for seven years, and that when he reappeared he had the gift of prophecy. Because he was able to foretell events, he was given the name of True Thomas.

All through Scotland, from the Cheviot Hills to the Pentland Firth, the story of Thomas the Rhymer has long been known.

During his seven years' absence from home he is said to have dwelt in Fairyland. One evening, so runs the tale, he was walking alone on the banks of Leader Water when he saw riding towards him the Fairy Queen on her milk-white steed, the silver bells tinkling on its mane and the silver bridle jingling sweet and clear. He was amazed at her beauty, and thinking she was the Queen of Heaven, bared his head and knelt before her as she dismounted, saying: 'All hail, mighty Queen of Heaven! I have never before seen your equal.'

Said the green-clad lady: 'Ah! Thomas, you have named me wrongly. I am the Queen of Fairyland, and have come to visit you.'

'What seek you with me?' Thomas asked.

Said the Fairy Queen: 'You must hasten at once to Fairyland, and serve me there for seven years.'

Then she laid a spell upon him, and he had to obey her will. She mounted her milk-white steed and Thomas mounted behind her, and they rode off together. They crossed Leader Water, and the horse went swifter than the wind over hill and dale until a great wide desert was reached. No house nor human being could be seen anywhere. East and west, north and south, the level desert stretched as far as eye could see. They rode on and on until at length the Fairy Queen spoke: 'Dismount, Thomas, and I shall show you three wonders.'

Thomas dismounted and the Fairy Queen dismounted also. Said she: 'Look, yonder is a narrow road full of thorns and briers. That is the path to Heaven. Yonder is a broad highway which runs across a lily lea. That is the path of wickedness. Yonder is another road. It twines round the hillside towards the west. That is the way to Fairyland, and you and I must ride thither.'

Again she mounted her milk-white steed and Thomas mounted behind. They rode on and on, crossing many rivers. Nor sun or moon could be seen nor any stars, and in the silence and thick darkness they heard the deep voice of the roaring sea.

At length a light appeared in front of them, which grew larger and brighter as they rode on. Then Thomas saw a beautiful country. The horse halted and he found himself in the midst of a green garden. When they had dismounted, the Fairy Queen plucked an apple and gave it to Thomas, saying: 'This is your reward for coming with me. After you have eaten of it you will have power to speak truly of coming events, and men will know you as "True Thomas".'

Thomas ate the apple and then followed the queen to her palace. He was given clothing of green silk and shoes of green velvet, and he dwelt among the fairies for seven years. The time passed so quickly that the seven years seemed no longer than seven hours.

After his return to Ercildoune, where he lived in a castle, Thomas made many songs and ballads and pronounced in rhyme many prophecies. He travelled up and down the country, and wherever he went he foretold events, some of which took place while yet he lived among men, but others did not happen until long years afterwards. There are still some prophecies which are as yet unfulfilled.

It is said that when Thomas was an old man the Fairy Queen returned for him. One day, as he stood chatting with knights and ladies, she rode from the riverside and called: 'True Thomas, your time has come.'

Thomas cried to his friends: 'Farewell, all of you, I shall return no more.' Then he mounted the milk-white steed behind the Fairy Queen, and galloped across the ford. Several knights leapt into their saddles and followed the Rider of the Shee, but when they reached the opposite bank of the river they could see naught of Thomas and the Fairy Queen.

It is said that Thomas still dwells in Fairyland, and that he goes about among the Riders of the Shee when they come forth at the beginning of each summer. Those who have seen him ride past tell that he looks very old, and that his hair and long beard are white as driven snow. At other times he goes about invisible, except when he attends a market to buy horses for a fairy army which is to take part in a great battle. He drives the horses to Fairyland and keeps them there. When he has collected a sufficient number, it is told, he will return again to wage war against the invaders of his country, whom he will defeat on the banks of the Clyde.

Thomas wanders far and wide through Scotland. He has been seen, folks have told, riding out of a fairy dwelling below Eildon Hills, from another fairy dwelling below Dumbuck Hill, near Dumbarton, and from a third fairy dwelling below the boat-shaped mound of Tom-na-hurich at Inverness.

Once a man who climbed Dumbuck Hill came to an open door and entered through it. In a dim chamber he saw a little old man resting on his elbow, who spoke to him and said: 'Has the time come?'

The man was stricken with fear and fled away. When he pressed through the doorway, the door shut behind him, and turf closed over it.

Another story about Thomas is told at Inverness. Two fiddlers, named Farquhar Grant and Thomas Gumming, natives of Strathspey, who lived over three hundred years ago, once visited Inverness during the Christmas season. They hoped to earn money by their music, and as soon as they arrived in the town began to show their skill in the streets. Although they had great fame as fiddlers in Strathspey, they found that the townspeople took little notice of them. When night fell, they had not collected enough money to buy food for supper and to pay for a night's lodging. They stopped playing and went, with their fiddles under their right arms, towards the wooden bridge that then crossed the River Ness.

Just as they were about to walk over the bridge they saw a little old man coming towards them in the dusk. His beard was very long and very white, but although his back was bent his step was easy and light. He stopped in front of the fiddlers, and, much to their surprise, hailed them by their names saying: 'How fares it with you, my merry fiddlers?'

'Badly, badly!' answered Grant.

'Very badly indeed!' Gumming said.

'Come with me,' said the old man. 'I have need of fiddlers tonight and will reward you well. A great ball is to be held in my castle, and there are no musicians.'

Grant and Gumming were glad to get the chance of earning money by playing their fiddles and said they would go. 'Then follow me and make haste,' said the old man. The fiddlers followed him across the wooden bridge and across the darkening moor beyond. He walked with rapid strides, and sometimes the fiddlers had to break into a run to keep up with him. Now and again that strange, nimble old man would turn round and cry: 'Are you coming, my merry fiddlers?'

'We are doing our best,' Grant would answer, while Gumming would mutter: 'By my faith, old man, but you walk quickly!'

'Make haste, Grant; make haste, Gumming,' the old man would then exclaim; 'my guests will be growing impatient.'

In time they reached the big boat-shaped mound called Tom-na-hurich, and the old man began to climb it. The fiddlers followed at a short distance. Then he stopped suddenly and stamped the ground three times with his right foot. A door opened and a bright light streamed forth.

'Here is my castle, Gumming; here is my castle, Grant,' exclaimed the old man, who was no other than Thomas the Rhymer. 'Come within and make merry.'

The fiddlers paused for a moment at the open door, but Thomas the Rhymer drew from his belt a purse of gold and made it jingle. 'This purse holds your wages,' he told them. 'First you will get your share of the feast, then you will give us fine music.'

As the fiddlers were as hungry as they were poor, they could not resist the offer made to them, and entered the fairy castle. As soon as they entered, the door was shut behind them.

They found themselves in a great hall filled with brilliant light. Tables were spread with all kinds of food, and guests sat round them eating and chatting and laughing merrily.

Thomas led the fiddlers to a side table, and two graceful maidens clad in green came forward with dishes of food and bottles of wine, and said: 'Eat and drink to your hearts' content, Farquhar Grant and Thomas Gumming – Farquhar o' Feshie and Thomas o' Tom-an-Torran. You are welcome here tonight.'

The fiddlers wondered greatly that the maidens knew not only their personal names but even the names of their homes. They began to eat, and, no matter how much they ate, the food on the table did not seem to grow less. They poured out wine, but they could not empty the bottles.

Said Gumming: 'This is a feast indeed.'

Said Grant: 'There was never such a feast in Strathspey.'

When the feast was ended the fiddlers were led to the ballroom, and there they began to play merry music for the gayest and brightest and happiest dancers they ever saw before. They played reels and jigs and strathspeys, and yet never grew weary. The dancers praised their music, and fair girls brought them fruit and wine at the end of each dance. If the guests were happy, the musicians were happier still, and they were sorry to find at length that the ball was coming to an end. How long it had lasted they could not tell. When the dancers began to go away they were still unwearied and willing to go on playing.

Thomas the Rhymer entered the ballroom, and spoke to the fiddlers, saying: 'You have done well, my merry men. I will lead you to the door, and pay you for your fine music.'

The fiddlers were sorry to go away. At the door Thomas the Rhymer divided the purse of gold between them, and asked: 'Are you satisfied?'

'Satisfied!' Gumming repeated. 'Oh, yes, for you and your guests have been very kind!'

'We should gladly come back again,' Grant said.

When they had left the castle the fiddlers found that it was bright day. The sun shone from an unclouded sky, and the air was warm. As they walked on they were surprised to see fields of ripe corn, which was a strange sight at the Christmas season. Then they came to the riverside, and found instead of a wooden bridge a new stone bridge with seven arches.

'This stone bridge was not here last night,' Gumming said.

'Not that I saw,' said Grant.

When they crossed the bridge they found that the town of Inverness had changed greatly. Many new houses had been built; there were even new streets. The people they saw moving about wore strange clothing. One spoke to the fiddlers, and asked: 'Who are you, and whence come you?'

They told him their names, and said that on the previous night they had played their fiddles at a great ball in a castle near the town.

The man smiled. Then Farquhar said: 'The bridge we crossed over last evening was made of wood. Now you have a bridge of stone. Have the fairies built it for you?'

The man laughed, and exclaimed, as he turned away: 'You are mad. The stone bridge was built before I was born.'

Boys began to collect round the fiddlers. They jeered at their clothing, and cried: 'Go back to the madhouse you have escaped from.'

The fiddlers hastened out of the town, and took the road which leads to Strathspey. Men who passed them stopped and looked back, but they spoke to no one, and scarcely spoke, indeed, to one another.

Darkness came on, and they crept into an empty, half-ruined house by the wayside and slept there. How long they slept they knew not, but when they came out again they saw that the harvesting had begun. Fields were partly cut, but no workers could be seen in them, although the sun was already high in the heavens. They drank water from a well, and went on their way, until at length they reached their native village. They entered it joyfully, but were unable to find their homes. There, too, new houses had been built, and strange faces were seen. They heard a bell ringing, and then knew it was Sabbath day, and they walked towards the church. A man spoke to them near the gate of the churchyard and said: 'You are strangers here.'

'No, indeed, we are not strangers,' Grant assured him. 'This is our native village.'

'You must have left it long ago,' said the man, 'for I have lived here all my life, and I do not know you.'

Then Grant told his name and that of his companion, and the names of their fathers and mothers. 'We are fine fiddlers,' he added; 'our equal is not to be found north of the Grampians.'

Said the man: 'Ah! you are the two men my grandfather used to speak of. He never saw you, but he heard his father tell that you had been decoyed by Thomas the Rhymer, who took you to Tom-na-hurich. Your friends mourned for you greatly, but now you are quite forgotten, for it is fully a hundred years since you went away from here.'

The fiddlers thought that the man was mocking them, and turned their backs upon him. They went into the churchyard, and began to read the names on the gravestones. They saw stones erected to their wives and children, and to their children's children, and gazed on them with amazement, taking no notice of the people who passed by to the church door.

At length they entered the church hand in hand, with their fiddles under their arms. They stood for a brief space at the doorway, gazing at the congregation, but were unable to recognise a single face among the people who looked round at them.

The minister was in the pulpit. He had been told who the strangers were, and, after gazing for a moment in silence, he began to pray. No sooner did he do so than the two fiddlers crumbled into dust.

Such is the story of the two fiddlers who spent a hundred years in a fairy dwelling, thinking they had played music there for but a single night.

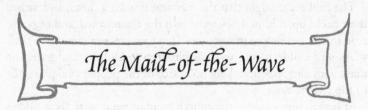

The Maid-of-the-Wave

The mermaid, or, as she is called in Gaelic, Maid-of-the-Wave, has great beauty and is sweet-voiced. Half her body is of fish shape, and glitters like a salmon in sunshine, and she has long copper-coloured hair which she loves to comb as she sits on a rock on a lonely shore, gazing in a mirror of silver, and singing a song in praise of her own great beauty. Sometimes, on moonlight nights, she takes off her skin covering and puts on sea-blue garments, and then she seems fairer than any lady in the land.

Once a young crofter was wandering below the cliffs on a beautiful summer night when the wind was still and the silver moon shone through the clear depths of ocean, casting a flood of light through Land-under-Waves. He heard sounds of song and laughter. He crept softly towards a shadowy rock, and, climbing it, looked down on a bank of white sand. There he beheld a company of mermaids dancing in a ring round a maid who was fairest of the fair. They had taken off their skin coverings, and were gowned in pale blue, and, as they wheeled round about, their copper tresses streamed out behind their backs, glistening in the moonlight. He was delighted by their singing and amazed at their beauty.

At length, he crept stealthily down the rock and ran towards the skin coverings lying on the sand. He seized one and ran off with it. When the mermaids saw him they screamed and scattered in confusion, and snatching up their skin coverings, leapt into the sea and vanished from sight. One maid remained behind. This was the fair one round whom the others had been dancing. Her skin covering was gone, and so she could not return to her sea home.

Meanwhile the crofter ran to his house and hid the skin covering in a box, which he locked, placing the key in his pocket. He wondered what would happen next, and he had not long to wait. Someone came to his door and knocked softly. He stood listening in silence. Then he heard the knocking again, and opened the door.

A Maid-of-the-Wave, clad in pale sea-blue garments, stood before him, the moonlight glistening on her wet copper hair. Tears stood in her soft blue eyes as she spoke sweetly saying: 'I beg you, have pity and give me back my skin covering so that I may return to my sea home.'

She was so gentle and so beautiful that the crofter did not wish her to go away, so he answered: 'What I have got I keep. Do not sorrow, fair one. Remain here and be my bride.'

The mermaid turned away and wandered along the shore, but the crofter did not leave his house. In the morning she returned again, and the crofter said to her: 'Be my bride.'

The mermaid consented saying: 'I cannot return to my fair sea home. I must live now among human beings, and I know no one except you alone. Be kind to me, but do not tell man or woman who I am or whence I came.'

The crofter promised to keep her secret, and that day they were married. All the people of the township loved Maid-of-the-Wave, and rejoiced to have her among them. They thought she was a princess from a far country who had been carried away by the fairies.

For seven years the crofter and his wife lived happily together. They had three children, two boys and a girl, and Maid-of-the-Wave loved them dearly.

When the seventh year was drawing to a close the crofter set out on a journey to Big Town, having business to do there. His wife was lonely without him, and sat often on the shore singing songs to her baby girl and gazing over the sea.

One evening, as she wandered among the rocks, her elder boy, whose name was Kenneth, came to her and said: 'I found a key which opened father's box, and in the box I saw a skin like the skin of a salmon, but brighter and more beautiful, and very large.'

His mother gasped with surprise and secret joy, and asked softly: 'Will you give me the key?'

Kenneth handed the key to her, and she hid it in her bosom. Then she said: 'It is getting late. The moon will not rise till near midnight. Come home, little Kenneth, and I shall make supper, and put you to bed, and sing you to sleep.'

As she spoke she began to sing a joyous song, and Kenneth was glad that his mother was no longer sad because his father was from home. He grasped his mother's hand, and tripped lightly by her side as they went homeward together.

When the two boys had had supper and were slumbering in bed, the crofter's wife hushed her girl-baby to sleep, and laid her in her cradle. Then she took the key from her bosom and opened the box. There she found her long-lost skin covering. She wished to return to her fair sea home, yet she did not care to leave her children. She sat by the fire for a time, wondering if she should put on the skin covering or place it in the box again. At length, however, she heard the sound of singing coming over the waves, and the song she heard was like this:

'Maid-of-the-Wave, the dew mist is falling,
      Thy sisters are calling and longing for thee;
Maid-of-the-Wave, the white stars are gleaming,
      Their bright rays are streaming across the dark sea.
Maid-of-the-Wave, would thou wert near us!
      Come now to cheer us – Oh, hear us! Oh, hear us!

Maid-of-the-Wave, a sea-wind is blowing,
      The tide at its flowing hath borne us to thee;
Maid-of-the-Wave, the tide is now turning –
      Oh! we are all yearning our sister to see.
Maid-of-the-Wave, come back and ne'er leave us,
      The loss of thee grieves us – believe us! believe us!

Maid-of-the-Wave, what caredst thou in childhood
      For moorland or wildwood? thy home was the sea.
Maid-of-the-Wave, thine exile and sorrow
      Will end ere the morrow, and thou shalt be free.
Maid-of-the-Wave, tonight from our sea-halls
      A heart-spell on thee falls – the sea calls! the sea calls!'

She kissed the two boys and wept over them. Then she knelt beside her little baby girl, who smiled in her sleep, and she sang:

'Sleep, oh! sleep my fair, my rare one,
      Sleep, oh! sleep nor sigh nor fret thee.
Though I leave thee it doth grieve me –
      Ne'er, oh! ne'er will I forget thee.

Sleep, oh! sleep, my white, my bright one,
  Sleep, oh! sleep and know no sorrow.
Soft I kiss thee, I who'll miss thee
  And thy sire who'll come tomorrow.

Sleep, oh! sleep my near, my dear one,
  While thy brothers sleep beside thee.
They will waken all forsaken –
  Fare thee well, and woe betide me!'

When she had sung this song she heard voices from the sea calling low and calling sweet:

'Maid-of-the-Wave, oh! list to our singing;
  The white moon is winging its way o'er the sea.
Maid-of-the-Wave, the white moon is shining,
  And we are all pining, sweet sister, for thee.
Maid-of-the-Wave, would thou wert near us!
  Come now to cheer us – Oh, hear us! Oh, hear us!'

The weeping mother kissed her boys and her baby girl once again. Then she put on her skin covering and, hastening down the beach, plunged into the sea. Ere long, sounds of joy and laughter were heard far out amongst the billows, and they grew fainter and fainter until they were heard no more. The moon rose high and fair, and shone over the wide solitary ocean, and whither the mermaids had gone no one could tell.

When the crofter returned next morning he found the children fast asleep. He wakened Kenneth, who told him about finding the key and opening the box.

'Where is the key now?' the crofter asked.

'I gave it to mother,' said the boy.

The crofter went towards the box. It was open, and the skin covering was gone. Then he knew what had happened, and sat down and sorrowed because Maid-of-the-Wave had gone.

It is told that the lost mother often returned at night-time to gaze through the cottage windows on her children as they lay asleep. She left trout and salmon for them outside the door. When the boys found the fish they wondered greatly, and their father wept and said: 'Your mother is far away, but she has not forgotten you.'

'Will mother return again?' the boys would ask.

'No, mother will not return,' their father would say. 'She now dwells in the home of her people, to which you and I can never go.'

When the boys grew up they became bold and daring seamen, and no harm ever came to them in storm or darkness, for their mother, Maid-of-the-Wave, followed their ship and protected it from all peril.

A mermaid has power to grant three wishes, for she is one of the fairy folk of ocean and a subject of Queen Beira's.

Once a seaman saw a Maid-of-the-Wave sitting on a rock. He crept towards her, unheard and unseen, and seized her in his arms.

'Let me go!' the mermaid cried, 'or I shall drag you into the sea.'

'I shall not let you go,' said the seaman, who was very strong, 'until you have granted me three wishes.'

'What are your wishes?' asked the mermaid.

'Health, wealth and prosperity.'

'Your wishes are granted,' exclaimed the mermaid, who, being then released, plunged into the sea and vanished from sight.

Sometimes a mermaid will give good advice to human beings. There was once a man in Galloway who had skill as a curer of diseases, and it was said that he received some of his knowledge from a mermaid. A beautiful girl named May was ill with consumption. The Galloway herbalist tried in vain to cure her, and as he loved her dearly and wished to marry her, his heart was very sad when he found that his herbs did not do her any good. One evening as he sat sorrowing on the shore, a mermaid raised her head above the waves and sang:

> 'Would you let bonnie May die in your hand
> And the mugwort flowering in the land?'

Then she vanished.

The man went at once and gathered the flowers of the mugwort, and made a medicine. This he gave to May, who was soon restored to health.

A mermaid may be offended by anyone who interferes with her, and if she is offended she may do harm.

An old family once lived in a house called Knockdolion, which stood on the banks of the Water of Girvan in Ayrshire. There was a black stone at the end of the house, and a mermaid used to come and sit on it, combing her hair and singing for hours on end. The lady of the house could not get her baby to sleep because of the loud singing of the mermaid, so she told her menservants to break up the stone.

This they did, and when the mermaid came on the night that followed she found no stone to sit upon. She at once flew into a rage, and cried to the lady of the house:

> 'Ye may think on your cradle –
> I think on my stane;
> There will ne'er be an heir
> To Knockdolian again.'

Not long after this the baby died. He was the only child in the house, and when his father and mother died the family became extinct.

Once a Forfarshire landowner nearly lost his life by rushing into a lake towards a mermaid. He thought she was a young lady who had got beyond her depths while bathing. As she struggled in the water she called to him: 'Help! help! or I'll drown.' When the landowner entered the lake his manservant followed him and hauled him back. 'That wailing woman,' the servant said, 'is not a human being but a mermaid. If you had touched her, she would have dragged you down and drowned you.' As he spoke the sound of laughter came over the lake, and the mermaid was seen swimming away in the dusk.

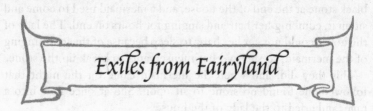

Exiles from Fairyland

The Fairy Queen banishes from Fairyland any fairy who disobeys her orders. Then the exile wanders about alone through the land in search of companions. As the queen's subjects shun the banished fairy man or woman, he or she must needs make friends with human beings.

The Goona is the name given to one class of fairy exiles. A Goona is very kindly and harmless, and goes about at night trying to be of service to mankind. He herds the cattle on the hills, and keeps them away from dangerous places. Often he is seen sitting on the edge of a cliff, and when cattle come near he drives them back. In the summer and autumn seasons he watches the cornfields, and if a cow should try to enter one, he seizes it by a horn and leads it to hill pasture. In winter time, when the cattle are kept in byres, the Goona feels very lonely, having no work to do.

Crofters speak kindly of the Goona, and consider themselves lucky when one haunts their countryside. They tell that he is a little fairy man with long golden hair that falls down over his shoulders and back. He is clad in a fox's skin, and in wintry weather he suffers much from cold, for that is part of his punishment. The crofters pity him, and wish that he would come into a house and sit beside a warm fire, but this he is forbidden to do. If a crofter were to offer a Goona any clothing the little lonely fellow would have to go away and he could never return again. The only food the exiled fairy can get are scraps and bones flung away by human beings. There are songs about the Goona. One tells:

> He will watch the long weird night,
> When the stars will shake with fright,
> Or the ghostly moon leaps bright
>   O'er the ben like Beltane fire.
> If my kine should seek the corn
> He will turn them by the horn,

>And I 'll find them all at morn
>Lowing sweet beside the byre.

Only those who have 'second sight' – that is, the power to see supernatural beings and future events – can behold a Goona. So the song tells:

>Donald Ban has second sight,
>And he'll moan the Goona's plight
>When the frosts are flickering white,
>   And the kine are housed till day;
>For he'll see him perched alone
>On a chilly old grey stone,
>Nibbling, nibbling at a bone
>   That we've maybe thrown away.

>He's so hungry, he's so thin,
>If he'd come we'd let him in;
>For a rag of fox's skin
>   Is the only thing he'll wear.
>He'll be chittering in the cold
>As he hovers round the fold,
>With his locks of glimmering gold
>   Twined about his shoulders bare.

Another exiled fairy is called 'The Little Old Man of the Barn'. He lives to a great age – some say until he is over two hundred years old – but he remains strong and active although his back is bent and his long grey beard reaches to his ankles. He wears grey clothing, and the buttons of his coat are of silver. On his high peaked cap there is a white owl's feather. The face of the little old man is covered with wrinkles, but his eyes are bright and kindly. He is always in a hurry, and hobbles about, leaning on his staff, but he walks so quickly that the strongest man can hardly keep up with him. When he begins to work he works very hard and very quickly. He will not hold a conversation with anyone once he begins to perform a task. If a man who has second sight should address him, saying: 'How are you, old man?' he will answer: 'I'm busy, busy, busy.' If he should be asked: 'What are you doing?' he will give the same answer, repeating it over and over again. It is no use trying to chat with the little old man.

There was once an old crofter whose name was Callum. He had seven strong sons, but one by one they left him to serve as keepers of the deer. Callum was left to do all the work on the croft. He had to cut the corn and thresh it afterwards, and had it not been for the assistance given him by the 'Little Old Man of the Barn', he would never have been able to get the threshing done. Each night the fairy man entered the barn and worked very hard.

The following verses are from a song about Callum:

> When all the big lads will be hunting the deer,
> And no one for helping old Callum comes near,
> Oh, who will be busy at threshing his corn?
> Who will come in the night and be going at morn?
>> The Little Old Man of the Barn.
>> Yon Little Old Man –
>> So tight and so braw, he will bundle the straw,
>> The Little Old Man of the Barn.
>
> When the peat will turn grey, and the shadows fall deep,
> And weary old Callum is snoring asleep;
> When yon plant by the door will keep fairies away,
> And the horseshoe sets witches a-wandering till day,
>> The Little Old Man of the Barn,
>> Yon Little Old Man
>> Will thrash with no light in the mouth of the night –
>> The Little Old Man of the Barn.

There was once a fairy exile who lived in a wood in Gairloch, Ross-shire. He was called the Gillie Dhu, which means 'dark servant', because he had dark hair and dark eyes. He wore a green garment made of moss and the leaves of trees. Nobody feared him, for he never did any harm.

Once a little girl, whose name was Jessie Macrae, was wandering in the wood and lost her way. It was in summertime, and the air was warm. When evening came on Jessie began to grow afraid, but although she hastened her steps she could not find her way out of the wood. At length, weary and footsore, she sat down below a fir tree and began to weep. A voice spoke to her suddenly from behind, saying: 'Why are you crying, little girl?'

Jessie looked round and saw the Gillie Dhu. He had hair black as the wing of a raven, eyes brown as hazelnuts in September, and his mouth was large; he had a hundred teeth, which were as small as herring bones. The Gillie Dhu was smiling: his cream-yellow cheeks had merry dimples, and his eyes were soft and kindly. Had Jessie seen him at a distance, with his clothing of moss and leaves, she would have run away in terror, but as he seemed so kindly and friendly she did not feel the least afraid.

'Why are you crying, little girl?' the Gillie asked again. 'Your teardrops are falling like dew on the little blue flowers at your feet.'

'I have lost my way,' said Jessie in a low voice, 'and the night is coming on.'

Said the Gillie: 'Do not cry, little girl; I shall lead you through the wood. I know every path – the rabbit's path, the hare's path, the fox's path, the goat's path, the path of the deer and the path of men.'

'Oh, thank you, thank you!' Jessie said. She looked the fairy up and down, and wondered to see his strange clothing.

'Where do you dwell, little girl?' asked the Gillie Dhu.

Jessie told him, and he said: 'You have been walking every way but the right way. Follow me, and you'll reach home before the little stars come out to peer at me through the trees.'

The Gillie turned round about, and began to trip lightly in front of the girl. He went so fast that she feared she would lose sight of him, but he turned round again and again, and when he found she was far behind, he danced a pretty dance until she came up to him. Then he scampered on as before.

At length Jessie reached the edge of the wood, and saw her home beside the loch. The Gillie bade her goodbye, and said: 'Have I not led you well? Do not forget me. I am the Gillie Dhu, and I love little girls and little boys. If ever you get lost in the wood again, I shall come to your aid. Goodbye, little girl, goodbye.'

He laughed merrily, and then trotted away and was soon lost to sight among the trees.

There was once a fairy exile who was mute. The Fairy Queen had punished him for some offence by taking away his powers of speech and hearing, and she forbade any other fairy to go near him. He wore a bright red jacket and green breeches, and from beneath his little red cap his long curling hair, which was yellow as broom, dropped down on his shoulders. The little fairy man had cheeks red as rowan berries and laughing blue eyes, and he was always smiling. It made one happy to look at him. He was always so contented and pleased and playful, although he was deaf and dumb, that he put everyone who met him in a good humour.

For a long time the fairy man lived all alone beneath a great heap of stones, called the Grey Cairn, on a lonely moor in the Black Isle, in Ross-shire. This cairn is in a fir wood which skirts the highway.

When a cart came along the highway the fairy man used to steal out from behind a big grey stone, smiling and smiling. Then he would jump on the axle of a wheel, and whirl round and round; and the faster the cart would go the better he would be pleased. He would drop off the axle at the edge of the wood, but he never forgot to turn round and smile to the driver as he ran away.

The people liked to see the little fairy man whirling round and round on the cartwheel, because they believed he always brought them luck.

One day a farmer and his wife were going to the Fair of St Norman at Cromarty to sell their butter and eggs, but when they reached the big grey stone the little red man did not come in sight.

The farmer, who was ill-tempered that day, wanted to go on without giving the little fellow a whirl on the cartwheel, but his wife said: 'No, no; if you will not wait for him, I'll get down and walk home; for we would have no luck at the fair if we missed the bonnie wee red man.'

The woman was looking through the trees, and suddenly she began to laugh.

'Look, Sandy dear, look!' she cried, 'there comes the bonnie wee man – oh, the dear little fairy!'

The farmer was frowning and ill-tempered, but when he looked round he began to smile, for the little red fairy was smiling so sweetly to him. He whipped up his mare, and cried over his shoulder to his wife: 'Is he on the wheel yet, Kirsty dear; is he on the wheel?'

'Yes, yes, Sandy dear,' Kirsty answered, 'he's on now. Go faster, Sandy – the faster you go the better he'll be pleased.'

The farmer cried to the mare: 'Gee-up, Jenny, gee-up, my lass!'

and the old mare went trotting along the highway, while the little red fairy sat on the axle, whirling round and round with the wheel, and smiling and smiling all the time.

When he dropped off at the edge of the wood, his bright yellow hair was streaming over his laughing eyes, and his cheeks were redder than hazel-berries. The fairy smiled to Sandy and smiled to Kirsty, looking over his shoulder as he ran away.

'The dear wee man!' cried the farmer's wife.

'The happy little chap,' cried the farmer.

They both looked back to see the glint of the fairy's red jacket as he ran merrily through the trees. They both felt very happy, and they were happier still when they were on their way homeward, because they had secured good prices for their butter and eggs at the fair.

There was a miller who had a mill with a water-wheel in a woody dell not far from the Grey Cairn. The little fairy man was fond of him, because he got many a fine whirl on the mill-wheel. Every morning and every evening the miller left a little cog of oatmeal porridge on the window-sill for the wee red man. Sometimes, when he was busy tying the bags of meal, the fairy would look in at the door and smile and smile, until the miller felt so happy that he forgot he was old, and began to whistle or sing like a young lad on a bright May morning.

When the miller was getting frail, the little red fairy used to help him at his work. Every now and then he would run out to whirl round the mill-wheel, and he would come back with the spray clinging to his hair like dewdrops on whin blossom.

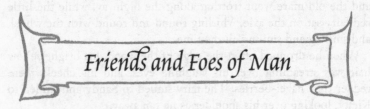

Friends and Foes of Man

In ancient days, the dog was looked upon as man's best friend, and the enemy of all supernatural beings: fairies, giants, hags and monsters of the sea and the Underworld. When the seasons changed, on the four 'quarter days' of the year, and the whole world, as the folks believed, was thrown into confusion, the fairies and other spirits broke loose and went about plundering houses and barns and stealing children. At such times the dogs were watchful and active, and howled warning when they saw any of the supernatural creatures. They even attacked the fairies, and sometimes after such fights they returned home with all the hair scraped off their bodies.

A story is still current in Edinburgh about a piper and his dog who met with a monster of the Underworld. This monster haunted an underground passage, which is said to run from Edinburgh Castle to Holyrood Palace, and it was called Great-Hand, for no one ever saw aught of it except its gigantic grisly hand with nails like an eagle's claw.

In days of long ago, the underground passage was used by soldiers when the enemies of the King of Scotland invaded the kingdom and laid siege to Edinburgh Castle, his chief stronghold. The soldiers could leave the castle and fall upon the besiegers from behind, and through it reinforcements could be sent to the castle. When, however, the spirit called Great-Hand began to haunt the tunnel, it could not be used any longer, for every man who entered it perished in the darkness.

The piper was a brave man, and he resolved to explore the tunnel with his dog. 'I shall play my bagpipes all the way through,' he said to his friends, 'and you can follow the sound of the piping above the ground.'

There is a cave below the castle which leads to the tunnel, and the piper entered it one morning, playing a merry tune. His faithful dog followed him. The people heard the sound of the bagpipes as they walked down High Street, listening intently, but when they reached the spot which is called the 'Heart of Midlothian' the piping stopped abruptly, as if the pipes had been torn suddenly from the piper's hands. The piper was never seen again, but his dog, without a hair on its body, came running out of the cave below the castle.

There are other strange passages below hills, and even below the sea, about which stories have been told. The longest of these is one that is supposed to stretch from a cave in Oban to another cave in the Island of Mull. A Gaelic legend tells that a piper once entered the cave at Oban to explore the tunnel, but was never seen again. His dog returned with every hair torn from its body, and died soon afterwards.

It is said that most of these passages have been made by fairies for the monster with the gigantic grisly hand, and there are two stories about men who once caught glimpses of the hand inside caves, and yet managed to escape from it.

The first story is about an underground passage, over three miles long, that is said to connect the Dropping Cave, near Cromarty, with another cave in the fairy-haunted dell of Eathie, which is situated beside Navity Moor, where in ancient times the Earth Goddess was worshipped within a grove. It is told that when fires are lit in one of the caves the smoke comes out of the other.

The Dropping Cave is so called because drops of water are constantly falling from its ceiling, which bristles with long tapering stalactites that look like icicles. There are lots of strange stories about this cave. Fishermen have told that they have seen blue lights hovering near it in the darkness, and also that often, on moonlight nights, a mermaid sits on a rock below it, combing her long yellow hair with her fingers and singing a low sad song.

Once upon a time a little old man, with a pale wrinkled face and long grey beard, was seen sitting near the cave, gazing over the sea. He did not move for three days. People crept along the lonely shore to watch him from a distance, and fishermen, passing in their boats, stared at him with wondering eyes. No one dared to go near him except a half-witted lad, who first walked round the little old man, and then spoke, saying: 'Why are you sitting here? Are you not tired yet?'

The little old man made no answer, but shivered all over. Terrified by his appearance, the lad turned at once and fled homeward, crying: 'He is shivering now, he is shivering now.'

On the evening of the third day the little old man disappeared. Soon afterwards a terrible storm broke out. It raged fiercely for several days and when it was over the shores were strewn with wreckage and the bodies of drowned sailors. The people believed that the little old man was one of the inhabitants of the Underworld, and some have declared he was no other than Thomas the Rhymer.

A Cromarty man, named William Millar, who lived over a hundred years ago, is said to have entered the Dropping Cave and explored part of the underground passage. When he returned he told that he had caught a glimpse of the great hand.

Before he entered the cave, Millar sewed sprigs of rowan and witch hazel in the hem of his vest. Into one of his pockets he put a Bible and in his right hand he held a staff of blackthorn which he had cut on a calm night when the moon was full, and he had dressed without using anything made of iron. With the aid of these charms he hoped to be able to protect himself against the spirits of the Underworld.

Having lit a torch, Millar climbed up to the mouth of the dark wet cave and entered it just as the sun was beginning to rise. He walked forward until the passage became so low and narrow that he had to crawl on his hands and knees. He crawled for some distance until the cave began to widen, and at length he found himself in a big underground chamber which was full of blue mist. A small and beautiful rainbow appeared round his flaming torch. For a time he stood gazing around him and above. The roof seemed to be very high, and the rocky walls were rough and bare. He walked onward, and as he did so the sound of his footsteps awoke many echoes loud and faint. It seemed as if a hundred people were walking through the cave.

Suddenly Millar heard a curious humming noise. He stopped to listen, and when he did so the humming grew louder. He peered through the blue mist for a time, fearing to advance farther into the depths of that fearsome place. Then a fierce gust of wind blew in his face. The flames of the torch were swept backwards, flickered and went out. Just as this happened, Millar caught a glimpse of many dim forms flitting round about him. A cry of fear came from his lips, and he turned to run away, but stumbled over a stone, fell heavily, and became unconscious.

How long he lay there he never could tell. When he woke, the chamber was no longer dark, for a red light shone through it. The humming noise had grown very loud and seemed to be the noise of falling water. Thinking he was not far from the waterfalls of Eathie burn, he rose up and hastened forward. The passage grew narrow, and led to another large chamber, where he saw a great fire of fir logs burning fiercely, and a waterfall dashing over a rock into a deep pool beneath. In front of the pool was a big stone chest. The floor of the rocky chamber was strewn with human bones.

Millar crept forward cautiously until he saw a big iron mace, red with rust and blood, lying at one end of the stone chest, and a horn dangling on a chain which came down from the rocky ceiling.

He gazed at the horn for a minute; then he grasped it in his hands and blew a single blast which awoke a hundred echoes. No sooner did he do so than the waters ceased to fall. Millar was astonished, and thought he would blow the horn once again to see what would happen. But when he leaned forward to grasp it, he saw the lid of the stone chest rising slowly. He stepped back at once, for a sudden panic struck him, and he began to tremble like an aspen leaf.

The lid rose and rose and suddenly fell backwards with a crash. Then out of the chest came a gigantic grisly hand which grasped the big rusty mace. Millar shrieked and fled out of the rocky chamber. A fierce yell broke out behind him, and, turning round, he saw the hand throwing down the mace, the lid of the chest closing and the waterfall beginning to pour again over the rocks into the deep pool.

With hasty steps he ran into the chamber in which he had lain in a swoon, and having found his torch, lit it again and crept forward until he reached the narrow passage through which he had crawled. When at length he got out of the Dropping Cave, he found that the sun was setting over the western hills. He vowed never again to attempt to explore the underground passage to Eathie.

Another cave story is told about a west-coast man named Mac-Fadyen who had a wonderful black dog which he had got from a fairy. This animal was very lazy and used to sleep a great deal and eat huge quantities of food. MacFadyen's wife hated it, and often said to her husband: 'Your black dog is quite useless – it eats too much food and never does anything to help you. I think it should be drowned.'

MacFadyen would not drown it, however. 'Leave it alone,' he would say; 'the dog will have its day.'

One morning many of the villagers went out to hunt the wild deer on the mountains. They roused a great fleet-footed stag which ran towards the village. All the dogs were behind it in full chase, except MacFadyen's dog, which lay sleeping in the sunshine at the corner of his house. The stag was heading for the loch, over which it could swim and so escape its pursuers, but it had first to pass MacFadyen's dog. Someone said: 'Now the dog's great day has come at last.'

The hunters shouted and their dogs bayed aloud. MacFadyen's dog was awakened by the tumult, and rising up, stretched itself and looked round about. It saw the great stag, but never moved to attack. Instead, it just lay down again and closed its eyes, and the stag entered the water and swam across the loch.

'Kill that lazy dog of yours, MacFadyen,' the hunters cried out; 'it is of no use.'

Said MacFadyen: 'Leave the dog alone; the dog will have its day.'

One morning MacFadyen and another two men went out to fish round the shores of a lonely island. When the boat was launched the dog walked down the beach, and leaping into it, stretched itself at MacFadyen's feet and went to sleep.

'We do not require a dog when we go fishing,' one of the men said. 'Put your dog ashore, MacFadyen.'

Said MacFadyen: 'Leave the dog alone; the dog will have its day.'

The men fished round the island all day, and when evening was coming on they landed and went to a cave. They lit a fire there and cooked some fish. MacFadyen's dog ate as much fish as did the three men together.

Night came on, and the men lay down to sleep. MacFadyen had his dog beside him, and in the middle of the night the dog woke him with its growling. MacFadyen sat up. The fire was burning low, and in the silence he heard a dripping sound. He threw some dry twigs on the fire, and when the flames from them lit up the cave, he saw that both his friends were dead. The dripping he heard was the dripping of their blood flowing over the flat stones. The light went out, and MacFadyen sat trembling in the darkness while the dog kept growling angrily. Then MacFadyen heard a rustling sound, and saw, passing over the embers of the low fire, a great grisly hand. It was feeling round about the cave for something, and MacFadyen shrank back to escape from it. Suddenly his dog leapt up and attacked the giant hand. A fierce struggle followed. The hand tried to grasp the dog, and the dog tried to tear the hand to pieces. For several minutes the fight was waged with fury, and then the hand was withdrawn. The dog followed it, and scampered out of the cave, and MacFadyen, trembling in the darkness, heard a great stamping overhead.

He waited until the dawn began to break. Then he rose and left the cave, and ran down the beach. With a great effort he launched the boat, and leaping into it, began to row away from the haunted island.

He had not rowed a hundred yards when he saw two bright lights following him in the murk of the dawn. Terrified by the lights, he bent himself to the oars and rowed faster and faster. The boat went quickly through the water, but the lights came quickly after him. In the growing brightness of early morning, MacFadyen saw at length that the lights he dreaded were the flaming eyes of his dog, which was swimming from the island and endeavouring to reach the boat. The fury of the fight had roused all the slumbering energy of the dog, and MacFadyen was afraid of it. He did not wait for it, but kept on rowing until the dog became exhausted and, sinking below the waves, was drowned.

'The dog has had its day,' said MacFadyen. 'It saved my life.'

There are many Gaelic stories about faithful dogs, and some examples of these are as follows.

A man named Colin Cameron had once a great fleet-footed greyhound. He went out to hunt with it on a September morning, and lost his way among the mountains. Night came on, and he allowed the dog to go ahead and followed it. In time he came to a lonely shieling on a hillside, and saw a light issuing from it. The door was open, and he looked in. He saw an old woman clad in green sitting on the floor. She looked up and spoke, saying: 'Are you not coming in, Colin Cameron?'

Colin suspected that the woman was an evil spirit, and answered: 'Not just now.'

'You have lost your way,' she said.

'Perhaps I shall find it ere long,' he told her.

'If you do not come in,' she replied, 'I had better go with you and show you the way to your house.'

'Do not trouble yourself,' he answered; 'I shall find my way myself.'

Having spoken thus, Colin turned and ran down the hillside. Soon he found that his dog was not following him, and he stopped to call it. As he did so, the sound of a fierce struggle fell on his ears, and he began to run again. He ran a great distance. Then the moon rose up, and he found himself in a glen he knew, and turned his face homewards. He reached his own house in safety, and soon after he entered it his dog came in. The animal had not a hair left on its body except on its ears. It was panting with exhaustion and pain. Lying down at Colin's feet, it licked his hand and then fell over on its right side and died.

Colin realised at once what had happened. His faithful greyhound had waited behind at the shieling to prevent the green woman from following him.

Another story is told about three men who once crossed a lonely moor in the night-time. They had a dog with them, and when they were halfway on their journey it began to run round and round them in ever-widening circles. At length the men heard the sound of fairy music, and one said to another: 'The wee folk are dancing and making merry somewhere near us.'

They hastened on their way, fearing to meet the fairies. At length the sound of the dog howling and barking mingled with the music. Suddenly the music stopped abruptly, and they heard the trampling of many feet on the dark moor. They ran as fast as they were able until the sounds died away in the distance, and they reached in safety the house to which they were going. Early next morning, the dog made its appearance. All the hair on its body had been scraped off as if with long nails, and soon after it entered the house it lay down and died.

A man named Malcolm MacPhee was once walking along a lonely rocky beach in Islay when a mermaid seized him. She thrust him into a cave, and there kept him a prisoner.

Now MacPhee had a big black dog, and his wife sent it out to search for its master. The wise animal at once ran towards the cave on the beach, where it found MacPhee. No sooner did it arrive, however, than the mermaid rose out of the sea to prevent her prisoner escaping. The dog growled fiercely when it saw her, and she tried to drive it away.

Said MacPhee: 'You had better let me go, or my dog will attack you.'

The mermaid laughed, and answered: 'I shall keep you here until you die.'

No sooner did she say that than the dog sprang at her. A fierce struggle took place, and the mermaid tried to escape by leaping back into the sea. The dog followed her, and fought until it killed the mermaid, but was itself so severely wounded that it was drowned before it reached the shore. MacPhee hastened homeward, lamenting the loss of his faithful dog.

It is told that dogs can see the spirit messenger of death coming nigh in the darkness. When they catch sight of it they begin to howl. People who hear dogs howling at night fear that someone they know will meet with a fatal accident or die suddenly while asleep.

The Banshee is dreaded by dogs. She is a fairy woman who washes white sheets in a ford by night when someone near at hand is about to die. It is said she has the power to appear during daytime in the form of a black dog, or a raven, or a hoodie-crow.

The following is a Highland poem about the Banshee, who is supposed to sing a mournful song while she washes the death-clothes of one who is doomed to meet with a sudden and unexpected death:

> Knee-deep she waded in the pool –
>   The Banshee robed in green –
> Singing her song the whole night long,
>   She washed the linen clean;
> The linen that must wrap the dead
>   She beetled on a stone;
> She washed with dripping hands, blood-red,
>   Low singing all alone:
>
>> *The Banshee I with second sight,*
>> *Singing in the cold starlight;*
>> *I wash the death-clothes pure and white,*
>> *For Fergus More must die tonight.*

'Twas Fergus More rode o'er the hill,
    Come back from foreign wars;
His horse's feet were clattering sweet
    Below the pitiless stars;
And in his heart he would repeat:
    'Oh never again I'll roam;
All weary is the going forth,
    But sweet the coming home.'

> *The Banshee I with second sight,*
> *Singing in the cold starlight;*
> *I wash the death-clothes pure and white*
> *For Fergus More must die tonight.*

He saw the blaze upon his hearth
    Bright-gleaming down the glen;
O, he was fain for home again!
    He'd parted with his men.
' 'Tis many a weary day,' he'd sigh,
    'Since I did leave her side;
I'll never more leave Scotland's shore
    And Una Ban, my bride.'

> *The Banshee I with second sight,*
> *Singing in the cold starlight;*
> *I wash the death-clothes pure and white,*
> *For Fergus More must die tonight.*

With thought of Una's tender love
Soft tears his eyes did blind,
When up there crept and swiftly leapt
A man who stabbed behind.
' 'Tis you,' he cried, 'who stole my bride.
This night shall be your last.' . . .
As Fergus fell, the warm red tide
Of life came ebbing fast.

> *The Banshee I with second sight,*
> *Singing in the cold starlight;*
> *I wash the death-clothes pure and white,*
> *For Fergus More must die tonight.*

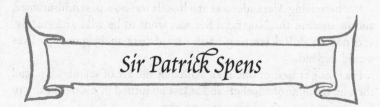

Sir Patrick Spens

The king sits in Dunfermline town,
Drinking the blood-red wine;
'Oh, where will I get a skilful skipper,
To sail this new ship o' mine?'

*   *   *

Half o'er, half o'er to Aberdour,
'Tis fifty fathoms deep,
And there lies good Sir Patrick Spens,
Wi' the Scots lords at his feet.

Now hearken to me, all ye who love old stories, and I will tell you how one of the bravest and most gallant of Scottish seamen came by his death. 'Tis the story of an event which brought mourning and sorrow to many a fair lady's heart in the far-off days of long ago.

Now all the world knows that his majesty, King Alexander III, who afterwards came by his death on the rocks at Kinghorn, had only one daughter, named Margaret, after her ancestress, the wife of Malcolm Canmore, whose life was so holy and her example so blessed that, to this day, men call her St Margaret of Scotland.

King Alexander had had much trouble in his life, for he had already buried his wife and his youngest son David, and 'twas no wonder that, as he sat in the great hall of his palace at Dunfermline, close to the Abbey Church, where he loved best to hold his court, his heart was sore at the thought of parting with his motherless daughter.

She had lately been betrothed to Eric, the young King of Norway, and it was now full time that she went to her new home. So a stately ship had been prepared to convey her across the sea; the amount of her dowry had been settled; her attendants chosen; and it only remained to appoint a captain to the charge of the vessel.

But here King Alexander was at a loss. It was now past midsummer, and in autumn the Northern Sea was wont to be wild and stormy, and on the skilful steering of the royal bark many precious lives would depend.

He thought first of one man skilled in the art of seamanship, and then he thought of another, and at last he turned in his perplexity to his nobles who were sitting around him.

'Canst tell me,' he said, fingering a glass of red French wine as he spoke, 'of a man well skilled in the knowledge of winds and tides, yet of gentle birth withal, who can be trusted to pilot this goodly ship of mine, with her precious burden, safely over the sea to Norway?'

The nobles looked at one another in silence for a moment, and then one of them, an old grey-haired baron, rose from his seat by Alexander's side.

'Scotland lacks not seamen, both gentle and simple, my liege,' he said, 'who could be trusted with this precious charge. But there is one man of my acquaintance, who, above all others, is worthy of such a trust. I speak of young Sir Patrick Spens, who lives not far from here. Not so many years have passed over his head, but from a boy he has loved the sea, and already he knows more about it, and its moods, than white-haired men who have sailed on it all their lives. 'Tis his bride, he says, an' I trow he speaks the truth, for, although he is as fair a gallant as ever the eye of lady rested on, and although many tender hearts, both within the court and without, beat a quicker measure when his name is spoken, he is as yet free of love fancies, and aye bides true to this changeful mistress of his. Truly he may well count it an honour to have the keeping of so fair a flower entrusted to him.'

'Now bring me paper and pen,' cried the king, 'and I will write to him this instant with mine own hand.'

Slowly and laboriously King Alexander penned the lines, for in these days kings were readier with the sword than with the pen; then, folding the letter and sealing it with the great signet ring which he wore on the third finger of his right hand, he gave it to the old baron, and commanded him to seek Sir Patrick Spens without loss of time.

Now Sir Patrick dwelt near the sea, and when the baron arrived he found him pacing up and down on the hard white sand by the seashore, watching the waves, and studying the course of the tides. He was quite a young man, and 'twas little wonder if the story which the old baron had told was true, and if all the ladies' hearts in Fife ached for love of him, for I trow never did goodlier youth walk the earth, and men said of him that he was as gentle and courteous as he was handsome.

At first when he began to read the king's letter, his face flushed with pride, for who would not have felt proud to be chosen before all others in Scotland to be the captain of the king's royal bark? But the smile passed away almost as soon as it appeared, and a look of great sadness took its place. In silence he gazed out over the sea. Did something warn him at that moment that this would prove his last voyage – that never again would he set foot in his beloved land?

It may be so; who can tell? Certain it is – the old baron recalled it to his mind in the sad days that were to come—that, when the young sailor handed back the king's letter to him, his eyes were full of tears.

' 'Tis certainly a great honour,' he said, 'and I thank his majesty for granting it to me, but methinks it was no one who loved my life, or the lives of those who shall sail with me, who suggested our setting out for Norway at this time of year.'

Then, anxious lest the baron thought that he said this out of fear, or cowardice, he changed his tone, and hurried him up to his house to partake of some refreshment after his ride, while he gave orders to his seamen to get everything ready.

'Make haste, my men,' he shouted in a cheerful, lusty voice, 'for a great honour hath fallen to our lot. His majesty hath deigned to entrust to us his much loved daughter, the Princess Margaret, that we may convey her, in the stately ship which he hath prepared, to her husband's court in Norway. Wherefore, let every man look to himself, and let him meet me at Aberdour, where the ship lies, on Sunday by nightfall, for we sail next day with the tide.'

So on the Monday morning early, ere it struck eight of the clock, a great procession wound down from the king's palace at Dunfermline to the little landing-stage at Aberdour, where the stately ship was lying, with her white sails set, like a gigantic swan.

Between the king and his son, the Prince of Scotland, rode the Princess Margaret, her eyes red with weeping, for in those days it was no light thing to set out for another land, and she felt that the parting might be for ever. And so, in good sooth, it proved to be, in this world at least, for before many years had passed all three were in their graves; but that belongs not to my tale.

Next rode the high and mighty persons who were to accompany the princess to her husband's land, and be witnesses of the fulfilment of the marriage contract. These were their graces the Earl and Countess of Menteith, his Reverence the Abbot of Balmerino, the good Lord Bernard of Monte-Alto, and many others, including a crowd of young nobles, five and fifty in all, who had been asked to swell the princess's retinue, and who were only too glad to have a chance of getting a glimpse of other lands.

Next came a long train of sumpter mules, with the princess's baggage, and that of her attendants. And last of all, guarded well by men-at-arms, came the huge iron-bound chests which contained her dowry: seven thousand merks in good white money and surety for seven thousand more laid out for her in land in Scotland.

Sir Patrick Spens was waiting to receive the princess on board the ship. Right courteously, I ween, he handed her to her cabin, and saw that my Lady of Menteith, in whose special care she was, was well lodged also, as befitted her rank and station. But I trow that his lip curled with scorn when he saw that the five and fifty young nobles had provided themselves with five and fifty feather beds to sleep on. He himself was a hardy man, as a sailor ought to be, and he loved not to see men so careful of their comfort.

At last the baggage, and the dowry, and even the feather beds were stowed away; and the last farewells having been said, the great ship weighed anchor and sailed slowly out of the Firth of Forth.

Ah me, how many eyes there were which watched it sail away, with husband, or brother, or sweetheart on board, which would wait in vain for many a long day for its return!

Sir Patrick made a good voyage. The sea was calm, the wind was in his favour, and by the evening of the third day he brought his ship with her precious burden safe to the shores of Norway.

'Now the saints be praised,' he said to himself as he cast anchor, 'for the princess is safe, let happen what may on our return voyage.'

In great state, and with much magnificence, Margaret of Scotland was wedded to Eric of Norway, and great feasting and merry-making marked the event. For a whole month the rejoicing went on. The Norwegian nobles vied with each other who could pay most attention to the Scottish strangers. From morning to night their halls rang with music, and gaiety, and dancing. No wonder that the young nobles – nay, no wonder that even Sir Patrick Spens himself, careful seaman though he was, forgot to think of the homeward journey, or to remember how soon the storms of winter would be upon them.

In good sooth they might have remained where they were till the spring, and then this tale need never have been told, had not a thoughtless taunt touched their Scottish pride to the quick.

The people of Norway are a frugal race, and to the older nobles all this feasting and junketing seemed like wild, needless extravagance.

'Our young men have gone mad,' they said to each other; 'if this goes on, the country will be ruined. 'Tis those strangers who have done it. It would be a good day for Norway if they would bethink themselves, and sail for home.'

That very night there was a great banquet, and there was dire confusion in the hall when a fierce old noble of royal blood, an uncle of the king, spoke aloud to Sir Patrick Spens in the hearing of all the company.

'Now little good will the young queen's dowry do either to our king or to our country,' he said, 'if it has all to be eaten up feasting a crowd of idle youngsters who ought to be at home attending to their own business.'

Sir Patrick turned red, and then he turned white. What the old man said was very untrue, and he knew it. For, besides the young queen's dowry, a large sum of money had been taken over in the ship to pay for the expenses of her attendants, and of the nobles in her train.

' 'Tis false. Ye lie,' he said bluntly; 'for I brought as much white money with me as would more than pay for all that hath been spent on our behalf. If these be the ways of Norway, then beshrew me, but I like them not."

With these words he turned and left the hall followed by all the Scottish nobles. Without speaking a word to any of them, he strode down to the harbour, where his ship was lying, and ordered the sailors to begin to make ready at once, for he would sail for home in the morning.

The night was cold and dreary; there was plainly a storm brewing. It was safe and snug in the harbour, and the sailors were loth to face the dangers of the voyage. But their captain looked so pale and stern, that everyone feared to speak.

'Master,' said an old man at last – he was the oldest man on board, and had seen nigh seventy years – 'I have never refused to do thy bidding, and I will not begin tonight. We will go, if go we must; but, if it be so, then may God's mercy rest on us. For late yestreen I saw the old moon in the sky, and she was nursing the new moon in her arms. It needs not me to tell you, for you are as weather-wise as I am, what that sign bodes.'

'Say ye so?' said Sir Patrick, startled in spite of his anger; 'then, by my troth, we may prepare for a storm. But tide what may, come snow or sleet, come cold or wet, we head for Scotland in the morning.'

So the stately ship set her sails once more, and for a time all went well. But when they had sailed for nigh three days, and were thinking that they must be near Scotland, the sky grew black and the wind arose, and all signs pointed to a coming storm.

Sir Patrick took the helm himself, and did his best to steer the ship through the tempest which soon broke over them, and which grew worse and worse every moment. The sailors worked with a will at the ropes, and even the foolish young nobles, awed by the danger which threatened them, offered their assistance. But they were of little use, and indeed, one would have laughed to have seen them, had the peril not been so great, with their fine satin cloaks wrapped round them, and carrying their feathered hats under their arms, trying to step daintily across the deck, between the rushes of the water, in order that they might not wet their tiny, cork-heeled, pointed-toed shoes.

Alack, alack, neither feathered hats, nor pointed shoon, availed to save them! Darker and darker grew the sea, and every moment the huge waves threatened to engulf the goodly vessel.

Sir Patrick Spens had sailed on many a stormy sea, but never in his life had he faced a tempest like this. He knew that he and all his gallant company were doomed men unless the land were near. That was their only hope, to find some harbour and run into it for shelter.

Soon the huge waves were breaking over the deck, and the bulwarks began to give way. Truly their case was desperate, and even the gay young nobles grew grave, and many hearts were turned towards the homes which they would never see again.

'Send me a man to take the helm,' shouted Sir Patrick hoarsely, 'while I climb to the top of the mast, and try if I can see land.'

Instantly the old sailor who had warned him of the coming storm, the night before, was at his side.

'I will guide the ship, captain,' he said, 'if you are bent on going aloft; but I fear you will see no land. Sailors who are out on their last voyage need not look for port.'

Now Sir Patrick was a brave man, and he meant to fight for life; so he climbed up to the mast head, and clung on there, despite the driving spray and roaring wind, which were like to tear him from his foothold. In vain he peered through the darkness, looking to the right hand and to the left; there was no land to be seen, nothing but the great green waves, crested with foam, which came springing up like angry wolves, eager to swallow the gallant ship and her luckless crew.

Suddenly his cheek grew pale and his eyes dark with fear. 'We are dead men now,' he muttered; for, not many feet below him, seated on the crest of a massive wave, he saw the form of a beautiful woman, with a cruel face and long fair hair, which floated like a veil on the top of the water. 'Twas a mermaid, and he knew what the sight portended.

She held up a silver bowl to him, with a little mocking laugh on her lips. 'Sail on, sail on, my guid Scots lords,' she cried, and her sweet, false voice rose clear and shrill above the tumult of the waves, 'for I warrant ye'll soon touch dry land.'

'We may touch the land, but 'twill be the land that lies fathoms deep below the sea,' replied Sir Patrick grimly, and then the weird creature laughed again, and floated away in the darkness.

When she had passed, Sir Patrick glanced down at the deck, and the sight that met him there only deepened his gloom. Worn with the beating of the waves, a bolt had sprung in the good ship's side, and a plank had given way, and the cruel green water was pouring in through the hole.

Verily, they were facing death itself now; yet the strong man's heart did not quail.

He had quailed at the sight of the mermaid's mocking eyes, but he looked on the face of death calmly, as befitted a brave and a good man. Perhaps the thought came to him, as it came to another famous seaman long years afterwards, that heaven is as near by sea as by land, and in the thought there was great comfort.

There was but one more thing to be done; after that they were helpless. 'Now, my good Scots lords,' he cried, and I trow a look of amusement played round his lips even at that solemn hour, 'now is the time for those featherbeds of yours. There are five and fifty of them, and odds take it if they be not enough to stop up one little hole.'

At the words the poor young nobles set to work right manfully, forgetting in their fear that their white hands were bruised and bleeding, and their dainty clothes all wet with seawater.

Alack! alack! ere half the work was done, the good ship shivered from bow to stern, and went slowly down under the waves; and Sir Patrick Spens and his whole company met death, as, in their turn, all men must.

So there, under the waters of the grey Northern Sea, he rested, lying in state, as it were, with the Scottish lords and his own faithful sailors round him; while there was grief and woe throughout the length and breadth of Scotland, and fair women wept as they looked in vain for the husbands, and the brothers, and the lovers who would return to them no more.

And, while the long centuries come and go, he is resting there still, with the Scots lords and his faithful sailors by him, waiting for a day, whose coming may be long, but whose coming will be sure, when the sea shall give up its dead.

The Good Housewife and the Little People

Once upon a time there was a rich farmer who had a very thrifty wife. She used to go out and gather all the little bits of wool which she could find on the hillsides and bring them home. Then, after her family had gone to bed, she would sit up, and card the wool, and spin it into yarn; then she would weave the yarn into warm cloth, to make garments for her children.

But, as you can fancy, all this work made her feel very tired. Indeed, she was so tired that one night, sitting at her loom, she laid down her shuttle, buried her head in her hands and burst out crying.

'Oh, that someone would come, from near or far, from land or sea, to help me,' she sobbed.

No sooner had the words left her lips than she heard someone knocking at the door. 'Who is there?' she cried, going to the door and placing her ear to the keyhole.

'Tall Quary, good housewife, open the door to me. As long as I have, you'll get,' was the answer, spoken in a strange, unknown tongue.

After some hesitation she opened the door, and there, on the threshold, stood the oddest little woman she had ever seen, dressed in a green dress and wearing a white mutch on her head.

The good housewife was so astonished, that she simply stood and stared at her strange visitor; but without uttering another word, the little woman ran past her and seated herself at the spinning-wheel.

The mistress shut the door, and turned to go back into the kitchen, but before she had reached it, she heard another knock, and when she went and asked who was there, another queer, shrill voice answered, 'Tall Quary, good housewife, open the door to me. As long as I have, you'll get;' and when she opened the door there was another queer little woman, in a white mutch and a lilac frock, standing on the threshold.

She too ran into the house without waiting to say, 'By your leave,' and picking up the distaff, began to put some wool on it.

Then, before the good wife could get the door shut, a funny little mannikin, with green trousers and a red pirnie, came out of the darkness, and following the tiny women into the kitchen, seized hold of a handful of wool and began to card it, and another wee wee woman followed him, and then another tiny mannikin, and another, and another, until it seemed to the good housewife that all the fairies and pixies in Scotland were coming to her house.

The kitchen was alive with them. Some of them were hanging the great pot on the fire to boil water to wash the wool that was dirty, some were teasing the clean wool, and some were carding it, some were spinning it into yarn, and some were weaving the yarn into great webs of cloth.

And the noise they made was enough to make her head run round. Splash! splash! Whirr! whirr! Clack! clack! The water in the pot bubbled over; the spinning-wheel whirred; the shuttle in the loom flew backwards and forwards. It seemed as if she would be deafened by the fray!

And the worst of it was that they all cried out for something to eat, and although she put on her gridle and baked bannocks as fast as she could the bannocks were eaten up the moment they were taken off the fire, and yet her uncanny visitors shouted for more.

At last the poor woman was so perplexed that she went to the next room to wake her husband, and see if he could not still the tumult.

But to her horror she found that, although she shook him with all her might, she could not wake him. It was very plain to see that he was bewitched.

Terrified almost out of her senses at this new misfortune, and leaving the fairies eating her last batch of bannocks, she stole out of the house and ran as fast as she could to the cottage of a wise man, who lived about a mile away.

She knocked at his door until he got up and put his head out of the window to see who was there; then she told him the whole story.

He listened in silence until she was finished, then he shook his head at her gravely. 'You foolish woman,' he said, 'let this be a lesson to you never to pray for things that you do not want. For your prayer may be granted, as it has been granted tonight, and the answer may only bring trouble on your own head. For before your husband can be loosed from the spell with which these little people have bound him, they must be got out of the house and the fulling-water, which they have boiled, must be thrown over him.

'And in order to get them out of the house, you must hurry to the top of that little hill which lies behind the cottage, which some of the country folk call Burg Hill, and others the Fairie Knowe. And when you have climbed to the top of it, you must shout three times with all your might, "Burg Hill is on fire!"

'Then will all the fairies run out to see if it be true, for that is where they dwell; and when they are out of the cottage, you must slip inside and bar the door; and as quickly as you can, you must turn the kitchen topsy-turvy, and upset everything that the fairies have worked with, else if they return before you have done so, the things that their fingers have touched will open the door and let them in, in spite of you.'

So the housewife went away, and climbed to the top of the hillock, and cried three times with all her might, "Burg Hill is on fire!" And, sure enough, almost before she had finished, the door of the cottage was flung wide open, and all the little fairie folk came running out, knocking one another over in their eagerness to be first at the hill, and each of them calling for the thing which they valued most, and had left behind them in the Fairie Knowe.

In the confusion the good housewife slipped down the back of the Knowe, and ran as fast as she could to her cottage, and I can tell you that when she was once inside it did not take her long to bar the door and turn everything upside down.

She took the band off the spinning-wheel, and twisted the head of the distaff the opposite way. She lifted the pot of fulling-water off the fire, and turned the room topsy-turvy, and threw down the carding-combs.

Then, when she had done everything she could think of, she put the gridle once more on the fire, and set to work to bake a gridleful of bannocks for her husband's breakfast, for the fairies had eaten up every bite of bread in the house.

She was busy at this when the little folk (who had soon found out that Burg Hill was not on fire at all) returned, and knocked at the door. 'Good housewife, let us in!' they cried.

'I cannot open the door,' she answered, 'for my hands are fast in the dough.'

Then the fairies began to appeal to the things which they had been working with.

'Good Spinning-wheel! get up and open the door,' they whispered.

'How can I,' answered the spinning-wheel, 'seeing that my band is undone.'

'Kind distaff! open the door for us.'

'That would I gladly do,' said the distaff, 'but I cannot walk, for my head is turned the wrong way.'

'Weaving-loom! have pity, and open the door.'

'I am all topsy-turvy, and cannot help myself, far less anyone else,' sighed the loom.

'Fulling-water! open the door,' they implored.

'I am off the fire,' growled the fulling-water, 'and all my strength is gone.'

The fairies were getting tired and impatient.

'Oh! Is there nothing that will come to our aid, and open the door?' they cried.

'I will,' said a little barley bannock that was lying toasting on the hearth, and she rose and trundled quickly across the floor.

But, luckily, the housewife saw her, and she nipped her between her finger and thumb, just as she was halfway across the kitchen, and, because she was only half-baked, she fell with a 'splatch' on the cold flags.

Then the fairies gave up the attempt to get back to the kitchen, and instead they climbed up by the windows into the room where the good housewife's husband was sleeping, and they swarmed up on his bed and tickled him until he became quite light-headed, and talked nonsense, and flung himself about, as if he had a fever.

'What in the world shall I do now?' said the good housewife to herself, and she wrung her hands in despair.

Then, all of a sudden, she remembered what the wise man had said about the fulling-water; and she ran to the kitchen, and lifted a little out of the pot, and carried it back, and threw it over the bed where her husband was.

In an instant he woke up in his right senses; and, jumping out of bed, he ran across the room and opened the door, and the fairies vanished, and they have never been seen again from that day to this.

The Son of the Strong Man of the Woods

There was once a man who lived in a tiny hut on the borders of a mighty forest. The neighbours wondered that he chose to live there, for the forest was full of all manner of wild animals, some of them timid and gentle enough, but some of them fierce and cruel.

People called him the 'Strong Man of the Wood', and the name was well chosen, he was so tall and cheerful and brave.

He was married to a sweet young wife whom he loved dearly; and every night when he returned from hunting, he used to look about for any withered branches which had been blown off the trees in the winter's storms, and he would drag them to the door of the hut, and cut them up for firewood, so that she should have no trouble when the fire came to be lit in the morning.

In this way time passed happily on, until at last a terrible thing happened.

There was a great oak tree growing a little way from the hut, and as no wood burns so brightly as oak wood, the good-hearted man made up his mind that he would prepare a little surprise for his wife by cutting down the massive tree, and carrying home a nice stock of firewood.

But, sad to relate, as he was bending over the root, plying his axe with all his might, the mighty tree bent over and crashed down on him, almost crushing him beneath its weight. He managed to scramble out from under it, however, and with a great effort he raised it on his shoulder, and staggered home with weak and tottering steps.

His strength was quite exhausted ere he reached the door, and when at last he threw down his burden, he fell beside it with a cry of pain.

At the unwonted sound his wife hurried out, and greatly alarmed, helped him to rise and to walk into the house.

'I have received my death-blow,' he murmured, as he sank down on the bed. 'As the tree crashed over, something within me broke, and I feel my life ebbing fast.'

His poor wife tried to cheer him with hopeful words, but he only shook his head, and signed to her to be quiet.

'See,' said he, opening his right hand, and showing her a little acorn lying in his palm, 'here is an acorn from the tree that killed me. I want you to promise that, as soon as I am dead, you will plant it on the top of the dung-heap which stands close by the byre door. There it will germinate and grow, and by the time its tiny leaves have pierced through the rubbish that covers it, you will have a little son to cheer you. He will not be like other children, who learn in a few years to run about and take care of themselves, for you must care for him and nurse him until he is strong enough to pull up by its roots the tree into which this acorn will grow.'

Having said this, the Strong Man of the Wood turned his face to the wall and died, leaving his poor young widow full of sorrow at his loss, and of wonder at the strange words which he had spoken to her.

But, true to her promise, she planted the acorn, and it all came to pass as her husband had foretold. By the time two tiny brown oak leaves were peeping up above the dung-heap, a little son had been born to her, and, remembering his father's words, she nursed him on her knee until he was seven years old.

Then she carried him out, and, setting him down on the dung-heap, she told him to try and pull up the tender sapling which was growing there.

The little fellow did as he was bid, and tugged, and tugged, but he could not uproot the oak.

'You are not strong enough yet, my son,' said his mother, and she picked him up again, and carried him back to the house.

Another seven years passed, and the child had grown into a sturdy boy, bigger by far than most lads of his age, while the tiny sapling had almost grown into a small tree.

'I will try his strength once more,' said his mother, so she bade her son run out and try to pull up the young oak tree by its roots.

Alas, alas! To her great disappointment he failed again. He was strong, but the tree was stronger.

So for another seven weary years she nursed him, and then he tried again. And this time he succeeded, for he pulled the oak tree up by its roots, and threw it down with a shout of triumph at his mother's feet.

' 'Twill make good firewood for you, mother,' he said.

'That it will,' said his mother, 'and the first use I will put it to is to kindle a fire, and bake a pocketful of bannocks for you, for it is high time that you set out to seek your fortune. I have cared for you for one-and-twenty years, and you must care for yourself now.'

So the son of the Strong Man of the Wood put his mother's bannocks in his pocket, and set out to seek his fortune.

At first he walked for many miles without seeing any place where it seemed likely that he could find work, but at last he came in sight of a large farmstead, where there was a stack-yard filled with more stacks than ever he had seen in his life before.

'If all these stacks are to be threshed there ought to be work enough and to spare here,' he said to himself, and he went straight up to the door of the farmhouse and knocked.

A waiting-maid came to the door, and she started back in amazement at the sight of the stranger, for the son of the Strong Man of the Wood was such a big lad that, in comparison with all the other folk she had ever seen in her life, he was quite a giant.

'What may you want?' she asked timidly, keeping well to the back of the door.

'To speak with thy master, if he be within,' said Ranald (for that was the big lad's name) promptly.

The maidservant turned and ran to the sitting-room, where her master was having his afternoon nap.

'Master, master, wake up!' she cried, 'for the biggest lad that ever I saw is at the door, and he is asking for you.'

The master rose and went out, and he too was astonished at the stranger's size. 'What do you want?' he said, eyeing him from head to foot.

'I want work,' said Ranald cheerfully. 'I am young and strong, and the man who hires me will have no cause to rue it.'

'By my troth you look strong enough,' said the farmer slowly. (It chanced that he needed help, and this lad seemed to have come just in the nick of time.) 'Can you thresh?'

'That can I,' answered Ranald, lifting one of his brawny arms, and swinging it round his head as if it were a flail.

'Well, I will try you,' said the farmer after a pause, 'and I hope that what you say will turn out to be true, and that I will have no cause to rue my choice.'

So the bargain was made, and without more ado Ranald asked when he should begin to work.

'Not till tomorrow morning,' answered the farmer, astonished at his zeal, for as a rule his servants were not in such a hurry to begin their work. 'There is as much corn waiting there to be threshed as will keep two men busy for six weeks, and after that there are all the stacks in the stackyard too.'

Now at that time farm-servants used to commence their work in the morning when the stars disappeared, and finish it at night, when they once more began to twinkle in the sky; so before it grew dark Ranald went and peeped into the barn where the men were still at work. He burst out laughing when he saw the flails that they were using; they seemed to him only fit for pigmies to use.

'These flails are useless,' he said contemptuously. 'When you come here in the morning, you will see the flail that *I* work with.'

Then he put his hands in his pockets, and strolled off to a wood which he saw up on the hillside, and when he got there he cut down a young tree, and shaped it into the handle of a flail; then he walked down the hill again with it upon his shoulder.

When the men saw it they looked at one another, whispering, 'What sort of lad is this, for he has made the mast of his flail as tall as the mast of a ship.'

Next day Ranald rose betimes, ere the morning star had quitted the sky, and set to work in the barn. He threshed and threshed with right good will, and his arm was so strong, and his flail so heavy, that before breakfast-time he had threshed out all the corn that was stored there. Then he went out to the stackyard, and seizing a stack under each arm, he carried them bodily down into the barn and threshed them. Then he went back for another two, and so the work went on, until at dinner-time the barn was full of golden grain, and the courtyard outside was almost buried in straw.

When all was finished he threw down his flail and walked towards the farmhouse, wondering that the farmer had never come out to see how he was getting on. Halfway across the courtyard, however, he came upon him, standing still, and gazing in bewilderment at the empty stackyard, and the great piles of straw which were heaped up in every direction.

'What shall I do next?' asked Ranald, going up to him and tapping him on the shoulder.

The master looked at him dully, as if he had just been wakened out of a dream.

'Do?' he said slowly, for he was feeling half afraid of this new man of his who could do the work of ten men and appear to be quite fresh when he was finished. 'You had better go into the barn and thresh the corn that you will find there.'

'I have threshed that too,' answered Ranald, with a twinkle in his eye, 'and now I want to know what you would have me do next.'

The farmer did not know what answer to make. He was feeling more afraid than ever of this strange servant of his, so he told him to go and get his dinner, while he went to the barn to see if what he said was true.

And when he saw that it was all true, his heart sank within him, and when his eyes fell on the enormous flail lying in the corner, he was overcome by terror, and fairly turned and fled.

'Whoever he is, or wherever he comes from, he is not canny,' he muttered to himself, and he took the back road to the house rather than the front one, for fear he should meet the newcomer, for he wanted to have some time to himself to think how he could get rid of him.

Meanwhile Ranald had finished his dinner, and now he was standing at the front door, and when he saw the farmer he went across and met him. 'And what can I do now?' he asked once more.

'Oh! anything you have a mind to,' stammered the farmer; 'you have been so busy all this forenoon, I think you had better rest this afternoon.'

'Very good,' said the big lad calmly, 'but ere I go to rest I would fain have a word with you. You have seen now how much work I can do, and the way in which I do it. But in order to work like that a man of my size needs food, and therefore I must in future have more dinner.'

'And how much must you have?' asked his master anxiously.

'Half a chalder of meal in brose, one day, and half a chalder of meal in bannocks, with the carcass of a two-year-old stot, another,' said Ranald quietly.

Then he walked on, while the farmer ran open-mouthed into the kitchen and began to tell his tale to his old servants who were assembled there.

'Haif a chalder of meal in brose, one day, and half a chalder of meal in bannocks, with the carcass of a two-year-old stot, another,' they repeated in horror when he had finished his story. 'Master, the place will be ruined unless you can get rid of him; for he certainly is not human if he can eat all that.'

'Get rid of him! That would I gladly,' said the farmer, 'but how? If any man can tell me that, I will give him an extra month's wages.'

But the servants only looked at one another and shook their heads; at last one of them spoke. 'Send for Big Angus of the Rocks,' he said; 'if he cannot tell us of a way, no one else can.'

So they sent for Big Angus of the Rocks, who was the oldest and wisest man in all the countryside, and when he was come they told him the whole story about the stacks, and the flail, and, what concerned them more than anything else, the enormous dinner which Ranald demanded.

The old man listened, shaking his head in dismay.

'Alas! Has he come at last?' he said. 'When I was a little boy, and my grandfather was an old man, about as old as I am now, I heard him foretell how some day this place would be ruined by a big giant, and I fear this stranger must be he.'

'But how can we get rid of him?' asked the farmer, for he had no wish to let his farm be ruined if he could help it.

'There is but one plan which I can think of,' answered the old man. 'Set him to open the well in the middle of the field yonder, and order him to dig on and on until he come to water. He will have to dig deep to reach that, I trow, for I know that the well has a sandy bottom; and when he has gone pretty far down into the earth, let all the men who can handle a shovel be gathered together on the bank, and let them shovel the loose stones and earth which he has thrown up down on him as fast as they can; so will he be smothered and crushed to death. But hark'ee! Do it when he is stooping, and if he stand up, let every man run, lest he spring out of the hole and try to kill them.'

That night the farmer sent for Ranald, and told him that water was getting so scarce that he thought there must be something wrong with the spring, and that, as there was a well in the middle of the ten-acre field, he would like him to open it, so that water could be drawn there.

'You must dig deep,' he added, 'for there is a sandy bottom, and the water is hard to come by.'

'All right,' said Ranald cheerfully; 'I'll start work on it in the morning.

Next morning the farmer and his men were astir early, but Ranald was up before them, already at work. The farmer and his men, armed with spades and shovels, crept up to the hole. Ranald was stooping down to lift a spadeful of earth.

'Quick, lads, we have him!' shouted the farmer, and one and all set to work to shovel the earth back into the well as hard as they could.

But what was their amazement when, just as they thought they had him covered, he stood up and shook himself as easily as if he had been shaking a few flakes of snow from his coat.

'Whist!' he said, and turned one ear up to the sky as if he were listening for something.

Then everyone remembered the words of Big Angus of the Rocks, and they turned and ran for their lives, in case he should jump out of the hole and kill them.

Meanwhile Ranald went calmly on with his work until it was finished. Then he laid his spade aside, and went home for his dinner.

To his astonishment he found that the door of the farmhouse was locked and bolted.

He knocked softly, then he knocked loudly, and at last, as nobody came to open it, he put his shoulder against it and burst it open.

He looked all round for the farmer, and, to his amazement, he discovered him hiding under the table, shaking with terror. When he saw that Ranald had no intention of harming him, however, he came slowly out, and stood up.

'Have you finished your work?' he asked.

'Ay,' said Ranald; 'but I was sore pestered by crows while I was at it, for they scratched and scratched in the heap of earth that I had thrown up till they sent down dust enough to blind me.

'What shall I do now?' he went on, looking at his master in the most simple way possible.

'Oh, go and get thy dinner!' answered the farmer in despair; and, with a smile, Ranald did as he was bid.

Meanwhile his master hurried off to Big Angus, and told him the whole story.

The old man shook his head. ' 'Tis plain we must try another plan,' he said, 'seeing that the first has failed.'

'But what plan can we try now?' asked the farmer.

'Send him to plough the crooked ridge of the Field of the Dark Lake,' replied Angus. 'Out of that came never man nor beast alive who ploughed there till the going down of the sun.'

So his master sent for Ranald once more, and told him to go and plough the crooked ridge of the Field of the Dark Lake.

'Very well,' said the big lad. 'I'll begin at star-setting tomorrow.'

So in the morning out he went, with his plough upon his shoulders, and leading a pair of horses behind him. When he reached the Field of the Dark Lake he laid down his plough and looked round him.

It was a great bare field, with a high ridge running through it, and one solitary tree growing in the middle of the ridge, with a dark lake lying by the side of it.

He ploughed all day, and everything went well, until, just as the sun was going down, he heard a great splash, and looking towards the lake, he saw a dark shapeless object in the water.

'It is a monster of some sort,' he said to himself, 'and that is why my fine master sent me here. Doubtless he hoped it would eat me alive: but if it wants me it must come for me,' and without troubling himself further, he went on with his ploughing.

Meanwhile the sun went down, and just as its last rays disappeared beneath the horizon, the huge shapeless monster came out of the water, and crawled up the bank on to the crooked ridge. Then it began to crawl slowly along the furrow from one end, while Ranald and his horses came to meet it from the other.

They met just under the solitary tree.

'Stand back,' he shouted, 'or you will see what will happen.'

The fierce beast paid no heed to his words; but opened his great jaws and swallowed one horse alive.

'That is enough!' said Ranald in a rage. 'I will make you give that horse back,' and letting go the plough, he tied the great beast's tail to the tree. Of course it struggled, and in its struggles it pulled up the tree by the roots.

'Oh! ho!' said Ranald, 'just what I wanted,' and he picked up the tree, and beat the monster with it, until the trunk broke into splinters. 'Give back that horse,' he cried. But the beast paid no heed. 'If you will not give it back, then you shall do its work,' he said grimly, and he seized hold of it, and yoked it to the plough.

As he was doing this, however, the remaining horse became so terrified at its strange companion, that it broke its traces and galloped home.

The farmer and his men rejoiced greatly when they saw it coming. 'Without doubt the big lad is dead at last,' they cried, 'the monster from the Dark Lake has swallowed him.'

But their joy was short-lived, for at that moment one of them chanced to look out of the window, and who should they see but Ranald coming quietly homewards, while beside him crawled the loathsome beast dragging the plough.

This was worse and worse. With a wild shriek everyone ran to hide himself as best as he might; and when Ranald reached the farm, he found naught save an empty house and silence.

He left the beast at the door, and strode into the kitchen.

'Where are you?' he cried.

There was no answer for a long time, and then at last the farmer came creeping down the stair from the attic where he had hidden himself, and asked him, in a trembling voice, what he wanted.

'I want to know what I have to do tomorrow,' said Ranald.

'Plough,' said the farmer, keeping tight hold of the door that led to the attic stairs.

'The ploughing is all finished,' said the big lad.

'That cannot be,' answered his master, 'there is as much land to plough in that field as would keep two men busy for six weeks.'

'But I tell you it is,' said Ranald. 'If you go out to look, you will not see a single furrow unploughed.'

'And did nothing trouble you when you were at the job?' asked the farmer faintly.

'Oh, nothing but a nasty thing of an ugly beast that came out of the lake and ate one of the horses,' said Ranald carelessly. 'I tried to make it give back the horse, but it did not seem to want to do so, so I did not waste time arguing with it, but I yoked it to the plough and made it pull it home.'

This was more than the farmer had bargained for. He crept forward and took hold of Ranald's coat.

'And where is he now?' he whispered.

'Outside the door,' answered Ranald.

The farmer nearly fell down with terror. 'What did you bring him here for?' he moaned. 'Send him away, oh! send him away!'

'I just brought him hither to let you see what manner of beast he is,' laughed Ranald. 'Now I will cut off his head, and put him in the great hole behind the dung-heap; then we will be able to plough the crooked ridge in peace hereafter.'

He went away to kill the monster, leaving the farmer wringing his hands in despair. 'Whatever shall we do?' he said to himself. With a woebegone face he betook himself to the house of Big Angus, and told him how the big lad had slain the monster, instead of the monster swallowing the big lad, as they had hoped and expected.

Old Angus could hardly believe his ears. 'There is but one thing more we can do,' he said, 'and I cannot but think that it will succeed. Pretend that all the meal is finished, and say to him that we can have nothing to eat until he takes a bag of corn to the Mill of Leckan, and has it ground there. Tell him he must stay all night if need be, for there is no meal about the place; and I warrant that if once he sets his head inside the Mill of Leckan after sunset, the big brownie of the mill will see to it that he never leaves it again alive. But hark'ee,' added the old man solemnly, 'be on the watch, and if by any chance he does escape – for, as you say, he seems to be more than mortal – take to your heels and run – men, and women and bairns.'

Once more the farmer sought Ranald. 'The meal has run down,' he said. 'Take the horse, therefore, and the sled, and a big bag of corn, and haste to the Mill of Leckan. I fear that you must grind all night, so as to be back with the meal in the morning, for there is not so much left in the barrel as would bake one single bannock.'

'Very well,' said Ranald, and he went off at once to yoke the sled.

He arrived at the Mill of Leckan in the gloaming, and as luck would have it, the miller had locked up the mill, turned his horse out to pasture, and gone to bed. Ranald went to the door of his cottage, and knocked loudly.

'Who is there?' shouted the miller.

' 'Tis I, Ranald, son of the Strong Man of the Wood,' was the reply.

'And what do you want?' asked the miller.

'I want you to get up and drive the mill, for I have brought with me a great bag of oats which must be ground before tomorrow morning.'

'For no man on earth will I enter the mill at this time of night,' said the miller.

'But I tell you you must,' repeated Ranald, 'for the folk where I come from are fasting till I take home the meal.'

'Fasting or no fasting, it makes no difference; I stir not from my house till the sun is up,' growled the miller.

'If you will not get up yourself to grind the corn,' said Ranald cheerily, 'waste no more of my time, but give me the key.'

Now the miller wanted to go to sleep, so he gave Ranald the key of the mill, and bade him begone, adding that if any misfortune befell him, as it was sure to do, it was his own fault.

Ranald took the key and opened the mill, then he carried in the bag of corn, and, making a fire of reeds and peats, he spread it out on the kiln to harden.

Then he put it into the hopper, and set the mill in motion, and in no very long time some of the corn was ground into meal.

When this was done, he began to feel hungry, which was little wonder, for the farmer had sent him away in such a hurry that he had had no time to take his supper.

So he made some of the meal into bannocks, and set them down on the hot kiln to bake. In a little while, when they were nice and crisp, and almost ready for eating, he heard a strange rustling in a dark corner, and looking round, he saw a great hairy figure rising up among the shadows, and stretching out a huge paw to seize one of the bannocks.

' 'Tis nothing but a brownie after all,' he said to himself; then he turned and faced his uncanny companion fearlessly.

'Keep back,' he said sharply; but the brownie paid no heed. It only stretched out its great paw farther, and seized one of the bannocks.

'Don't do that again,' said Ranald angrily.

The brownie paid no attention, but helped itself to another bannock.

'If you touch another one, dearly shall you regret it,' Ranald cried in a rage.

But the only answer the creature made was to seize the third, and last, bannock.

'Put them back,' shouted Ranald, almost beside himself with anger, and taking one leap, he seized hold of the brownie.

Then began a great and fearful struggle. At the first turn the roof of the mill crashed in; at the second, the kiln fell on the floor, a heap of ruins.

Outside, in his cottage, the miller heard the noise, and wrapping his head in the blankets, crept to the foot of the bed; while his wife, with one wild scream, jumped out of the bed altogether and hid underneath it.

Meanwhile Ranald had won the battle, and the brownie was meekly asking to be allowed to go away.

'Not until you have rebuilt the mill and the kiln, and put my bannocks where you found them,' answered Ranald sternly.

'Let go of me, and I will do it,' said the brownie.

'Nay, but you will do it before I let you go,' answered his captor. 'How am I to know that you will not run away?'

So with Ranald's hand firmly grasping the back of his neck, the brownie set to work to put the roof on the mill and build up the kiln.

At last all was finished. The mill and the kiln were just as they had been when Ranald arrived.

'Now let me go,' groaned the Brownie.

'Not until you have found the bannocks, and put them back on the kiln,' said Ranald. 'Do you think that I am going to be done out of my supper by you?' and he tightened his grip on the brownie's neck.

So the creature had to put his great paw up the chimney, and bring down the bannocks from where he had hidden them, and put them back on the kiln.

'Now you can go; and see to it that you never come back,' said Ranald, and, opening the door, he threw the brownie right out into the darkness. With three terrible shrieks the uncanny creature vanished, and so far as I have heard, he has never been seen from that day to this.

The miller heard the shrieks, although his head was hidden under the blankets. 'Alack! alack!' he moaned, 'why did I ever give him the key? for it is clear the brownie has killed him.'

When Ranald had finished his supper, he ground the rest of the corn, put the meal into the bag, put the bag on the sled, yoked the horse and locked the door.

The key he carried to the miller's house; but when he knocked, there was no answer.

He knocked again, and this time he heard a small faint voice, muffled by blankets, asking who was there.

' 'Tis I; here is the key of the mill,' he replied. 'If you will open the door I will give it you.'

The poor miller thought it was the brownie who was outside the door.

'Oh, be off! be off!' he entreated. 'Take the key if you want to, but spare my dwelling.'

Ranald laughed a hearty laugh. ' 'Tis I,' he said, 'and not the brownie, and here is your key,' and he pushed it under the door.

The miller jumped up in amazement. '*You!*' he cried in astonishment. 'Do you mean to tell me you are still alive, after spending a night in the Mill of Leckan?'

'Yes, I am,' answered Ranald, 'and so will you be if you have a mind to try it; for I have made the thing that dwelt there run away, and I promise you it will never trouble you again.'

Meanwhile, at the farm, the farmer was anxiously waiting to see whether his third plot had been successful or not. He had stationed men on all the hilltops to keep a lookout, and give him timely warning should they see Ranald returning. Great was his dismay and disappointment when one of them came running down to say that he had seen Ranald in the distance with the sled and the bag of meal.

'He will be here in less than an hour,' he gasped, for he was breathless with running, 'and then I know not what will become of us all, for he cannot be so blind as not to see that we are doing our best to destroy him.'

'Troth, we will not wait till he comes,' said the farmer, whose evil conscience made him a coward.

And so it came about that when honest, good-hearted Ranald came back with the meal, instead of finding a group of hungry folk waiting for him, as he had expected, he found the farm deserted, and every soul belonging to it fled.

' 'Tis none of my doing,' he said to himself, 'for I would have served my master faithfully, if he had been content to give me enough to eat. However, I need not grumble, for here is a well-stocked farm ready to my hand, and I will even bring my old mother here, and we will live peacefully together.'

So back he went to the hut by the forest, and told his mother all that had befallen him, and how he had gained possession of a well-stocked farm, and how she must needs come and keep his house.

But his mother was growing old, and the thought of the long miles she would have to go frightened her.

'I am old and frail, my son,' she said; 'journeys such as that are for young hearts and young limbs.'

Then the big lad stooped down and put his arm tenderly round her. 'You nursed me for one-and-twenty years,' he said. ' 'Tis my turn now to repay you;' and without more ado he lifted her on his back, and carried her safely to the farm; and there they lived in ease and plenty, and if they are not dead, they are living there still for all I know.

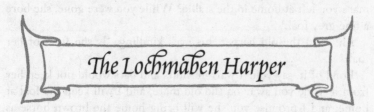

The Lochmaben Harper

Once upon a time, there was an old man in Lochmaben, who made his livelihood by going round the country playing on his harp. He was very old, and very blind, and there was such a simple air about him, that people were inclined to think that he had not all his wits, and they always called him the 'silly' Lochmaben Harper.

Now Lochmaben is in Dumfriesshire, not very far from the English border, and the old man sometimes took his harp and made long journeys into England, playing at all the houses that he passed on the road.

Once when he returned from one of these journeys, he told everyone how he had seen the English king, King Henry, who happened to be living at that time at a castle in the north of England, and although he thought the king a very fine-looking man indeed, he thought far more of a frisky brown horse which his majesty had been riding, and he had made up his mind that someday it should be his.

All the people laughed loudly when they heard this, and looked at one another and tapped their foreheads, and said, 'Poor old man, his brain is a little touched; he grows sillier, and sillier;' but the harper only smiled to himself, and went home to his cottage, where his wife was busy making porridge for his supper.

'Wife,' he said, setting down his harp in the corner of the room, 'I am going to steal the King of England's brown horse.'

'Are you?' said his wife, and then she went on stirring the porridge. She knew her husband better than the neighbours did, and she knew that when he said a thing, he generally managed to do it.

The old man sat looking into the fire for a long time, and at last he said, 'I will need a horse with a foal, to help me: if I can find that, I can do it.'

'Tush!' said his wife, as she lifted the pan from the fire and poured the boiling porridge carefully into two bowls; 'if that is all that you need, the brown horse is yours. Have you forgotten the old grey mare you left at home in the stable? While you were gone, she bore a fine grey foal.'

'Ah!' said the old harper, his eyes kindling. 'Is she fond of her foal?'

'Fond of it, say you? I warrant bolts and bars would not keep her from it. Ride you away on the old mare, and I will keep the foal at home; and I promise you she will bring home the brown horse as straight as a die, without your aid, if you desire it.'

'You are a clever woman, Janet: you think of everything,' said her husband proudly, as she handed him his bowlful of porridge, and then sat down to sup her own at the other side of the fire, chuckling to herself, partly at her husband's words of praise, and partly at the simplicity of the neighbours, who called him a silly old harper.

Next morning the old man went into the stable, and taking a halter from the wall he hid it in his stocking; then he led out his old grey mare, who neighed and whinnied in distress at having to leave her little foal behind her. Indeed, he had some difficulty in getting her to start, for when he had mounted her, and turned her head along the Carlisle road, she backed, and reared, and sidled, and made such a fuss, that quite a crowd collected round her, crying, 'Come and see the silly Harper of Lochmaben start to bring home the King of England's brown horse.'

At last the harper got the mare to start, and he rode, and he rode, playing on his harp all the time, until he came to the castle where the King of England was. And, as luck would have it, who should come to the gate, just as he arrived, but King Henry himself. Now his majesty loved music, and the old man really played very well, so he asked him to come into the great hall of the castle and let all the company hear him play.

At this invitation the harper jumped joyously down from his horse, as if to make haste to go in, and then he hesitated.

'Nay, but if it please your majesty,' he said humbly, 'my old nag is footsore and weary: mayhap there is a stall in your majesty's stable where she might rest the night.'

Now the King loved all animals, and it pleased him that the old man should be so mindful of his beast; and seeing one of the stable-men in the distance, he turned his head and cried carelessly, 'Here, sirrah! Take this old man's nag, and put it in a stall in the stable where my own brown horse stands, and see to it that it has a good supper of oats and a comfortable litter of hay.'

Then he led the harper into the hall where all his nobles were, and I need not tell you that the old man played his very best. He struck up such a merry tune that before long everybody began to dance, and the very servants came creeping to the door to listen. The cooks left their pans, and the chambermaids their dusters, the butlers their pantries; and, best of all, the stablemen came from the stables without remembering to lock the doors.

After a time, when they had all grown weary of dancing, the clever old man began to play such soft, soothing, quiet music, that everyone began to nod, and at last fell fast asleep.

He played on for a time, till he was certain that no one was left awake, then he laid down his harp, and slipped off his shoes, and stole silently down the broad staircase, smiling to himself as he did so.

With noiseless footsteps he crept to the stable door, which, as he expected, he found unlocked, and entered, and for one moment he stood looking about him in wonder, for it was the most splendid stable he had ever seen, with thirty horses standing side by side, in one long row. They were all beautiful horses, but the finest of all, was King Henry's favourite brown horse, which he always rode himself.

The old harper knew it at once, and, quick as thought, he loosed it, and drawing the halter which he had brought with him out of his stocking, he slipped it over its head.

Then he loosed his own old grey mare, and tied the end of the halter to her tail, so that, wherever she went, the brown horse was bound to follow. He chuckled to himself as he led the two animals out of the stable and across the courtyard, to the great wrought-iron gate, and when he had opened this, he let the grey mare go, giving her a good smack on the ribs as he did so. And the old grey mare, remembering her little foal shut up in the stable at home, took off at the gallop, straight across country, over hedges, and ditches, and walls, and fences, pulling the king's brown horse after her at such a rate that he had never even a chance to bite her tail, as he had thought of doing at first, when he was angry at being tied to it.

Although the mare was old, she was very fleet of foot, and before the day broke she was standing with her companion before her master's cottage at Lochmaben. Her stable door was locked, so she began to neigh with all her might, and at last the noise awoke the harper's wife.

Now the old couple had a little servant girl who slept in the attic, and the old woman called to her sharply, 'Get up at once, you lazy wench! Don't you hear your master and his mare at the door?'

The girl did as she was bid, and dressing herself hastily, went to the door and looked through the keyhole to see if it were really her master. She saw no one there save the grey mare and a strange brown horse.

'Oh mistress, mistress, get up,' she cried in astonishment, running into the kitchen. 'What do you think has happened? The grey mare has had a brown foal.'

'Hold your clavers!' retorted the old woman; 'you must be blinded by the moonlight if you don't know the difference between a full-grown horse and a two-month-old foal. Go and look out again and bring me word if 'tis not a brown horse which the mare has brought with her.'

The girl ran to the door, and presently came back to say that she had been mistaken, and that it was a brown horse, and that all the neighbours were peeping out of their windows to see what the noise was about.

The old woman laughed as she rose and dressed herself, and went out with the girl to help her to tie up the two horses.

' 'Tis the silly old Harper of Lochmaben they call him,' she said to herself, 'but I wonder how many of them would have had the wit to gain a new horse so easily?'

Meanwhile, at the English castle the harper had stolen silently back to the hall after he had let the horses loose, and taking up his harp again, he harped softly until the morning broke, and the sleeping men round him began to awake.

The king and his nobles called loudly for breakfast, and the servants crept hastily away, afraid lest it might come to be known that they had left their work the evening before to listen to the stranger's music.

The cooks went back to their pans, and the chambermaids to their dusters, and the stablemen and grooms trooped out of doors to look after the horses; but presently they all came rushing back again, helter-skelter, with pale faces, for the stable door had been left open, and the king's favourite brown horse had been stolen, as well as the harper's old grey mare. For a long time no one dare tell the king, but at last the head stableman ventured upstairs and broke the news to the master-of-the-horse, and the master-of-the-horse told the lord chamberlain, and the lord chamberlain told the king.

At first his majesty was very angry, and threatened to dismiss all the grooms, but his attention was soon diverted by the cunning old harper, who threw down his harp and pretended to be in great distress.

'I am ruined, I am ruined!' he exclaimed, 'for I lost the grey mare's foal just before I left Scotland, and I looked to the price of it for the rent, and now the old grey mare herself is gone, and how am I to travel about and earn my daily bread without her?'

Now the king was very kind-hearted, and he was sorry for the poor old man, for he believed every word of his story, so he clapped him on the back, and bade him play some more of his wonderful music, and promised to make up to him for his losses.

Then the wicked old harper rejoiced, for he knew that his trick had succeeded, and he picked up his harp again, and played so beautifully that the king forgot all about the loss of his favourite horse.

All that day the harper played to him, and on the morrow, when the old man would set out for home, in spite of all his entreaties that he would stay longer, the king made his treasurer give him three times the value of his old grey mare, in solid gold, because he said that if his servants had locked the stable door, the mare would not have been stolen; and, besides that, he gave him the price of the foal, which the wicked old man had said that he had lost. 'For,' said the king, ' 'tis a pity that such a marvellous harper should lack the money to pay his rent.'

Then the cunning old harper went home in triumph to Loch-maben, and the good king never knew till the end of his life how terribly he had been cheated.

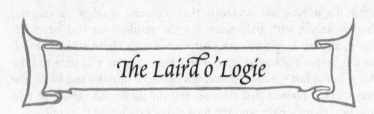

The Laird o' Logie

It was Twelfth Night, and in the royal Palace of Holyrood a great masked ball was being held, for the king, James VI, and his young wife, Anne of Denmark, had been keeping Christmas there, and the old walls rang with gaiety such as had not been since the ill-fated days of Mary Stuart.

It was a merry scene; everyone was in fancy dress, and wore a mask, so that even their dearest friends could not know them, and great was the merriment caused by the efforts which some of the dancers made to guess the names of their partners.

One couple in the throng, however, appeared to know and recognise each other, for as a tall slim maiden dressed as a nun, who had been dancing with a stout old monk, passed a young man in the splendid dress of a French noble, she dropped her handkerchief, and as the young Frenchman picked it up and gave it to her, she managed to exchange a whisper with him, unnoticed by her elderly partner.

Ten minutes later she might have been seen stealing cautiously down a dark, narrow flight of stairs that led to a little postern, which she opened with a key which she drew from her girdle, and closing it behind her, stepped out on the stretch of short green turf which ran along one side of the quaint chapel. It was bright moonlight, but she stole behind one of the buttresses that cast heavy shadows on the grass, and waited.

Nearly a quarter of an hour passed before another figure issued from the same little postern and joined her. This time it was the young French noble, his finery hidden by a guard's long cloak.

'Pardon me, sweetheart,' he said, throwing aside his disguise and putting his hand caressingly on her shoulder, 'but 'tis not my fault that you are here before me. I had to dance a minuet with the queen; she was anxious to show the court dames how 'tis done in Denmark, and, as you know, I have learned the Danish steps passably well dancing it so often with you. So I was called on, and Arthur Seaton, and a mention was made of you, but Gertrud Van Hollbell volunteered to fill your place.'

'Gertrud is a good-natured wench, and I will tell her so; but did her majesty not notice my absence?'

'No, she was so busy talking with me, and I gave her no time to miss you,' said the young man, laughing, but his companion's face was troubled. They had taken off their masks, and a stranger looking at them would have taken them for what they seemed to be, a dark-haired, black-eyed Frenchman, and a fair English nun. But Hugh Weymes of Logie was a simple Scottish gentleman, in spite of his dress, and looks; and the maiden, Mistress Margaret Twynlace, was a Dane, who had come over, along with one or two others, as maid-in-waiting to the young queen, who had insisted on having some of her own countrywomen about her.

Mistress Margaret's fair hair, and fairer skin, so different from that of the young Scotch ladies, had quite captivated young Weymes, and the two had been openly betrothed.

They had plenty of chances of speaking to each other in the palace, where Weymes was stationed in his capacity of gentleman of the king's household, and the young man was somewhat at a loss to understand why Margaret should have arranged a secret meeting which might bring them both into trouble were it known, for Queen Anne was very strict, and would have no lightsome maids about her, and were it to reach her ears that Margaret had met a man in the dark, even although it was the man she intended to marry, she would think nothing of packing her off to Denmark at a day's notice.

Now, as this was the very last thing that Hugh wanted to happen, his voice had a touch of reproach in it, as he began to point out the trouble that might ensue if any prying servant should chance to see them, or if Margaret's absence were noticed by the queen.

But the girl hardly listened to him.

'What does it matter whether I am sent home or not?' she said passionately. 'You can join me there and Denmark is as fair as Scotland; but it boots not to joke and laugh, for I have heavy news to tell you. You must fly for your life. 'Tis known that you have had dealings with my Lord of Bothwell, that traitor to the king, and your life is in danger.'

The young man looked at her in surprise. 'No, sweet Meg,' he said, 'but methinks the Christmas junketing has turned your brain, for no man can bring a word against me, and I stand high in his majesty's favour. Someone has been filling your ears with old wives' tales.'

'But I know you are in danger,' she persisted, wringing her hands in despair when she saw how lightly he took the news. 'I do not understand all the court quarrels, for this land is not my land, but I know that Lord Bothwell hates the king, and that the king distrusts Lord Bothwell, and, knowing this, can I not see that there is danger in your having been seen talking to the earl in a house in the Cowgate? and, moreover, it is said that he gave you a packet which you are supposed to have carried here. Would that I could persuade you to fly, to take ship at Leith, and cross over to Denmark; my parents would harbour you till the storm blew past.'

Margaret was in deadly earnest, but her lover only laughed again, and assured her that she had been listening to idle tales. To him it seemed incredible that he could get into any trouble because he had lately held some intercourse with his father's old friend, the Earl of Bothwell, and had, at his request, carried back a sealed packet to give to one of the officials at the palace, on his return from a trip to France. It was true that Lord Bothwell was in disfavour with the king, who suspected him of plotting against his person, but Hugh believed that his royal master was mistaken, and, as he had only been about the court a couple of months or so, he had not yet learned how dangerous it was to hold intercourse with men who were counted the king's enemies.

So he soothed Margaret's fears with playful words, promising to be more discreet in the future, and keep aloof from the earl, and in a short time they were back in the ballroom, and he, at least, was dancing as merrily as if there was no such word as treason.

For two or three weeks after the Twelfth Night ball, life at Holyrood went on so quietly that Margaret Twynlace was inclined to think that her lover had been right, and that she had put more meaning into the rumours which she had heard than they were intended to convey, and, as she saw him going quietly about his duties, apparently in as high favour as before with the king, she shook off her load of anxiety, and tried to forget that she had ever heard the Earl of Bothwell's name.

But without warning the blow fell. One morning, as she was seated in the queen's ante-chamber, busily engaged, along with the other women, in sewing a piece of tapestry which was to be hung, when finished, in the queen's bedroom, Lady Hamilton entered the room in haste, bearing dire tidings.

It had become known at the palace the evening before that a plot had been discovered, planned by the Earl of Bothwell, to seize the king and keep him a prisoner while the earl was declared regent. As it was known that young Hugh Weymes, one of the king's gentlemen, had been seen in conversation with him some weeks before, he had been seized and his boxes searched, and in them had been found a sealed packet, containing letters to one of the king's councillors, who was now in France, asking his assistance, and signed by Bothwell himself.

The gentleman had not returned – probably word had been sent to him of his danger – but young Weymes had been promptly arrested, although he disclaimed all knowledge of the contents of the packet, and had been placed under the care of Sir John Carmichael, keeper of the king's guard, until he could be tried.

'And there will only be one sentence for him,' said the old lady grimly; 'it's beheaded he will be. 'Tis a pity, for he was a well-favoured youth; but what else could he expect, meddling with such matters?' and then she left the room, eager to find some fresh listeners to whom she could tell her tale.

As the door closed behind her a sudden stillness fell over the little room. No one spoke, although some of the girls glanced pityingly at Margaret, who sat, as if turned to stone, with a still, white face, and staring eyes. Gertrud Van Hollbell, her countrywoman and bosom friend, rose at last, and went and put her arms round her.

'He is a favourite with the queen, Margaret, and so are you,' she whispered, 'and after all it was not he who wrote the letter. If I were in your place, I would beg her majesty, and she will beg the king, and he will be pardoned.'

But Margaret shook her head with a wan smile. She knew too well the terrible danger in which her lover stood, and she rightly guessed that the queen would have no power to avert it.

At that moment the door opened, and the queen herself entered, and all the maidens stood up to receive her. She looked grave and sad, and her eyes filled with tears as they fell on Margaret, who had been her playmate when they were both children in faraway Denmark, and who was her favourite maid-of-honour.

Seeing this, kind-hearted Gertrud gave her friend a little push. 'See,' she whispered, 'she is sorry for you; if you go now and beg her she will grant your request.'

Slowly, as if in a dream, the girl stepped forward, and knelt at her royal mistress's feet, but the queen laid her hand gently on her shoulder.

' 'Tis useless asking me, Margaret,' she said. 'God knows I would have granted his pardon willingly. I do not believe that he meant treason to his grace, only he should not have carried the packet; but I have besought the king already on his behalf and he will not hear me. Or his lords will not,' she added in an undertone.

Then the girl found her voice. 'Oh, madam, I will go to the king myself,' she cried, 'if you think there is any chance. Perhaps if I found him alone he might hear me. I shall tell him what I know is true, that Hugh never dreamt that there was treason in the packet which he carried.'

'You can try it, my child,' said the queen, 'though I fear it will be but little use. At the same time, the king is fond of you, and your betrothal to young Weymes pleased him well.'

So, with a faint hope rising in her heart, Margaret withdrew to her little turret chamber, and there, with the help of the kind-hearted Gertrud, she dressed herself as carefully as she could.

She remembered how the king had praised a dull-green dress which she had once worn, saying that in it she looked like a lily, so she put it on, and Gertrud curled her long yellow hair, and fastened it in two thick plaits behind, and sent her away on her errand with strong encouraging words; then she sat down and waited, wondering what the outcome of it all would be.

Alas! in little more than a quarter of an hour she heard steps coming heavily up the stairs, and when Margaret entered, it needed no look at her quivering face to know that she had failed.

'It is no use, Gertrud,' she moaned, 'no use. His majesty might have let him off – I saw by his face that he was sorry – but who should come into the hall but my Lords Hamilton and Lennox, and then I knew all hope was gone. They are cruel, cruel men, and they would not hear of a pardon.'

Gertrud did not speak; she knew that words of comfort would fall on deaf ears, even if she could find any words of comfort to say, so she only held out her arms, and gathered the poor heartbroken maiden into them, and in silence they sat, until the light faded, and the stars came out over Arthur's Seat. At last came a sound which made them both start. It was the grating noise of a key being turned in a lock, and the clang of bolts and bars, and then came the sound of marching feet, which passed right under their little window. Gertrud rose and looked out, but Margaret only shuddered. 'They are taking him before the king,' she said. 'They will question him, and he will speak the truth, and he will lose his head for it.'

She was right. The prisoner was being conducted to the presence of the king and the Lords of Council, to be questioned, and, as he openly acknowledged having spoken to the Earl of Bothwell, and did not deny having carried the packet, although he swore that he had no idea of its contents, his guilt was considered proved, and he was taken back to prison, there to await sentence, which everyone knew would be death.

From the little window Gertrud watched the soldiers of the king's guard lock and bar the great door, and give the key to Sir John Carmichael, their captain, who crossed the square swinging it on his finger. 'Would that I had that key for half an hour,' she muttered to herself. 'I would let the bird out of his cage, and old Karl Sevgen would do the rest.'

Margaret started up from the floor where she had been crouching in her misery. 'Old Karl Sevgen,' she cried; 'is he here?'

The old man was the captain of a little schooner which plied between Denmark and Leith, who often carried messages backwards and forwards between the queen's maids and their friends.

'Ay,' said Gertrud, glad to have succeeded in rousing her friend, and feeling somehow that there was hope in the sound of the old man's familiar name. 'He sent up a message this evening – 'twas when you were with the king – and if we have anything to send with him it must be at Leith by the darkening tomorrow. I could get leave to go, if you had any message,' she added doubtfully, for she saw by Margaret's face that an idea had suddenly come to her, for she sat up and gazed into the twilight with bright eyes and flushed cheeks.

'Gertrud,' she said at last, 'I see a way, a dangerous one, 'tis true, but still it is a way. I dare not tell it you. If it fails, the blame must fall on me, and me alone; but if you can get leave to go down to Leith and speak with old Karl alone, could you tell him to look out for two passengers in the small hours of Wednesday morning? And say that when they are aboard the sooner he sails the better; and, Gertrud, tell him from me, for the love of heaven, to be silent on the matter.'

Gertrud nodded. 'I'll do as you say, dear heart,' she said, 'and pray God that whatever plan you have in your wise little head may be successful; but now you must go to the queen. It is your turn tonight to sleep in the ante-room.'

'I know it,' answered the girl, with a strange smile, and without saying any more she kissed her friend, and, bidding her good-night, left the room.

Outside the queen's bedchamber was a little ante-chamber, opening into a tiny passage, on the other side of which was a room occupied by the members of the king's bodyguard, who happened to be on duty for the week.

It was the queen's custom to have one of her maids sleeping in the ante-room in case she needed her attendance through the night, and this week the duty fell to Margaret.

After her royal mistress had retired, the girl lay tossing on her narrow bed, thinking how best she could rescue the man she loved, and by the morning her plans were made.

'Gertrud,' she said next day, when the two were bending over their needlework, somewhat apart from the other women, 'do you think that Karl could get you a length of rope? It must be strong, but not too thick, so that I could conceal it about my person when I go to the queen's closet tonight. You could carry it home in a parcel, and the serving man who goes with you will think that it is something from Denmark.'

'That can I,' said Gertrud emphatically; 'and if I have not a chance to see you, I will leave it on the coffer in your chamber.'

'Leave what?' asked the inquisitive old dowager who was supposed to superintend the maids and their embroidery and who at that moment crossed the room for another bundle of tapestry thread; she had overheard the last remark.

'A packet for Mistress Margaret, which she expects by the Danish boat,' answered Gertrud promptly. 'I have permission from her majesty to go this evening on my palfrey to Leith, to deliver some mails to Captain Karl Sevgen, and to receive our packets in return.'

'Ah,' said the old dame kindly, ' 'tis a treat for you doubtless to see one of your own countrymen, even although he is but a common sailor,' and she shuffled back placidly to her seat.

Margaret went on with her work in silence, blessing her friend in her heart for her ready wit, but she dare not look her thanks, in case some curious eye might note it.

Gertrud was as good as her word. When Margaret went up to her little room late in the evening, to get one or two things which she wanted before repairing to the queen's private apartments, she found a packet, which would have disarmed all suspicions, lying on her coffer. For it looked exactly like the bundles which found their way every month or two to the Danish maids at Holyrood. It was sewn up in sailcloth, and was addressed to herself in rude Danish characters; but she knew what was in it, and in case the queen might ask questions and laughingly desire to see her latest present from home, she slit off the sailcloth, which she hid in the coffer, and, unfolding the coil of rope, she wound it round and round her body, under her satin petticoat. Luckily she was tall, and very slender, and no one, unless they examined her very closely, would notice the difference in her figure. Then, taking up a great duffle cloak which she used when riding out in dirty weather, she made her way to her post.

It seemed long that night before Queen Anne dismissed her. The king lingered in the supper chamber, and the gentle queen, full of sympathy for her favourite, sat in the little ante-room and talked to her of Denmark, and the happy days they had spent there. At last she departed, just as the clock on the tower of St Giles struck twelve, and Margaret was at liberty to unwind the coil of rope, and hide it among the bedclothes, and then, wrapping the warm cloak round her, she lay down and tried to wait quietly until it was safe to do what she intended to do.

There were voices for awhile in the next room – the king and queen were talking – then they ceased entirely; but still she waited, until one o'clock rang out, and she heard the guards pass on their rounds.

Then she rose, and, taking off her shoes, crept gently across the tiny room, stealthily opened the door of the queen's bedroom and listened. All was quiet except for the regular breathing of the sleepers. A little coloured lamp which hung from the ceiling was burning softly, and by its light she could see the different objects in the room. Stealing to the dressing-table, she looked about for any trinkets that would answer her purpose. The king's comb lay there, carefully cut from black ivory, with gold stars let in along the rim; and there, among other dainty trifles, was the mother-of-pearl and silver knife, set with emeralds, which his majesty had given the queen as a keepsake, about the time of their marriage. Margaret picked up both of these, and then, retracing her steps, she closed the door behind her, and flung herself on her bed to listen in breathless silence in case anyone had heard her movements and should come to ask what was wrong.

But all was quiet; not a soul had heard.

* * *

'The prisoner to be taken to the king now! Surely, fellow, you are dreaming.' Sir John Carmichael, captain of the king's guard, sat up in bed, and stared in astonishment at the soldier who had brought the order.

'No,' said the man stolidly. 'But 'twas one of the queen's wenches who came to the guardroom, and told us, and as a token that it is true, and no joke, she brought these from his majesty,' and he held out the gilded comb and the little jewelled knife.

Sir John took them and turned them over in silence. He knew them well enough, and, moreover, it was no uncommon thing for the king, when he sent a messenger, as he often did, at an unaccustomed hour, to send also some trinket which lay beside him at the moment, as a token; therefore the honest gentleman suspected nothing, although he was loth to get out of bed.

There was no help for it, however; the message had come from the king, and king's messages must be obeyed, even though they seemed ill-timed and ridiculous.

'What in the world has ta'en his majesty now?' he grumbled, as he got up reluctantly and began to hustle on his clothes. 'Even though he wants to question the lad alone, could he not have waited till the morning? 'Tis the queen's work, I warrant; she has a soft heart, and she will want his majesty to hear the young man's defence when none of the Lords of the Council are by.'

So saying, he took down the great key which hung on a nail at the head of his bed, and went off with the soldiers to arouse young Weymes, who seemed quite as surprised as Sir John at the sudden summons.

At the door of the queen's ante-chamber they were met by the same maid-of-honour who had taken the tokens to the guard, and she, modestly shielding her face with a fold of her cloak, asked Sir John if he would remain in the guardroom with the soldiers until she called for him again, as the king wanted to question the prisoner alone in his chamber.

At the sound of her voice Hugh Logie started, although Sir John did not seem to notice it, else his suspicions might have been aroused. He only waited until his prisoner followed the girl into the little room, then he locked the door behind them as a precaution, and withdrew with the soldiers into the guardroom, where he knew a bright fire and a tankard of ale were always to be found.

Once in the ante-room, the young man spoke. 'What means this, sweetheart?' he said. 'What can the king want with me at this hour of night?'

'Hush!' answered the girl, laying a trembling finger on her lips, while her eyes danced in spite of the danger. ' 'Tis I who would speak with you, but on board Karl Sevgen's boat at Leith, and not here. See,' and she drew the rope from its hiding-place, 'tie this round your waist, and I will let you down from the window; by God's mercy it looks out on a deserted part of the garden, where the guards but rarely come, and you can steal over the ditch, and down the garden, and round the Calton Hill, and so down to the sea at Leith. Karl's boat is there; he will be watching for you. You will know her by her long black hull, and by a red light he will burn in the stern. No, Hugh,' for he would have taken her in his arms. 'The danger is not over yet, and we will have time to talk when we are at sea, for I am coming too; I dare not stay here to face the king alone. Only I can steal out by that little door in the tapestry' – luckily Sir John did not know that there was another way out – 'and meet you in the garden.'

The window was not very high, and the night was dark, and no one chanced to pass that way as a figure slung itself down, and dropped lightly into the ditch; and, when a guard did come round, Hugh lay flat among the mud and nettles until he had passed, and by that time Margaret had stolen out by the little postern, and was waiting for him at the foot of the garden, and hand in hand they made their way over the rough uneven fields which lay between them and Leith.

Meanwhile, Sir John Carmichael drank ale, and talked with the guards, and waited – and waited, and talked with the guards, and drank ale, until his patience was well-nigh gone. At last, just when the day was breaking, he went to the door of the ante-room to listen, and hearing nothing, he knocked, and receiving no answer, he unlocked the door and peeped in, not wishing to disturb the maid-of-honour, but merely to satisfy himself that all was right. The moment he saw the open window and the rope, he shouted to the guards, and rushed across the floor, and thundered at the door of the king's apartment, hoping against hope that the prisoner was still there.

But the king had been sleeping peacefully, and when he heard the story, he was very angry at first, and talked of arresting Sir John, and sent off horsemen, who rode furiously to Leith, in the hope of catching the Danish boat. But they came back with the news that she had sailed with the tide at three o'clock in the morning, after having taken two passengers on board; and, after all, he could say little to Carmichael, for had he not received the comb and the knife as tokens?

'You should not have lingered so long at supper,' said the Queen slyly, only too pleased at the turn events had taken. 'Then you would have slept lighter, and would have awaked when the wench stole in to take the things.'

King James burst into a great laugh. 'By my troth, you are right,' he said, slapping his thigh. 'The wench has been too clever for all of us, for the Lords of the Council, and Carmichael, and me, and she deserves her success. They must stay where they are for a time, for appearances' sake, but when you are writing to Denmark, you can say that you think that my wrath will not last for ever.'

Nor did it, and before many months had passed Hugh Weymes of Logie came home in triumph, bringing with him his young wife, who had dared so much and acted so boldly for his sake.

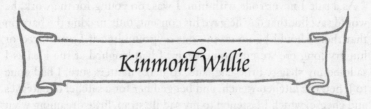

Kinmont Willie

I well remember the dull April morning, in the year 1596, when my father, William Armstrong of Kinmont, 'Kinmont Willie', as he was called by all the countryside, set out with me for a ride into Cumberland.

As a rule, when he set his face that way, he rode armed, and with all his men behind him, for these were the old reiving days, when we folk who dwelt on the Scottish side of the Border thought we had a right to go and steal what we could, sheep, or oxen, or even hay, from the English loons, who, in their turn, would come slipping over from their side to take like liberties with us, and mayhap burn down a house or two in the by-going.

My father was aye in the thick and throng of these raids, for he was such a big powerful man that he was more than a match for three Englishmen, did he chance to meet them. Men called him an outlaw, but we thought little of that; most of the brave men on our side had been outlawed at one time or another, and it did them little ill: indeed, it was aye thought to be rather a feather in their cap.

Well, as I say, my father was not riding on business, as it were, this morning, for just then there was a truce for a day or two between the countries, the two Wardens of the Marches, Sir Walter Scott of Buccleuch and Lord Scroope, having sent their deputies to meet and settle some affairs at the Dayholme of Kershope, where a burn divides England from Scotland. My father and I had attended the Truce Muster, and were riding homeward with but a handful of men, when I took a sudden notion into my head that I would like to cross the Border and ride a few miles on English ground.

My birthday had fallen the week before (I was just eleven years old), and my father, aye kind to his motherless bairns, had given me a new pony, a little shaggy beast from Galloway, and, as I was keen to see how it would run beside a big man's horse, I had pled hard for permission to accompany him on it to the Muster.

As a rule I never rode with him. I was too young for the work, he would say; but that day he gave his consent, only making the bargain that there should be no crying out or grumbling if I were tired or hungry long ere we got home again. I had laughed at the idea as I saddled my shaggy little nag, and, to make matters sure, I had gone to Janet, the kitchen wench, and begged her for a satchel of oatcakes and cheese, which I fastened to my saddle strap, little dreaming what need I would have of them before the day was out.

The Truce Muster had broken up sooner than he expected, so my father saw no reason why he should not grant my request, and let me have a canter on English soil, for on a day of truce we could cross the Border if we chose without the risk of being taken prisoners by Lord Scroope's men, and marched off to Carlisle Castle, while the English had a like privilege, and could ride down Liddesdale in open daylight, if they were so minded.

Scarce had we crossed the little burn, however, which runs between low-growing hazel bushes, and separates us from England, when two of the men rode right into a bog, and when, after some half-hour's work, we got the horses out again, we found that both of them wanted a shoe, and my father said at once that we must go straight home, in case they went lame.

At this I drew a long face. I had never been into England, and it was a sore disappointment to be turned back just when we had reached it.

'Well, well,' said my father, laughing, ever soft-hearted where I was concerned, 'I suppose we could ride into Bewcastle, lad, since we have got this length. The men can go back with the horses; 'tis safe enough to go alone today.'

So the men turned back, nothing loth, for Bewcastle Waste was no unknown land to them, and my father and I rode on for eight miles or so, over that most desolate country. Its bareness and loneliness disappointed me. Somehow I had expected that England would be quite different from Scotland, even although they were all one piece of land, with only a burn running between.

'Have you had enough?' said my father at last, noticing my down-cast face, and drawing rein. 'Did you expect all the trees to be made of silver, and all the houses to be built of gold? Never mind, lad, every place looks much the same in the month of April, I trow, especially when it has been a backward season; but when summer is here, I'll let you ride with the troop, and perhaps you will get a glimpse of "Merry Carlisle", as they call it. It lies over there, twelve miles or more from where we stand.'

As he pointed out the direction with his whip, we both became aware of a large body of men, riding rapidly over the moor as if to meet us. My father eyed them keenly, his face growing grave as he did so.

'Who are they, father?' I asked with a sinking heart. I had lived long enough at Kinmont to know that men did not generally ride together in such numbers unless they were bent on mischief.

'It's Sakelde, the English warden's deputy, and no friend of mine,' he answered with a frown, 'and on any other day I would not have met him alone like this for a hundred merks; but the truce holds for three days yet, so we are quite safe; all the same, lad, we had better turn our horses round, and slip in behind that little hill; they may not have noticed us, and in that case 'tis no use rousing their curiosity.'

Alas! we had no sooner set our horses to the trot, than it became apparent that not only were we observed, but that for some reason or other the leader of the band of horsemen was desirous of barring our way.

He gave an order – we could see him pointing with his hand – and at once his men spurred on their horses and began to spread out so as to surround us. Then my father swore a big oath, and plunged his spurs into his horse's sides. 'Come on, Jock,' he shouted, 'sit tight and be a man; if we can only get over the hill edge at Kershope, they'll pay for this yet.'

I will remember that race to my dying day. It appeared to last for hours, but it could not have lasted many minutes, ten at the most, during which time all the blood in my body seemed to be pounding and surging in my head, and the green grass and the sky to be flying past me, all mixed up together; and behind, and on all sides, came the pit-pat of horses' feet, and then someone seized my pony's rein, and brought him up with a jerk, and my father and I were sitting in the midst of two hundred armed riders, whose leader, a tall man, with a thin cunning face, regarded us with a triumphant smile.

'Neatly caught, you thieving rogue,' he said; 'by my troth, neatly caught. Who would have thought that Kinmont Willie would have been such a fool as to venture so far from home without an escort? But I can supply the want, and you shall ride to Carlisle right well attended, and shall never now lack a guard till you part with your life at Haribee.'

As the last word fell on my ear, I had much ado to keep my seat, for I turned sick and faint, and all the crowd of men and horses seemed to whirl round and round. Haribee! Right well I knew that fateful name, for it was the place at Carlisle where they hanged prisoners. They could not hang my father – they dare not – for although he had been declared an outlaw, and might perhaps merit little love from the English, was not this a day of truce, when all men could ride where they would in safety?

' 'Tis a day of truce,' I gasped with dry lips; but the men around me only laughed, and I could hear that my father's fierce remonstrance met with no better answer.

'You are well named, false Sakelde,' I heard him say, and his voice shook with fury, 'for no man of honour would break the king's truce in this way.'

But Sakelde only gave orders to his men to bind their prisoner, saying, as he did so, 'I warrant Lord Scroope will be glad to find you think so much about the truce, and if you are so scrupulous, you need not be hanged for a couple of days; the walls of Carlisle Castle are thick enough to guard you till then. Be quick, my lads,' he went on, turning to his men; 'we have a good fourteen miles to ride yet, and I have no mind to be benighted ere we reach firmer ground.'

So they tied my father's feet together under his horse, and his hands behind his back, and fastened his bridle rein to that of a trooper, and the word was given for the men to form up, and they began to move forward as sharply as the boggy nature of the ground would allow.

I followed in the rear with a heavy heart. I could easily have escaped had I wanted to do so, for no one paid any attention to me; but I felt that, as long as I could, I must stay near my father, whose massive head and proud set face I could see towering above the surrounding soldiers, for he was many inches taller than any of them.

The spring evening was fast drawing to a close as we came to the banks of the Liddle, and splashed down a stony track to a place where there was a ford. As we paused for a moment or two to give the horses a drink, my father's voice rang out above the careless jesting of the troopers.

'Let me say goodbye to my eldest son, Sakelde, and send him home; or do the English war with bairns?'

I saw the blood rise to the English leader's thin sallow face at the taunt, but he answered quietly enough, 'Let the boy speak to him and then go back,' and a way was opened up for me to where my father sat, a bound and helpless prisoner, on his huge white horse.

One trooper, kinder than the rest, took my pony's rein as I slid off its back and ran to him. Many a time when I was little had I had a ride on White Charlie, and I needed no help to scramble up to my old place on the big horse's neck.

My father could not move, but he looked down at me with all the anger and defiance gone out of his face, and a look on it which I had only seen there once before, and that was when he lifted me up on his knee after my mother died and told me that I must do my best to help him, and try to look after the little ones.

That look upset me altogether, and, forgetting the many eyes that watched us, and the fact that I was eleven years old, and almost a man, I threw my arms round his neck and kissed him again and again, sobbing and greeting as any bairn might have done, all the time.

'Ride home, laddie, and God be with you. Remember if I fall that you are the head of the house, and see that you do honour to our name,' he said aloud. Then he signed to me to go, and, just as I was clambering down, resting a toe in his stirrup, he made a tremendous effort and bent down over me. 'If you could but get word to the Lord of Buccleuch, laddie, 'tis my only chance. They dare not touch me for two days yet. Tell him I was ta'en by treachery at the time o' truce.'

The whisper was so low I could hardly hear it, and yet in a moment I understood all it was meant to convey, and my heart beat until I thought that the whole of Sakelde's troopers must read my secret in my face as I passed through them to where my pony stood.

With a word of thanks I took the rein from the kindly man who had held it, and then stood watching the body of riders as they splashed through the ford, and disappeared in the twilight, leaving me alone. But I felt there was work for me to do, and a ray of hope stole into my heart.

True, it was more than twenty miles, as the crow flies, to Branksome Tower in Teviotdale, where my Lord of Buccleuch lived, and I did not know the road, which lay over some of the wildest hills of the Border country, but I knew that he was a great man, holding King James's commission as Warden of the Scottish Marches, and at his bidding the whole countryside would rise to a man. 'Twas well known that he bore no love to the English, and when he knew that my father had been taken in time of truce . . . ! The fierce anger rose in my heart at the thought, and, burying my face in my pony's rough coat, I vowed a vow, boy as I was, to be at Branksome by the morning, or die in the attempt. I knew that it was no use going home to Kinmont for a man to ride with me, for it was out of my way, and would only be a waste of time.

It was almost dark now, but I knew that the moon would rise in three or four hours, and then there would be light enough for me to try to thread my way over the hills that lay between the valleys of the Teviot and Liddle. In the meantime, there was no special need to hurry, so I loosened my pony's rein, and let him nibble away at the short sweet grass which was just beginning to spring, while I unbuckled the bag of cakes which I had put up so gaily in the morning, and, taking one out, along with a bit of cheese, did my best to make a hearty meal. But I was not very successful, for when the heart is heavy, food goes down but slowly, and Janet's oatcake and the good ewe cheese, which at other times I found so tooth-some, seemed fairly to stick in my throat, so at last I gave it up, and, taking the pony by the head, I began to lead him up the valley.

Although I had been down the Liddle as far as the ford once or twice before, it had always been in daylight, and my father had been with me; but I knew that as long as I kept close to the river I was all right for the first few miles, until the valley narrowed in, and then I must strike off among the high hills on my left.

It was slow work, for it was too dark to ride, and I dare not leave the water in case I lost my way, and by the time we had gone perhaps four or five miles, I had almost lost heart, for I was both tired and cold, and it seemed to me that half the night at least must be gone, and at this rate we would never reach Branksome at all.

At last, just when the tears were getting very near my eyes – for I was but a little chap to be set on such a desperate errand – I struck on a narrow road which led up a brae to my left, and going along it for a hundred yards or so, I saw a light which seemed to come from a cottage window. I stopped and looked at it, wondering if I dare go boldly up and knock.

In those lawless days one had to be cautious about going up to strange houses, for one never knew whether one would find a friend or an enemy within, so I determined to tie my pony to a tree, and steal noiselessly up to the building, and see what sort of place it was.

I did so, and found that the light came from a tiny thatched cottage standing by itself, sheltered by some fir trees. There appeared to be no dogs about, so I crept quite close to the little window and peered in through a hole in the shutter. I could see the inside of the room quite plainly; it was poorly furnished, but beautifully clean. In a corner opposite the window stood a rough settle, while on a three-legged stool by the peat fire sat an old woman knitting busily, a collie dog at her feet.

There could be nothing to fear from her, so I knocked boldly at the door. The collie flew to the back of it barking furiously, but I heard the old woman calling him back, and presently she peeped out, asking who was there.

' 'Tis I, Jock Armstrong of Kinmont,' I said, 'and I fain would be guided as to the quickest road to Branksome Tower.'

The old woman peered over my head into the darkness, evidently expecting to see someone standing behind me.

'I ken Willie o' Kinmont; but he's a grown man,' she said suspiciously, making as though she would shut the door.

'He's my father,' I cried, vainly endeavouring to keep my voice steady, 'and – and – I have a message to carry from him to the Lord of Buccleuch at Branksome.' I would fain have told the whole story, but I knew it was better to be cautious. I was still no distance from the English Border, and it would take away the last chance of saving my father's life were Sakelde to get to know that word of his doings was like to reach the Scottish warden's ears.

'Loshsake, laddie!' exclaimed the old dame in astonishment, setting the door wide open so that the light might fall full on me, ' 'tis full twenty miles tae Branksome, an' it's a bad road ower the hills.'

'But I have a pony,' I said. ' 'Tis tied up down the roadway there, and the moon will rise.'

'That it will in an hour or two, but all the same I misdoubt me that you'll lose your road. What's the matter wi' Kinmont Willie that he has tae send a bairn like you with his messages? Ye needna' be feared to speak out,' she added as I hesitated; 'Kinmont Willie is a friend of mine – at least, he did my goodman and me a good turn once – and I would like to pay it back again if I could.'

I needed no second bidding; it was such a relief to have someone to share the burden, and I felt better as soon as I had told her, even although the telling brought the tears to my eyes.

The old woman listened attentively, and then shook her fist in the direction which the English had taken.

'He's a fause loon that Sakelde,' she said, 'and I'd walk to Carlisle any day to see him hanged. 'Twas he who stole our sheep, two years past at Martinmas, and 'twas your father brought them back again. But keep up your heart, my man; if you can get to the Bold Buccleuch he'll put things right, I'll warrant, and I'll do all I can for you. Go inbye, and sit down by the fire, and I'll go down the road and fetch the nag. You'll both be the better for a rest, and a bite o' something to eat, and when the moon is risen I'll take you up the hill, and show you the track. My goodman is away at Hawick market, or he would ha'e ridden a bit of the road wi' ye.'

When I was a little fellow, before my mother died, she used to read me lessons out of her great Bible with the silver clasps, and of all the stories she read to me, I liked the lesson of the Good Samaritan best, and, looking back, now that I am a grown man, it seems to me that I met the Good Samaritan that night, only he was a woman.

After Allison Elliot, for that was her name, had brought my pony into her cow-house, and seen that he was supplied with both hay and water, she returned to the cottage, and with her own hands took off my coarse woollen hose and heavy shoon, and spread them on the hearth to dry, then she made me lie down on the settle, and, covering me up with a plaid, she bade me go to sleep, promising to wake me the moment the moon rose.

It was nearly eleven o'clock when she shook me gently, bidding me get up and put on my shoon, as it was time to be going, and, sitting up, I found a supper of wheaten bread and hot milk on the table, which she told me to eat, while she wrapped herself in a plaid and went out for the nag.

What with the sleep, and the dry clothes, and the warm food, I promise you I felt twice the man I had done a few hours earlier, and I chattered quite gaily to her as she led my pony up a steep hillside behind the cottage, for the moon was only beginning to rise, and there was still but little light. After we had gone some two miles, we struck a bridle track, well trodden by horses' hoofs, which wound upwards between two high hills.

Here Allison paused and looked keenly at the ground.

'This is the path,' she said; 'you can hardly lose it, for there have been riders over it yesterday or the day before. Scott o' Haining and his men, most likely, going home from their meeting at the Kershope Burn. This will lead you over by Priesthaugh Swire, and down the Allan into Teviotdale. Beware of a bog which you will pass some two miles on this side of Priesthaugh. 'Tis the mire Queen Mary stuck in when she rode to visit her lover when he lay sick at Hermitage. May the Lord be good to you, laddie, and grant you a safe convoy, for ye carry a brave heart in that little body o' yours!'

I thanked her with all my might, promising to go back and see her if my errand were successful; then I turned my pony's head to the hills, and spurred him into a brisk canter. He was a willing little beast, and mightily refreshed by Allison Elliot's hay, and as the moon was now shining clearly, we made steady progress; but it was a long lonely ride for a boy of my age, and once or twice my courage nearly failed me: once when my pony put his foot into a sheep drain, and stumbled, throwing me clean over his head; and again when I missed the track, and rode straight into the bog Allison had warned me about, and in which the little beast was near sticking altogether, and I lost a good hour getting him to firm land and finding the track again.

The bright morning sun was showing above the eastern horizon before I left the weary hills behind me, but it was easy work to ride down the sloping banks of the Allan, and soon I came to the wooded valley of the Teviot.

Urging on my tired pony, I cantered down the level haughs which lay by the riverside, and it was not long before Branksome came in sight, a high square house, with many rows of windows, flanked by a massive square tower at each corner.

I rode up to the great doorway through an avenue of beeches and knocked timidly with the wrought-iron knocker, for I had never been to such a grand house in my life before, and I felt that I made but a sorry figure, splashed as I was with mud from head to foot.

The old seneschal who came to the door seemed to think so too, for he looked me up and down with a broad grin on his face before he asked who I was, and on what business I had come.

'To see my Lord of Buccleuch, and carry a message to him from William Armstrong of Kinmont,' I replied, with as much dignity as I could muster, for the fellow's smile angered me, and I feared that he might not think it worth his while to tell the warden of my arrival.

'Then you shall see Sir Walter at once, young sir, if you will walk this way,' said the man, mimicking my voice good-naturedly, and hitching my pony's bridle to an iron ring in the doorpost, he led me along a stone passage, straight into a great vaulted hall, in the centre of which stood a long wooden table, with a smaller one standing crossways on a dais at its head.

A crowd of squires and men-at-arms stood round the lower table, laughing and jesting as they helped themselves with their hunting knives to slices from the huge joints, or quaffed great tankards of ale, while up at the top sat my Lord of Buccleuch himself, surrounded by his knights, and waited on by smart pages in livery, boys about my own age.

As the old seneschal appeared in the doorway there was a sudden silence, in which he announced in a loud voice that a messenger had arrived from William Armstrong of Kinmont; but when he stepped aside, and everyone saw that the messenger was only a little eleven-years-old lad, a loud laugh went round the hall, and the smart pages whispered together and pointed to my muddy clothes.

When the old seneschal saw this, he gave me a kindly nudge.

'Yonder is my Lord of Buccleuch at the top of the table,' he whispered; 'go right up to him, and speak out thy message boldly.'

I did as I was bid, though I felt my cheeks burn as I walked up the great hall, among staring men and whispering pages, and when I reached the dais where the warden sat, I knelt at his feet, cap in hand, as my father had taught me to do before my betters.

Sir Walter Scott, Lord of Buccleuch, of whom I had heard so much, was a young, stern-looking man, with curly brown hair and keen blue eyes. His word was law on the Borders, and people said that even the king, in far-off Edinburgh, stood in awe of him; but he leant forward and spoke kindly enough to me.

'So you come from Armstrong of Kinmont, boy; and had Kinmont Willie no better messenger at hand, that he had to fall back on a smatchet like you?'

'There were plenty of men at Kinmont, if it please your lordship,' I answered, 'had I had time to seek them; but a man called Sakelde has taken my father prisoner, and carried him to Carlisle, and I have ridden all night to tell you of it, for he is likely to be hanged the day after tomorrow, if you cannot save him.'

Here my voice gave way, and I could only cling to the great man's knee, for my quivering lips refused to say any more.

Buccleuch put his arm round me, and spoke slowly, as one would speak to a bairn.

'And who is your father, little man?'

'Kinmont Willie,' I gasped, 'and he was ta'en last night, in truce time.'

I felt the arm that was round me stiffen, and there was silence for a moment, then my lord swore a great oath, and let his clenched fist fall so heavily on the table that the red French wine which stood before him splashed right out of the beaker, a foot or two in the air.

'My Lord of Scroope shall answer for this,' he cried. 'Hath he forgotten that men name me the Bold Buccleuch, and that I am Keeper o' the Scottish Marches, to see that justice is done to high and low, gentle and simple?'

Then he gave some quick, sharp orders, and ten or twelve men left the room, and a minute later I saw them, through a casement, throw themselves astride their horses and gallop out of the courtyard. At the sight my heart lightened, for I knew that whatever could be done for my father would be done, for these men had gone to 'warn the waters', or, in other words, to carry the tidings far and wide, and bid all the men of the Western Border be ready to meet their chief at some given trysting-place, and ride with him to the rescue.

Meanwhile, the warden lifted me on his knee, and began asking me questions, while the pages gathered round, no longer jeering, but with wide-open eyes.

'You are a brave lad,' he said at last, after I had told him the whole story, 'and, with your father's permission, I would like to have you for one of my pages. We must tell him how well you have carried the message, and ask him if he can spare you for a year or two.'

At any other time my heart would have leapt at this unheard-of good fortune, for to be a page in the warden's household was the ambition of every well-born lad on the Border; but at that moment I felt as if Buccleuch hardly realised my father's danger.

'But he is lodged in Carlisle Castle, and men say the walls are thick,' I said anxiously, 'and it is garrisoned by Lord Scroope's soldiers.'

The warden laughed. 'We will teach my Lord Scroope that there is no bird's nest that the Bold Buccleuch dare not harry,' he said, and, seeing the look on his face, I was content.

Then, noticing how weary I was, he called one of the older pages and bade him see that I had food and rest, and the boy, who had been one of the first to laugh before, but who now treated me with great respect, took me away to a little turret room which he shared with some of his fellows, and brought me a piece of venison pie, and then left me to go to sleep on his low pallet, promising to wake me when there were signs of the warden and his men setting out.

I must have slept the whole day, for the little room was almost dark again, and the rain was beating wildly on the casement, when the boy came back. 'My lord has given orders for the horses to be saddled,' he said, 'and the trysting-place is Woodhouselee. I heard one squire tell another in the hall, for as a rule we pages know nothing, and are only expected to do as we are bid. I know not if my lord means you to ride with him, but I was sent up to fetch you.'

It did not take me long to spring up and fasten my doublet, and follow my guide down to the great hall. Here all was bustle and confusion; men were standing about ready armed, making a hasty meal at the long table, which never seemed to be empty of its load of food, while outside in the courtyard some fifty or sixty horses were standing, ready saddled, with bags of fodder thrown over their necks.

Every few minutes a handful of men would ride up in the dusk, and leaving their rough mountain ponies outside, would stride into the hall and begin to eat as hard as they could, exchanging greetings between the mouthfuls. These were men from the neighbourhood, my friend informed me, mostly kinsmen of Buccleuch, and lairds in their own right, who had ridden to Branksome with their men to start with their chief.

There was Scott of Harden and Scott of Goldilands, Scott of Commonside and Scott of Allanhaugh, and many more whom I do not now remember, and they drank their ale and laughed and joked as if they were riding to a wedding, instead of on an errand which might cost them their lives.

Buccleuch himself was in the midst of them, booted and spurred, and presently his eye fell on me.

'Ha! my young cocksparrow,' he cried. 'Will you ride with us to greet your father, or are your bones too weary? Small shame 'twould be to you if they were.'

'Oh, if it please you, sire, let me ride,' I said; 'I am not too weary, if my pony is not,' at which reply everyone laughed.

'I hear thy pony can scarce hirple on three legs,' answered my lord, clapping me on my shoulder, 'but I like a lad of spirit, and go you shall. Here, Red Rowan, take him up in front of you, and see that a horse is led for Kinmont to ride home on.'

I was about to protest that I was not a bairn to ride in front of any man, but Buccleuch turned away as if the matter were settled, and the big trooper who came up and took me in charge persuaded me to do as I was bid. ' 'Tis a dark night, laddie, and we ride fast,' he said, 'and my lord would be angered if you lost your way, or fell behind,' and although my pride was nettled at first, I was soon fain to confess that he was right, for the horses swung out into the wind and rain, and took to the hills at a steady trot, keeping together in the darkness in a way that astonished me. Red Rowan had a plaid on his shoulders which he twisted round me, and which sheltered me a little from the driving rain, and I think I must have dozed at intervals, for it seemed no time until we were over the hills, and down at Woodhouselee in Canonbie, where a great band of men were waiting for us, who had gathered from Liddesdale and Hermitage Water.

With scarcely a word they joined our ranks, and we rode silently and swiftly on, across the Esk, and the Graeme's country, until we reached the banks of the Eden.

Here we came to a standstill, for the river was so swollen with the recent rains that it seemed madness for any man to venture into the rushing torrent; but men who had ridden so far, and on such an errand, were not to be easily daunted.

'This way, lads, and keep your horses' heads to the stream,' shouted a voice, and with a scramble we were down the bank, and the nags were swimming for dear life. I confess now that at that moment I thought my last hour had come, for the swirling water was within an inch of my toes, and I clung to Red Rowan's coat with all the strength I had, and shut my eyes, and tried to think of my prayers. But it was soon over, and on the other side we waited a minute to see if any man were missing. Everyone was safe, however, and on we went till we were close on Carlisle, and could see the lights of the castle rising up above the city wall.

Then Buccleuch called a halt, and everyone dismounted, and some forty men, throwing their bridle reins to their comrades, stepped to the front. Red Rowan was one of them, and I kept close to his side.

Everything must have been arranged beforehand, for not a word was spoken, but by the light of a single torch the little band arranged themselves in order, while I watched with wide-open eyes. They were not all armed, but they all had their hands full.

In the very front were ten men carrying hunting-horns and bugles; then came ten carrying three or four long ladders, which must have been brought with us on ponies' backs. Then came other ten, armed with great iron bars and forehammers; and only the last ten, among whom was the warden himself and Red Rowan, were prepared as if for fighting.

At the word of command they set out, with long steady strides, and as no one noticed me, I went too, running all the time in order to keep up with them.

The castle stood to the north side of the little city, close to the city wall, and the courtyard lay just below it. We stole up like cats in the darkness, fearful lest someone might hear us and give the alarm. Everyone seemed to be asleep, however, or else the roaring of the wind deadened the noise of our footsteps. In any case, we reached the wall in safety, and as we stood at the bottom of it waiting till the men tied the ladders together, we could hear the sentries in the courtyard challenge as they went their rounds.

At last the ladders were ready, and Buccleuch gave his whispered orders before they were raised.

No man was to be killed, he said, if it could possibly be helped, as the two countries were at peace with each other, and he had no mind to stir up strife. All he wanted was the rescue of my father.

Then the ladders were raised, and bitter was the disappointment when it was found that they were too short. For a moment it seemed as if we had come all the weary way for nothing.

'It matters not, lads,' said the warden cheerily; 'there be more ways of robbing a corbie's nest than one. Bide you here by the little postern, and Wat Scott and Red Rowan and I will prowl round, and see what we can see.'

Along with these two stalwart men he vanished, while we crouched at the foot of the wall and waited; nor had we long to wait.

In ten minutes we could hear the bolts and bars being withdrawn, and the little door was opened by Buccleuch himself, who wore a triumphant smile. He had found a loophole at the back of the castle left entirely unguarded, and without much difficulty he and his two companions had forced out a stone or two, until the hole was large enough for them to squeeze through; they had caught and bound the unsuspecting sentries as they came round, stuffing their mouths full of old clouts to hinder them from crying out and giving the alarm.

Once we were inside the courtyard he ordered the men with the iron bars and forehammers to be ready to beat open the doors, and then he gave the word to the men with the bugles and hunting horns.

Then began such a din as I had never heard before, and have never heard since. The bugles screeched, and the iron bars rang, and above all sounded the wild Border slogan, 'Wha dare meddle wi' me?' which the men shouted with all their might. One would have thought that all the men in Scotland were about the walls, instead of but forty.

And in good faith the people of the castle, cowards that they were, and even my Lord Scroope himself, thought that they were beset by a whole army, and after one or two frightened peeps from out of windows, and behind doors, they shut themselves up as best they might in their own quarters, and left us to work our will and beat down door after door until we came to the very innermost prison itself, where my father was chained hand and foot to the wall like any dog.

Just as the door was being burst open, my lord caught sight of me as I squeezed along the passage, anxious to see all that could be seen. He laid his hand on the men's shoulders and held them back.

'Let the bairn go first,' he said; 'it is his right, for he has saved him.'

Then I darted across the cell, and stood at my father's side. What he said to me I never knew, only I saw that strange look once more on his face, and his eyes were very bright. Had he been a bairn or a woman I should have said he was like to weep. It was past in a moment, for there was little time to lose. At any instant the garrison might find out how few in numbers we were, and sally out to cut us off, so no time was wasted in trying to strike his chains off him.

With an iron bar Red Rowan wrenched the ring, to which he was fastened, out of the wall, and, raising him on his back, carried him bodily down the narrow staircase and out through the courtyard.

As we passed under my Lord Scroope's casement, my father, putting all his strength into his voice, called out a lusty 'good-night' to his lordship, which was echoed by the men with peals of laughter.

Then we hurried on to where the main body of troopers were waiting with the horses, and I warrant the shout that they raised when they saw us coming with my father in the midst of us, riding on Red Rowan's shoulder, might almost have been heard at Branksome itself.

When it died away we heard another sound which warned us that the laggards at the castle had gathered their feeble courage, and were calling on the burghers of Carlisle to come to their aid, for every bell in the city was ringing, and we could see the flash of torches here and there.

Scarcely had the smiths struck the last fetter from my father's limbs than we heard the thunder of horses' hoofs behind us.

'To horse, lads,' cried Buccleuch, and in another moment we were galloping towards the Eden, I in front of Red Rowan as before, and close to my father's side.

The English knew the lie of the land better than we did, for they were at the river before us, well-nigh a thousand of them, with Lord

Scroope himself at their head. Apparently they never dreamed that we would attempt to swim the torrent, and thought we would have to show fight, for they were drawn up as if for a battle; but we dashed past them with a yell of defiance, and plunged into the flooded river, and once more we came safe to the other side. Once there we faced round, but the English made no attempt to follow; they sat on their horses, glowering at us in the dim light of the breaking day, but they said never a word.

Then my Lord of Buccleuch raised himself in his stirrups, and plucking off his right glove, he flung it with all his might across the river, and, the wind catching it, it was blown right into their leader's face. 'Take that, my Lord of Scroope,' he cried; 'perhaps it will cure you of your treachery, for if Sakelde took him, 'twas you who harboured him, and if you didn't like my mode of visiting your Castle of Carlisle, you can call and lodge your complaint at Branksome at your leisure.'

Then, with a laugh, he turned his horse's head and led us homewards, as the sun was rising and the world was waking up to another day.

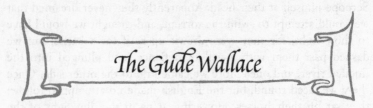

The Guide Wallace

I will tell you a tale of the Good Wallace, that brave and noble patriot who rose to deliver his country from the yoke of the English, and who spent his strength, and at last laid down his life, for that one end.

As all the world knows, the English king, Edward I, had defeated John Baliol at Dunbar, and he had laid claim to the kingdom of Scotland, and had poured his soldiers into that land. Some of these soldiers, hearing of the strength, and wisdom, and prowess of the young champion who had arisen, like Gideon of old, for the succour of his people, determined to try to take him by stealth, before venturing to meet him in the open field.

'Twas known that Wallace was in the habit of visiting a lady, a friend of his, in the town of Lanark, so a band of these soldiers went to her house, and surrounded it, while the captain knocked at the door. When the lady opened it, and saw him, and saw also that her house was surrounded by his men, she was very much alarmed, which perhaps was not to be wondered at, for everyone was afraid of the English at that time.

The officer spoke to her in quite a friendly manner, however, and began to tell her about his own country, and how much richer and finer everything was there than in Scotland, and at last, when she was thoroughly interested, he hinted that it was in her power to marry an English lord if she cared to do so, and go and live in England altogether.

Now I am afraid that the lady was both silly and discontented, and it seemed to her that it would be a very fine thing indeed to be an English nobleman's wife, so she blushed and bridled, and looked up and down, and at last she asked how the thing could be managed.

'Well,' said the officer cautiously, 'there is only one condition, and that doesn't seem to me to be a very hard one. It has been told me that there is a rough and turbulent fellow who visits this house.

His name is William Wallace, and because he is likely to stir up riots among the common people, it seems good to his majesty, King Edward, that he should be taken prisoner. Would it be possible,' and here his voice became very soft and persuasive, 'for you to let us know what night he intends to visit you?'

At first the lady started back, and was very indignant with him for daring to suggest that she should do such a dishonourable thing.

'I am no traitor,' she said proudly, 'nor am I like Jael of old, who murdered the man who took shelter in her tent.'

But the captain's voice was low and sweet, and the lady's nature was vain and fickle, and the prospect of marrying an English lord was very enticing, and so it came about that at last she yielded, and she told him how she was expecting young Wallace that very night at seven o'clock, and she promised to put a light in the window when he arrived.

Then the false woman went into her house and shut the door, and the soldiers set themselves to watch for the coming of their enemy.

How it happened I know not, but Wallace came, and walked boldly into the house without one of them seeing him, and he ran upstairs and knocked at the door of his friend's room.

When she opened it, he stood still, and stared at her in astonishment, for her face was pale and wild, and she looked at him with terror in her eyes. I warrant she had been wrestling with her conscience ever since she had spoken with the soldiers, and she had seen what an awful thing it is to be guilty of the blood of an innocent man.

'What's the matter?' cried Wallace, in his bluff, hearty way. 'You look all distraught, as if you had seen a ghost.'

Then he held out his hand as if to greet her, but she stretched forth hers and pushed him away. 'Touch me not. I am like Judas – Judas,' she moaned, 'who betrayed the innocent blood, and whose fate is written in the Holy Book for a warning to all poor recreants like to me.'

Sir William Wallace thought that she had gone mad. 'Calm yourself,' he said kindly. 'You have been been reading and thinking till you have fevered your poor brain. You are no Judas, but my own true friend, in whose house I find safe shelter when I need to visit Lanark.'

'Safe shelter!' she cried, with a bitter laugh, and she dragged him to the window, and pointed out in the dusk the figures of four soldiers who were leaning against the garden gate. 'Safe shelter, indeed, when I have betrayed you to the English; for this house is watched by fifteen soldiers; and I have but to put a lamp in the window, as a signal that you are here, and they will come and slay you.'

'And what is your reward for this deed of treachery?' asked Wallace, a look of contempt coming over his open face. 'What pay did the English loons promise you?'

'They promised me an English lord for a husband,' sobbed the wretched woman, who now would have done anything in her power to undo the wrong that she had done. 'But oh, sir, I fear I have brought sore affliction to you this day, and sore calamity to Scotland. If you can get free from this house, which I fear you will never do, you can denounce me as a traitor. I care not if I die the death.'

'Now heaven forfend!' said Wallace, whose kindly heart was touched by her distress, although he despised her for her false deed; 'it shall never be said that William Wallace avenged himself on a woman, no matter what her crime might be. I trusted you, and you have proved false, and so from henceforth we must go our different ways; but if you are truly sorry, you may yet help me, and, as for me, if once I get clear away from these southern knaves outside, I will think no more of the matter.'

'But can you get clear away?' questioned the lady anxiously. 'I fear now that it is past seven o'clock, they will keep stricter watch than they did when you came in. 'Twill be impossible for you to pass out in safety, and if you remain here, they will search the house when they tire of waiting for my signal.'

Wallace laughed. 'Impossible is not a word that I am well acquainted with, madam,' he said, 'and if, for the sake of the friendship that was between us in the days that are gone, you will lend me some of your clothes, a gown and kirtle maybe, and a decent petticoat of homespun, and a cap such as wenches wear to shield their faces from the sun, I hope I may make good my escape under the very noses of these fellows.'

Wondering to herself, the lady did as he asked her. She brought him a dark-coloured gown and kirtle, and a stout winsey petticoat, such as serving-maids wear, and after long search she found at the bottom of a drawer a milkmaid's cap.

Wallace proceeded to dress himself in these, and when he had put them all on, and had clasped a leather belt round his waist, and wound an apron about his head, as lassies do to protect themselves from the rain or sun, and put the milkmaid's bonnet on top of all, I warrant even his own mother would not have known him.

'Now fetch me a milk-can,' he said, 'for I am no longer a soldier, but a modest maiden going to the well to draw water.'

When she had brought it he bent low over her hand and gave it one kiss for the sake of old times; then he said farewell to her for ever, and opened the door, and walked boldly down the garden.

The four soldiers at the gate looked at one another in surprise when a tall damsel with a milk-can stood still at the foot of the garden path, and waited for them to lift the latch. They had not known that the lady had a serving-maid.

'If it please you, good sirs, to let me by,' broke in the maiden's voice in the gloom. 'My mistress has a sharp temper, and this water ought to have been fetched an hour ago.'

She spoke with a lisp, and her accent was so outlandish that the men scarce understood what she said; but this they saw, that she wanted to go and draw water from the well, and they opened the gate to let her pass.

'If I dared leave my post, I would gladly come and draw for you,' said one; 'shame is it that such a pretty wench be left to go to the well alone!'

The maiden paid no heed to the fellow's words, but tossed her head, and went quickly down the path to the well, taking such gigantic strides that the men gazed after her in wonder.

'Marry, but she covers the ground,' said one.

'Certs, but I would rather walk one mile with her than two,' said another.

'Methinks that we had better go after her and bring her back,' cried a third. 'I have heard say that this William Wallace, whom we are in search of, has mighty long legs.'

Horrified at the thought that they might have let the very man they were looking for escape, they hurried down the path after the serving-maid, and when they overtook her they found out in good sooth that she was William Wallace, for she drew a sword from under her kirtle and killed all four of them before they could lay hands on her.

When the four men lay dead before him, Wallace wasted no time over their burial, but drawing their bodies under a bush, where they were somewhat hidden from the passers-by, he hung the milk-can on a branch of a tree, and slipped quietly away in the gathering darkness. No one who met a simple country girl walking out of the town ever dreamt of asking her who she was, or where she was going, and ere morning came, I promise you, her garments had been cast, and buried in a hole in the ground, and Wallace was making his way northward as fast as ever he could.

He had to be very careful which way he travelled, for there were soldiers quartered in many of the towns, who knew that there was a price set on his head, and who were only too anxious to catch him. So he dared not venture into the towns, or into the districts where there were many houses, and by the time he was nearing Perth, he was acutely in need of food. He had eaten almost nothing for three days, nor had he money with which to buy provisions.

Now, near to Perth there is a beautiful haugh or common, called the North Inch, which stretches along the River Tay, and as he was crossing that, he saw a pretty, rosy country girl washing clothes under a tree, and spreading them out to bleach in the sun. She looked so kind and so good-tempered that he thought he would speak to her, and maybe, if he found that she lived near, he would ask her to give him something to eat.

So he went up to her, and greeted her pleasantly, and asked her what news there was in that part of the world.

'News?' said she, looking up at him with a roguish smile, for it was not often that she had the opportunity of talking with such a gallant knight. 'Nay, by my troth, I have no news, for I am but a poor working maiden, who toils hard for her living; but one thing I can tell you, an' if you are a true Scot at heart, you will do all in your power to shield him.'

'To shield whom?' asked Wallace in surprise. 'I know not of whom you speak.'

'Why! Sir William Wallace,' answered the girl, 'that gallant man who will deliver this poor country of ours. 'Tis known that he is in these parts; he has been traced from Lanark, and 'tis thought that he is making for the hills, where his followers are; and this very day a body of these cursed English have marched into the town, in order to search the country and take him. Look, do you see that little hostelry yonder? A band of them went in there not half an hour ago. Certs, had I been a man, I would e'en have gone myself, and measured my strength against theirs. I tell you this, because you seem a gallant fellow, and perchance you can do something to save the knight.'

Wallace smiled. 'Had I but a penny in my pocket,' he said, 'I would betake me to that little inn, just to see these English loons.'

The maiden hesitated. She was poor, as she had said, and had to work hard for her living, but it chanced that that day she had half a crown in her pocket, which she had intended to spend in the town on her way home. But her kind heart was stirred with pity at the thought of such a goodly young man having no money in his pocket, and at last she took out the half-crown and gave it to him.

'Take this,' she said, 'and go and buy meat and drink with it, and if you know where Wallace is, for the love of heaven, betray him not to these English knaves.'

'I will serve Wallace e'en as I serve myself,' he said, 'and more can no man promise,' and, thanking her heartily for the piece of silver, he strode off in the direction of the little hostler-house, leaving her wondering what he meant by his strange answer.

Wallace had not gone very far on his way before he met a beggar-man coming limping along, clad in an old patched cloak. This was the very thing the knight wanted.

'Hello, old man,' he said; 'how goes the world with you, and what news is there abroad in Perth?'

'News, master?' said the beggar. 'No news that I know of, save that 'tis said that Sir William Wallace is somewhere hereabouts, and a party of English soldiers have come to hunt for him. As I craved a bite of bread at the door of that hostler-house down yonder, I saw fifteen of them within, eating and drinking.'

'Say ye so, old man?' said Wallace. 'That is right good news to me, for I have long had a desire to see an English soldier close at hand. See,' and he drew the bright silver half-crown, which he had just received from the maiden, from his pocket, 'here is a piece of white money for you, if you will sell me that old cloak of yours, and your wallet. Faith, there be as many holes as patches in the cloak; it can scarce serve you for a covering, and 'twill answer my purpose right well.'

Joyfully the beggar agreed to the bargain, and Wallace was left with the cloak, which he threw over his shoulders, and which covered him from head to foot. Pulling his cap well over his eyes, and choosing a trusty thorn cudgel from a neighbouring thicket, he went limping up to the door of the little inn, and knocked.

The captain who was with the English soldiers opened it. He looked the lame beggar up and down. 'What do you want, you cruikit carle?' he asked haughtily.

'An alms, master,' answered the beggar humbly. 'I am a poor lame man, and unable to work, and I travel the country from end to end, begging my daily bread.'

'Ah,' thought the captain to himself, 'this man must hear all the country gossip. Likely enough he knows where Wallace is, or the direction in which 'tis thought he will travel.'

He took a handful of gold from his pouch, and held it before the beggar's eyes. 'Did you ever hear of a man called William Wallace?' he asked slowly; 'the country folk hereabouts talk a great deal of him. They call him "hero", and suchlike names. But he is a traitor to our rightful king, King Edward, and I am here to take him, alive or dead. Have you ever heard of the fellow?'

'Ay,' said the beggar, 'I have both heard of him and seen him. Moreover,' and he looked at the gold, 'I know where he is to be found.'

An eager look came into the English knight's face. 'I will pay you fifty pounds down,' he said, 'fifty pounds of good red money, if you will lead me to Sir William Wallace.'

'Tell down the money on this bench,' cried the beggar, 'for it is in my power to grant your request, and verily, I will never have a better offer, no, not if I wait till King Edward comes himself.'

The English captain counted down the money on the old worm-eaten wooden bench that stood beside the door of the inn, and the beggar counted it after him, and picked it up, and put it carefully away in his wallet. Then he faced the Englishman with a strange gleam in his eyes.

'You want to see William Wallace?' he said. 'Then see him you shall, and feel the might of his arm too, which is probably more than you bargained for,' and, before the astonished captain could grasp his sword, he had let the beggar's cloak fall to the ground, and, lifting his stout cudgel, he had given him such a clout over the head that his skull cracked like a nut and he fell dead at his feet.

Without waiting to take breath, Wallace drew his sword, and, running lightly upstairs, he burst into the room where the soldiers were just finishing their meal, and before they could rise from the table and grasp their weapons, he had stabbed every one of them to the heart.

The innkeeper's wife, who had just come from the kitchen, and was serving the men rather unwillingly, for she had no love for the English, stood still and stared in amazement.

'God save us!' she said at last, as Wallace stopped and wiped his sword. 'But are ye a man, or do you come from the Evil One himself?'

'I am William Wallace,' said the stranger, 'and I wish that all English soldiers who are in Scotland were even as these men are.'

'Amen to that,' said the old woman heartily, and then she dropped down on her knees before the embarrassed knight. 'Hech, sir,' she said fervently, 'to think that my eyes are looking on the Gude Wallace!'

'The Hungry Wallace, ye mean,' said the knight with a laugh. 'If ye love me, woman, get up from your knees, and set on meat and drink, for I have scarce tasted food these three days, and my strength is well-nigh gone.'

'That will I, right speedily,' she cried, and, jumping up, she ran to her husband and told him who the stranger was.

With great good will they began to prepare a meal, but hardly had it been dished up, and placed upon the table, before another band of soldiers marched up and surrounded the house. The beggarman had gone into Perth, and told people about the mysterious knight who had bought his old cloak in order that he might go and see the English soldiers, and when the rest of the soldiers in the town got to hear of it, they had suspected at once who he really was, and had come to the help of their companions.

Their suspicions proved true when they caught sight of Wallace through one of the windows.

'Come out, come out, false knight,' they cried exultingly, 'and don't think that you can escape our grasp. The fox is taken in his hole this time, and right speedily shall he die.'

With that they entered the house, and rushed upstairs, thinking that it would be an easy matter to capture the Scottish leader, for they knew that he had no follower with him. But the weak things of this world are able sometimes to confound the mighty, and they had not reckoned that the two old people to whom the inn belonged were prepared to shed the last drop of their blood, rather than let Wallace come to harm in their house.

So the old man had taken down his broad claymore from the wall, and the old woman had seized a lance, and they stood one on each side of their guest, grasping their weapons with fevered zeal.

Then began a fierce and deadly onslaught in that little room, and many a time it seemed as if the three brave defenders must go down; but Wallace's arm had the strength of ten, and the old man laid on right bravely, and the old woman gave many a deadly thrust with her lance from behind, where she saw it was needed; and so it came to pass that at last every Englishman was slain, and Wallace and his bold helpers were left triumphant.

'Now, surely, I can eat in peace,' said he, sitting down to his sorely needed meal, 'and then must I begone. For, with your help, I have done a work here this day that will raise all the English 'twixt Perth and Edinburgh. Maybe, goodman, you can get help to throw these bodies into the river. 'Twill be better for you that the English don't find them in your house, but I must up and away.'

'That can I,' said the old man, 'for the good folk of Perth think much of you, and very little of the English, therefore will they give me a hand.'

So once more Wallace took the road to the North, and as he retraced his steps across the North Inch, he passed the rosy-cheeked maiden again, busy at her work. She was laying the clothes out to bleach now, and she gave him a friendly nod as he approached.

'I hope, fair sir, that you have seen the English,' she said, 'and that you have come by food at the same time?'

'That have I,' said Wallace; 'thanks to thy gentle charity, I have eaten and drunk to my heart's content. I have seen the English soldiers too, and, by my troth, the English soldiers have also seen

me. The day that I visited that little hostler-house is not likely to be
forgotten by the English army.'

Then he put his hand in his pocket, and drew out twenty pounds
in good red gold.

'Take that,' he said to the astonished damsel, pressing the money
into her hand as he spoke. 'Your half-crown brought me luck, and
this is but your rightful share of it.'

So saying, he took his way quickly towards the hills, leaving the
girl so bewildered that, had it not been for the money in her hand,
she would have been inclined to think that it was all a dream.

As it was, she never quite believed that it was a human being who
had taken away her silver half-crown, and brought her back twenty
gold pieces, but talked of ghosts, and visions; and some people,
when they heard of the thirty English soldiers who lay dead in the
little hostler-house, were inclined to be of her opinion.

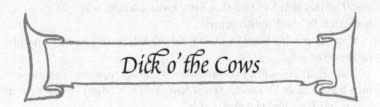

Dick o' the Cows

It was somewhere about the year 1592, and Thomas, Lord Scroope, sat at ease in his own apartment in Carlisle Castle. He had finished supper, and was now resting in a great oak chair before a roaring fire. A tankard of ale stood on a stool by his side (for my Lord of Scroope loved good cheer above all things), and his favourite hound lay stretched on the floor at his feet.

To judge by the look on his face, he was thinking pleasant thoughts just then. He held the office of Warden of the English Marches, as well as that of Governor of Carlisle Castle, and in those lawless days the post was not an easy one. There was generally some raid or foray which had to be investigated, some turbulent Scot pursued, or perhaps some noted freebooter hung; but just at present the countryside was at peace, and the Scotts, and Elliots, and Armstrongs, seemed to be content to stay quietly at home on their own side of the Border.

So that very day he had sent off a good report to his royal mistress, Queen Elizabeth, then holding her court in far-off London, and now he was dreaming of paying a long deferred visit to his Castle of Bolton in Lancashire.

A sharp knock at the door came as a sudden interruption to these dreams. 'Enter,' he cried hastily, wondering to himself what message could have arrived at the castle at that hour of night.

It was his own poor fool who entered, for in Carlisle Castle high state was kept, and Lord Scroope had his jester, like any king.

The man was known to everyone as 'Dick o' the Cow', the reason probably being that his wife helped to eke out his scanty wages by keeping three cows, and selling their milk to the honest burghers of Carlisle. He was a harmless, light-hearted fellow, whom some men called half-witted, but who was much cleverer than he appeared at first sight to be.

As a rule he was always laughing and making jokes, but tonight his face was long and doleful.

'What ails you, man?' cried Lord Scroope impatiently. 'Why does my jester come to me with a face that would make a merry man sad?'

'Alack, master,' answered the fool, 'up till now I have been an honest man, but at last I must turn my hand to thieving, and for that reason I would crave your leave to go over the Border into Liddesdale.'

'Tush!' said the warden impatiently, 'I love not such jesting. I hear enough about thieving and reiving, and suchlike business, without my own jester dinning it into my ears.'

But Dick knelt at his master's feet. 'This is no jest, my lord,' he said. 'For once in his life this poor fool is in earnest. For I am likely to be ruined if I cannot have revenge. You know how my wife and I live in a little cottage just outside the city walls, and how, with my small earnings, I bought three milch cows. My wife is a steady woman and industrious, and she sells the milk which these three cows give to the people in the city, and so she earns an honest penny.'

'In good sooth, a very honest penny,' repeated Lord Scroope, laughing, for 'twas well known in Carlisle that the milk which was sold by Dick o' the Cow's wife was thinner and dearer than any other milk sold in the town.

'Last night,' went on the fool, 'these Scottish thieves, the Armstrongs of Liddesdale, rode past the house, and, of course, they must needs drive these cows off, and, not content with that, they broke open the door, and stole the very coverlets off my bed. My wife bought these coverlets at the Michaelmas Fair, and what with the loss of them, and the loss of the cows, she is like to lose her reason. So, to comfort her, I have promised to bring them back. Therefore, my lord, I crave leave to go over into Liddesdale, and see what I can lay my hands on there.'

The blood rose to the warden's face. 'Am I not set here to preserve law and order, and would you have me give you permission to steal?'

'Nay, not to steal,' said the fool slyly; 'I only crave leave to get back my own, or, at least, the money's worth for what was my own.'

Lord Scroope pondered the request for a minute or two.

'After all,' he thought to himself, 'what can this one poor man do against such a powerful clan as the Armstrongs? He will be killed, most likely, and that will be the end of it. So there can be no great harm in letting him go.'

'If I give you leave, will you swear that you will steal from no one but those who stole from you?' he asked at last.

'That I will,' said Dick readily. 'I give you my word, and there is my right hand upon it. You can hang me for a thief myself if I take as much as a bannock of bread from the house of any man who has done me no harm.'

So Lord Scroope let him go.

A blithe man was Dick o' the Cow as he went down the streets of Carlisle next morning, for he had money in his pocket, and a big scheme floating in his brain. It mattered little to him that men smiled to each other as they passed him, and whispered, 'There goes Lord Scroope's poor jester.'

'He laughs the longest who laughs the last,' he thought to himself, 'and maybe all men will envy me before long.'

First of all, he went and bought a pair of spurs, and a new bridle, which he carefully hid in his breeches pocket, then he turned his back on Carlisle and set out to walk over Bewcastle Waste into Liddesdale. It was a long walk, but he footed it bravely, and at last he arrived at Puddingburn House, a strongly fortified place, held by John Armstrong, 'the Laird's Jock' as he was called, son of the Laird of Mangerton, and a man of importance in the clan. He was known to be both just and generous, and the poor fool thought that he would go to him, and tell him his story, in the hope that he would force the rest of the Armstrongs to give him back his three cows. But when he came near Puddingburn House, he found to his dismay that the two Armstrongs who had stolen his cows, Johnnie and Willie, had stopped there, on their way home, with all their men-at-arms, and from the sounds of feasting and mirth which he heard as he approached, he suspected that one, at least, of his three cows had been killed to provide the supper.

'Ah well,' thought he to himself, 'I am but a poor fool, and there are three-and-thirty armed men against me. To fight is impossible, so I must just set my wits to work against their strength of arms.'

So he walked boldly up to the house, and demanded to see the Laird's Jock. There was much laughter among the men-at-arms as he was led into the great hall, for everyone had heard of my Lord of Scroope's jester, and, when they knew that it was he, they all crowded round to see what he was like.

He knew his manners, and bowed right low before the master of the house. 'God save you, my good Laird's Jock,' he said, 'although I fear I cannot wish so well to all thy company. For I come here to bring a complaint against two of these men – against Johnnie and Willie Armstrong, who, with their followers, broke into my house near Carlisle these two nights past, and drove away my three good milk cows, forbye stealing three coverlets from my bed. And I crave that I get my own again, and that justice may be meted out to the dishonest varlets.'

These words were greeted by a shout of laughter, for these were rough and lawless times, when might was right, and the strong tyrannised over the weak, and it seemed ridiculous to see this poor fool standing in the middle of all these armed moss-troopers expecting to be heard.

'He deserves to be hanged for his insolence,' said Johnnie Armstrong, who had been the leader of the company.

'Run him through with a sword,' said Willie, laughing; ' 'tis less trouble, and 'twill serve the same end.'

'No,' cried another. ' 'Tis not worth while to kill him. He is but a fool at the best. Let us give him a good beating, and then let him go.'

But the Laird's Jock heard them, and his voice rang out high above the rest. 'Why harm the poor man?' he said. 'After all, he has but come to seek his property, and he must be both hungry and footsore.' Then, turning to the fool, he added kindly, 'Sit yourself down, my man, and rest a little. I am sorry that we cannot exactly give you your cattle back again, but at least we can give you a slice from the leg of one of them. Beshrew me if I have tasted finer beef for many a long day.'

Amid roars of laughter a slice of beef was cut from the enormous leg which lay roasted on the great table, and placed before Dick. But he could not eat it, he could only think what a fine cow it had been when it was alive. At last he slipped away unobserved out of the house, and, looking about for somewhere to sleep, he found an old tumbledown shed filled with peats.

He crept into it, and lay there, wondering and scheming how he could avenge himself.

Now it had always been the custom at Mangerton Hall, where the

Laird's Jock had been brought up, that whoever was not in time for one meal had to wait till the next, and he made the same rule hold good at Puddingburn House.

As the poor fool lay among the peats, he could see what was going on through a crack in the door, and he noticed that as more of the Armstrongs' men arrived both tired and hungry, they did not take time to put the key away safely after attending to their horses and locking the stable door, but flung it hastily up on the roof, where it could easily be found if it were wanted, and hurried off in case they were late for their supper.

'Here is my chance,' he thought to himself, and, as soon as they were all gone into the house, he crept out, and took down the key, and entered the stable. Then he did a very cruel thing. He cut every horse, except three, on one of its hind legs – 'tied it with St Mary's knot', as it was called – so that he made them all lame. Then he hastily drew the spurs and the new bridle out of his breeches pocket. He buckled on the spurs, and began to examine the three horses which he had not lamed. He knew to whom they belonged. Two of them, which were standing together, belonged to Johnnie and Willie Armstrong, and were the very horses they had ridden when they stole the cows. The third, a splendid animal, which had a stall to itself, plainly belonged to the Laird's Jock.

'I will leave the Laird's Jock's,' thought Dick to himself, 'for I cannot take three, and he is a kind man; but Johnnie's and Willie's must go. 'Twill perhaps teach them what comes of dishonest ways.'

So saying, he slipped the bridle over the head of one horse, and tied a rope round the neck of the other, and, opening the stable door, he led them out quietly, and then, mounting one of them, he galloped away as fast as he could.

The next morning, when the men went to the stable to see after their horses, there were shouts of anger and consternation. And no wonder. For it was easy to be seen that thirty of the horses would never put foot to the ground again; other two were stolen; and there was only one, the beautiful bay mare which belonged to the Laird's Jock, which was of any use at all.

'Now who hath done this cruel thing?' cried the master of the house in great anger. 'Let me know his name, and by my soul, he shall be punished.'

' 'Twas the varlet whom we all took to be such a fool,' cried Johnnie; 'the rascal who came here last night whining for his precious cows. A thousand pities we didn't do as I said, and hanged him on the nearest tree.'

'Hold thy tongue and take blame to thyself,' said the Laird's Jock sharply. 'Did I not tell you, before you rode to Carlisle, you and Willie and your thieving band, that the two countries were at peace, and if you began this work once more, 'twas hard to say where it would end? Truly the tables are turned. For this poor fool, as you call him, has befooled us all, for the men's horses are maimed and useless, your own and your brother's are stolen, and there but remains this good bay mare of mine. Beshrew me, but it seems as if the fellow had some gratitude left that he did not touch her, for I love her as I never loved a horse before.'

'Give her to me,' cried Johnnie Armstrong quickly, stung by this well-earned reproof, 'and I will bring the two horses back, and the cunning fool with them, either alive or dead. 'Tis a far cry from here to Carlisle, and I trow he could ride but slowly in the darkness.'

'A likely story,' said the Laird's Jock. 'The fool, as you call him, has already stolen two good horses, and to send another after him would but be sending good silver after bad.'

'An' do you think that he could take the horse from me?' asked Johnnie indignantly, and he pleaded so hard to be allowed to pursue Dick, that at last the Laird's Jock gave him leave.

He wasted no time in seeking his own armour, but snatching up hastily his kinsman's doublet, sword and helmet, he leaped on the bay mare and galloped away.

He rode so furiously that by midday he overtook Dick on Canonbie Lee, not far from Longtown.

The poor fool had had to ride slowly, for he was not very much accustomed to horses, and it was not easy for him to manage two. He looked round in alarm when he heard the thunder of hoofs behind him, but his face cleared when he saw that Johnnie Armstrong was alone.

'I have outwitted a whole household,' he thought to himself; 'beshrew me if I cannot tackle one man, even although it be Johnnie Armstrong.' All the same he put his horses to the gallop, and went on as fast as he could.

'Now hold, you traitor thief, and stand for your life,' shouted Johnnie in a passion.

Dick glanced hastily over his shoulder, and then he pulled his horses round suddenly. He could fight better than most men thought, when he was put to it.

'Are you alone, Johnnie?' he asked tauntingly. 'Then must I tell you a little story. I am an unlettered man, being but a poor fool, as you know, but I try to do my duty, and every Sunday I go to church in Carlisle city with my betters. And at our church we have a right good preacher, though his sermons run through my poor brain as if it were a sieve; but there are three words which I aye remember. The first two of these are "faith" and "conscience", and it seems to me that ye lacked both of them when ye came stealing in the dark to my humble cottage, knowing full well that I could not defend myself, and stole my cows and took my wife's coverlets. What the third word is, I cannot at this moment remember, but it means that when a man lacks faith and conscience he deserves to be punished, and therefore have I punished you.'

Johnnie Armstrong felt that he was being laughed at, and, blind with fury, he took his lance and flung it at the fool, thinking to kill him. But he missed his aim, and it only glanced against Dick's doublet, and fell harmless to the ground.

Dick, seeing his advantage, rode his horse straight at his enemy, and, taking his cudgel by the wrong end, he struck Johnnie such a blow on the head that he fell senseless to the ground.

Then was the fool a proud man. 'Lord Scroope shall hear of this, Johnnie,' he said to himself, with a chuckle of delight, as he dismounted and stripped the unconscious man of his coat-of-mail, his steel helmet and his two-handed sword. He knew that if he went home empty-handed, and told his master that he had fought with Johnnie Armstrong and defeated him, Lord Scroope would laugh him to scorn, for Johnnie was known to be one of the best fighters on the Borders; but these would serve as proofs that his story was true.

Then, taking the bay mare by the bridle, he mounted his horse once more, and rode on to Carlisle in triumph.

When Johnnie Armstrong came to his senses, he cursed the English and all belonging to them with a right good will. 'Now verily,' he said to himself, as he turned his face ruefully towards Liddesdale, ' 'twill be a hundred years and more ere anyone finds me fighting with a man who is called a fool again.'

When Dick o' the Cow rode into the courtyard of Carlisle Castle with his three horses, the first man he met was Lord Scroope. Now the warden knew the Laird's Jock's bay mare at once, and at the sight of her he flew into a violent passion. For he knew well enough that if Dick had stolen three horses from the Armstrongs, that powerful clan would soon ride over into Cumberland to avenge themselves, and had he not written to Queen Elizabeth, not three days before, of the peace which prevailed on the Borders?

'By my troth, fellow,' he said in deep vexation, 'I'll have you hanged for this.'

Poor Dick was much taken aback at this unlooked-for welcome. He had expected to be greeted as a hero, instead of being threatened with death.

' 'Twas yourself gave me leave to go, my lord,' he said sullenly.

'Yes, I gave you leave to go and steal from those who stole from you, if you could,' said Lord Scroope in reply; 'but beshrew me if I ever gave you leave to steal from the good Laird's Jock. He is a peaceful man, and a true, and meddles not with the Border folk. 'Twas not he who stole your cows.'

Then Dick held up the coat-of-mail, and the helmet, and the two-handed sword. 'On my honour, I won them all in fair and open fight,' he cried. 'Johnnie Armstrong stole my cows, and 'twas he who followed me on the Laird's Jock's mare, and clad in the Laird's Jock's armour. He would have slain me with his lance, but by God's grace it glanced from my doublet, and I felled him to the ground with my cudgel.'

'Well done!' cried the warden, slapping his thigh in his delight. 'By my soul, but it was well done. My poor fool is more of a man than I thought he was. If the horse be the fair spoil of war, then I will buy her from you. See, I will give you fifteen pounds for her, and throw a milk cow into the bargain. 'Twill please your wife to have milk again.'

But Dick was not satisfied with this offer. 'May the mother of all the witches fly away with me,' he said, 'if the horse is not worth more than fifteen pounds. No, no, my lord, twenty pounds is her price, and if you will not pay that for her, she goes with me tomorrow to be sold at Morton Fair.'

Now Lord Scroope happened to know the worth of the mare, so he paid the money down without more ado, and he kept his word about the milk cow.

As Dick pocketed the money, and took possession of the cow, he thought what a very clever fellow he was, and he held his head high as he rode out of the courtyard, and down the streets of Carlisle, still leading one horse, and driving the cow in front of him.

He had not gone very far before he met Lord Scroope's brother.

'Well met, fool,' he cried, laying his hand on Dick's bridle rein. 'Where in all the world did you get Johnnie Armstrong's horse? I know 'tis his by the white feet and white forelock. Has my brother been having a fray with Scotland?'

'No,' said the fool proudly, 'but I have. The horse is mine by right of arms.'

'Will you sell him me?' asked the warden's brother, who loved a good horse if only he could get him cheaply. 'I will give you ten pounds for him, and a milk cow into the bargain.'

'Say twenty pounds,' said Dick contemptuously, 'and keep your word about the milk cow, else the horse goes with me to Morton Fair.'

Now the warden's brother needed the horse, and, besides, it was not dear even at twenty pounds, so he paid down the money, and told the fool where to go for the milk cow.

An hour later Dick appeared at his own cottage door, and shouted for his wife. She rubbed her eyes and blinked with astonishment when she saw her husband mounted on a good black horse, and driving two fat milk cows before him.

Like everyone else, she had always counted him a fool, and had never looked for much help from him. So the loss of the three cows had been a serious matter to her, for the money which their milk brought had done much towards keeping up the house and clothing the children.

'Here, woman,' he cried joyously, leaping from his horse and emptying the gold out of his pockets into her apron. 'You made a great to-do over your coverlets, but I think that forty pounds of good red money will pay for them fully, and the three cows which we lost were but thin, starved creatures, compared with these two that I have brought back, and here is a good horse into the bargain.'

It all seemed too good to be true, and Dick's wife rubbed her eyes once more. 'Take care that they are not taken from you,' she said. 'Methinks the Armstrongs will demand vengeance.'

'They will not get it from Lord Scroope,' answered Dick, 'for 'twas he who gave me leave to go and steal from them. But perhaps we live too near the Borders for our own comfort, now that we are so rich. When a man hath made his fortune by his wits, as I have, he deserves a little peace in his old age. What would you think of going farther south into Westmoreland, and taking up house near your mother's kinsfolk?'

'I would think 'twas the wisest plan that ever entered that silly pate of yours,' answered his wife, who had never liked to live in such an unsettled region.

So they packed up their belongings, and getting leave from Lord Scroope, they went to live at Burgh-under-Stanmuir, where they passed for quite rich and clever people.

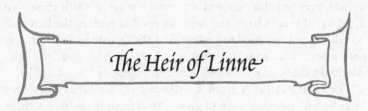

The Heir of Linne

There was trouble in the ancient Castle of Linne. Upstairs in his low-roofed, oak-panelled chamber the old lord lay dying, and the servants whispered to one another that when all was over, and he was gone, there would be many changes at the old place. For he had been a good master, kind and thoughtful to his servants, and generous to the poor. But his only son was a different kind of man, who thought only of his own enjoyment; and John o' the Scales, the steward on the estate, was a hard taskmaster, and was sure to oppress the poor and helpless when the old lord was no longer there to keep an eye on him.

By the sick man's bedside sat an old nurse, the tears running down her wrinkled face. She had come to the castle long years before, with the fair young mistress who had died when her boy was born. She had taken the child from his dying mother's arms, and had brought him up as if he had been her own, and many a time since he became a man she had mourned, along with his father, over his reckless and sinful ways.

Now she saw nothing before him but ruin, and she shook her head sadly, and muttered to herself as she sat in the darkened room.

'Janet,' said the old lord suddenly, 'go and tell the lad to speak to me. He loves not to be chided, and of late years I have said but little to him. It did no good, and only angered him. But there are things which must be said, and something warns me that I must make haste to say them.'

Noiselessly the old woman left the room, and went to do his bidding, and presently slow, unwilling footsteps sounded on the staircase, and the Lord of Linne's only son entered.

His father's eye rested on him with a fondness which nothing could conceal. For, as is the way with fathers, he loved him still, in spite of all the trouble and sorrow and heartache which he had caused him.

He was a fine-looking young fellow, tall and strong and debonair, but his face was already beginning to show traces of the wild and reckless life which he was leading.

'I am dying, my son,' said his father, 'and I have sent for you to ask you to make me one promise.'

A shadow came over the young man's careless face. He feared that his father might ask him to give up some of his boon companions, or never to touch cards or wine again, and he knew that his will was so weak that even if he made the promise he would break it within a month.

But his father knew this as well as he did, and it was none of these things that he was about to ask, for he knew that to ask them would be useless.

' 'Tis but a little promise, lad,' he went on, 'and one that you will find easy to keep. I am leaving you a large estate, and plenty of gold, but I know too well that in the days to come you will spend the gold and sell the land. You cannot do otherwise, if you continue to lead the life you are leading now. But don't think that I sent for you to chide you, lad; the day is past for that. Promise only that when the time comes, and you must needs sell the land, that you will refuse to part with one corner of it. 'Tis the little lodge which stands in the narrow glen far up on the moor. 'Tis a tumbledown old place, and no man would think it worth his while to pay you a price for it. Therefore I pray you to give me your solemn promise that when you part with all the rest, you will still remain master of that. For remember this, lad,' and in his eagerness the old man raised himself in his bed, 'when all else is lost, and the friends you have trusted turn their backs and frown on you, then go to that old lodge, for in it, though you may not think so now, there will always be a trusty friend waiting for you. Say, will you promise?'

'Of course I will, father,' said the young man, much moved; 'but I never mean to sell any of the land. I am not so bad as all that. But if it makes you happier, I swear now in your presence that I will never part with the old lodge.'

With a sigh of satisfaction the old lord fell back on his pillow, and before his son could call for help he was dead.

For the first few weeks after his father's death, the Heir of Linne seemed sobered, and as if he intended to lead a better life; but after a little while he began to riot and drink and gamble as hard as ever. He filled the old house with his friends, and wild revelry went on in it from morning till night.

He had always been weak and reckless; he was worse than ever now.

His father's friends shook their heads when they heard of his dissolute doings. 'It cannot go on,' they said. 'He is doing no work, and he is throwing away his money right and left. Had he all the gold of the Indies, it would soon come to an end at this rate.'

And they were right. It could not go on.

One day the young man found that not one penny remained of all the money which his father had left him, and there seemed nothing for it but to sell some of his land. Money must be got somehow, for he was deeply in debt. Besides, he had to live, and he had never been taught to work, and, even if he had, he was too lazy and idle to do it.

So away he went, and told his dilemma to his father's steward, John o' the Scales, who, as I have said, was a hard man, and a rogue into the bargain. He knew far more about money matters than his master's son, and when he heard the story which he had to tell him, his wicked heart gave a throb of joy.

Here, at last, was the very opportunity which he had been looking for: for, while the heir had been wasting his time and spending his money instead of looking after his estates, the dishonest steward had been filling his own pockets; and now he would fain turn a country gentleman.

So, with many fair words, and a great show of sympathy, he offered to buy the land for himself.

Young men would be young men, he said, and 'twas no wonder that a dashing young fellow, like the Heir of Linne, should wish to see the world, rather than stay quietly at home and look after his land. That was only fit for old men when they were past their prime. So, if he desired to part with the land, he would give him a fair price for it, and then there would be no need for him to trouble any more about money matters.'

The foolish young man was quite ready to agree to this. All that he cared about was how to get money to pay his debts, and to enable him to go on gambling and drinking with his companions.

So when John o' the Scales named a price for the land, and drew up an agreement, he signed it readily, never dreaming that the cunning steward was cheating him, and that the land was worth at least three times as much as he was paying for it. There was only one corner of the estate which he refused to sell, and that was the narrow glen, far out on the hillside, where the old tumbledown lodge stood.

For the Heir of Linne was not wholly bad, and he had enough manliness left in him to remember the promise which he had made to his dying father.

So John o' the Scales became Lord of Linne, and a mighty big man he thought himself. He went to live, with his wife Joan, in the old castle, and he turned his back on his former friends, and tried to make everyone forget that up till now he had only been a steward.

Meanwhile the Heir of Linne, as people still called him – though, like Esau, he had sold his birthright – went away quite happily now that his pockets were once more filled with gold, and went on in his old ways, drinking, and gambling, and rioting, with his boon companions, as if he thought that this money would last for ever.

But of course it did not, and one fine day, nearly a year after he had sold his land, he found that his purse was quite empty again, except for a few small coins.

He had no more land to sell, and for the first time in his life he grew thoughtful, and began to wonder what he should do. But he never took the trouble to worry about anything, and he trusted that in the end it would all come right.

'I have no lack of friends,' he thought to himself, 'and in the past I have entertained them right royally; surely now it is their turn to entertain me, and by and by I shall look for work.'

So with a light heart he travelled to Edinburgh, where most of his fine friends lived, never thinking but that they would be ready to receive him with open arms. Alas! he had yet to learn that the people who are most eager to share our prosperity are not always those who are readiest to share our adversity. With all his faults he had ever been open-handed and generous, and had lent his money freely, and he went boldly to their doors, intending to ask them to lend him money in return, now that he was in need of it.

But, to his surprise, instead of being glad to see him, one and all gave him the cold shoulder.

At the first house the servant came to the door with the message that his master was not at home, though the heir could have sworn that a moment before he had seen him peeping through the window.

The master of the next house was at home, but he began to make excuses, and to say how sorry he was, but he had just paid all his bills, and he had no more money by him; while at the third house his friend spoke to him quite sharply, just as if he had been a stranger, and told him that he ought to be ashamed of the way he had wasted his father's money, and sold his land, and that certainly he could not think of lending gold to him, as he would never expect to see it back again.

The poor young man went out into the street, feeling quite dazed with surprise.

'Ah, lack-a-day!' he said to himself bitterly. 'So these are the men who called themselves my friends. As long as I was Heir of Linne, and master of my father's lands, they seemed to love me right well. Many a meal have they eaten at my table, and many a pound of mine has gone into their pockets; and this is how they repay me.'

After this things went from bad to worse. He tried to get work, but no one would hire him, and it was not very long before the Heir of Linne, who had been so proud and reckless in his brighter days, was going about in ragged clothes, begging his bread from door to door. No one who saw him now would have known him to be the bright-faced, handsome lad of whom the old lord had been so proud a few years before.

At last, one day when his courage was almost gone, the words which his father had spoken on his deathbed, and which he had forgotten up till now, flashed into his mind.

'He said that I would find a faithful friend in the little lodge up in the glen, when all my other friends had forsaken me,' he said to himself. 'I cannot think what he meant, but surely now is the time to test his words, for surely no man could be more forsaken than I am.'

So he turned his face from the city, and wended his way over hill and dale, moor and river, till he came to the little lodge, standing in the lonely glen, high up on the moors near the Castle of Linne.

He had hardly seen the tumbledown old place since he was a boy, and somehow, from his father's words, he expected to find someone living in it – his good old nurse, perhaps. He was so worn out and miserable that the tears came into his eyes at the mere thought of seeing her kindly face. But the old building was quite deserted, and, when he forced open the rusty lock, and entered, he found nothing but a low, dark, comfortless room. The walls were bare and damp, and the little window was so overgrown with ivy that scarcely any light could get in. There was not even a chair or a table in it, nothing but a long rope with a noose at the end of it, which hung dangling down from the ceiling.

As his eyes grew accustomed to the darkness, he noticed that on the rafter above the rope there was written in large letters:

Ah, graceless wretch, I knew that you would soon spoil all, and bring yourself to poverty. So, to hide your shame and bring your sorrows to an end, I left this rope, which will prove your best friend.

'So my father knew the straits which my foolishness would bring me to, and he thought of this way of ending my life,' said the poor young man to himself, and he felt so heartbroken, and so hopeless, that he put his head in the noose and tried to hang himself.

But this was not the end of which his father had been thinking when he wrote the words; he had only meant to give his son a lesson, which he hoped would be a warning to him. So, when he put his head in the noose, and took hold of the rope, the beam that it was fastened to gave way, and the whole ceiling came tumbling down on top of him.

For a long time he lay stunned on the floor, and when at last he came to himself, he could hardly remember what had happened. At last his eye fell on a packet, which had fallen down with the wood and the mortar, and was lying quite close to him.

He picked it up and opened it.

Inside there was a golden key, and a letter which told him that if he would climb up through the hole in the ceiling, he would find a hidden room under the roof, and there, built into the wall, he would see three great chests standing together.

Wondering greatly to himself, he climbed up among the broken rafters, and he found that what the letter said was true. Sure enough there was a little dark room hidden under the roof, which no one had known of before, and there, standing side by side in the wall, were three iron-bound chests.

There was something written above them, as there had been something written above the rope, but this time the words filled him with hope. They ran thus:

> Once more, my son, I set you free;
> Amend your life and follies past:
> For if you do not mend thy ways,
> The rope will be your end at last.

With trembling hands the Heir of Linne fitted the golden key into the lock of one of the chests. It opened it easily, and when he raised the lid, what was his joy to find that the chest was full of bags of good red gold. There was enough of it to buy back his father's land, and when he saw it he hid his face in his hands, and sobbed for very thankfulness.

The key opened the other two chests as well, and he found that one of them was also full of gold, while the other was full of silver.

It was plain that his father had known how recklessly he would spend his money, and had stored up these chests for him here in this hidden place, where no one was likely to find them, so that when he was penniless, and had learned how wicked and stupid he had been, he might get another chance if he liked to take it.

He had indeed learned a lesson.

With outstretched hands he vowed a vow that he would follow his father's advice and mend his ways, and that from henceforth he would try to be a better man, and lead a worthier life, and use this money in a better way.

Then he lifted out three bags of gold, and hid them in his ragged cloak, and locked up the chests again, and took his way down the hill to his father's castle.

When he arrived, he peeped in at one of the windows, and there he saw John o' the Scales, fat and prosperous-looking, sitting with his wife Joan at the head of the table, and beside them three gentlemen who lived in the neighbourhood. They were laughing, and feasting, and pledging each other in glasses of wine, and, as he looked at them, he wondered how he had ever allowed the sleek, cunning-looking steward to become Lord of Linne in his father's place.

With something of his old pride he knocked at the door, and

demanded haughtily to speak with the master of the castle. He was taken straight to the dining-hall, and when John o' the Scales saw him standing in his rags he broke into a rude laugh.

'Well, spendthrift,' he cried, 'and what may your errand be?'

The heir wondered if this man, who, in the old days had flattered and fawned upon him, had any pity left, and he determined to try him.

'Good John o' the Scales,' he said, 'I have come here to crave your help. I pray you to lend me forty pence.'

It was not a large sum. John o' the Scales had often had twice as much from him, but the churlish fellow started up in a rage.

'Begone, you thriftless loon,' he cried; 'you need not come hither to beg. I swear that not one penny will you get from me. I know too well how you squandered your father's gold.'

Then the heir turned to John o' the Scales' wife Joan. She was a woman; perhaps she would be more merciful.

'Sweet madam,' he said, 'for the sake of blessed charity, bestow some alms on a poor wayfarer.'

But Joan o' the Scales was a hard woman, and she had never loved her master's son, so she answered rudely, 'No, by my troth, but you shall get no alms from me. You are little better than a vagabond; if we had a law to punish such, right gladly would I see you get your deserts.'

Now one of the guests who sat at the board with this smug and prosperous couple was a knight called Sir Ned Agnew. He was not rich, but he was a gentleman, and he had been a friend of the old lord, and had known the heir when he was a boy, and now, when he saw him standing, ragged and hungry, in the hall that had once been his own, he could not bear that he should be driven away with hard and cruel words. Besides, he felt very indignant with John o' the Scales, for he knew that he had bought the land far too cheaply. He had not much money to lend, but he could always spare a little.

'Come back, come back,' he cried hastily, as he saw the heir turn as if to leave the house. 'Whatever you are now, you were once a right good fellow, and you were always ready to part with your money to anyone who needed it. I am a poor man myself, but I can lend you forty pence at least; in fact I think that I could lend you eighty, if you are in sore want.' Then, turning to his host, he added,

'The Heir of Linne is a friend of mine, and I will count it a favour if you will let him have a seat at your table. I think it is the least you can do, seeing that you had the best of the bargain about his land.'

John o' the Scales was very angry, but he dared not say much, for he knew in his heart that what the knight said was true, and, moreover, he did not want to quarrel with him, for he liked to be able to go to market, where people were apt to think of him still as the castle steward, and boast about 'my friend, Sir Ned'.

'That's not true,' he blustered, 'and I'll take my vow that, far from making a good bargain, I lost money over that matter, and to prove what I say, I am willing to offer this young man, in the presence of you all, his lands back again, for a hundred merks less than I gave for them.'

' 'Tis done,' cried the Heir of Linne, and before the astonished John o' the Scales could speak, he had thrown down a piece of money on the table before him.

' 'Tis a God's-penny,' cried the guests in amazement, for when anyone threw down a piece of money in that way, it meant that they had accepted the bargain, and that the other man could not draw back.

Then the heir pulled out the three bags of gold from under his cloak, and threw them down on the table before John o' the Scales, who began to look very grave. He had never dreamt, when he offered to let the young man buy back the land, that he would ever be able to do it. He had meant it as a joke, and the joke was very much like turning into a reality. His face grew longer and longer as the heir emptied out the good red gold in a heap.

'Count it,' he cried triumphantly. 'It is all there, and honest money. It is yours, and the land is mine, and once more I am the Lord of Linne.'

Both John o' the Scales and his wife were very much taken aback; but there was nothing to be done but to count the money and to gather it up. John would fain have asked to be taken back as steward again, but the young lord knew now how dishonest he had been, and would not hear of such a thing.

'No, no,' he said, 'it is honest men whom I want now, and men who will be my friends when I am poor, as well as when I am rich. I think I have found such a man here,' and he turned to Sir Ned

Agnew. 'If you will accept the post, I shall be glad to have you for my steward, and for the keeper of my forests, and my deer, as well. And for every one of the pence which you were willing to lend me, I will pay you a full pound.'

So once more the rightful lord reigned in the Castle of Linne, and to everyone's surprise he settled down, and grew so like his father that strangers who came to the neighbourhood would not believe the stories people told them of the wild things he had done in his youth.

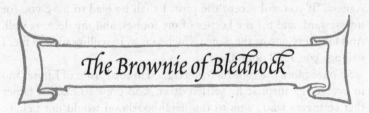

The Brownie of Blednock

Did you ever hear how a brownie came to our village of Blednock, and was frightened away again by a silly young wife, who thought she was cleverer than anyone else, but who did us the worst turn that she ever did anybody in her life when she made the queer, funny, useful little man disappear?

Well, it was one November evening, in the gloaming, just when the milking was done, and before the bairns were put to bed, and everyone was standing on their doorsteps, having a crack about the bad harvest, and the turnips, and what chances there were of good prices for the bullocks at the Martinmas Fair, when the queerest humming noise started down by the river.

It came nearer and nearer, and everyone stopped their idle talk and began to look down the road. And, 'deed, it was no wonder that they stared, for there, coming up the middle of the highway, was the strangest, most frightsome-looking creature that human eyes had ever seen.

He looked like a little wee, wee man, and yet he looked almost like a beast, for he was covered with hair from head to foot, and he wore no clothing except a little kilt of green rushes which hung round his waist. His hair was matted, and his head hung forward on his breast, and he had a long blue beard, which almost touched the ground.

His legs were twisted, and knocked together as he walked, and his arms were so long that his hands trailed in the mud.

He seemed to be humming something over and over again, and as he came near us we could just make out the words, 'Hae ye wark for Aiken-Drum?'

Eh, but I can tell you the folk were scared. If it had been the Evil One himself who had come to our quiet little village, I doubt if he would have caused more excitement. The bairns screamed, and hid their faces in their mothers' gown-tails; while the lassies, idle hussies that they were, threw down the pails of milk, which should have been in the milk-house long ago if they had not been so busy gossiping; and the very dogs crept in behind their masters, whining, and hiding their tails between their legs. The grown men, who should have known better, and who were not frightened to look the wee man in the face, laughed and hooted at him.

'Did ye ever see such eyes?' cried one.

'His mouth is so big, he could swallow the moon,' said another.

'Hech, sirs, but did ye ever see such a creature?' cried a third.

And still the poor little man went slowly up the street, crying wistfully, 'Hae ye wark for Aiken-Drum? Any wark for Aiken-Drum?'

Some of us tried to speak to him, but our tongues seemed to be tied, and the words died away on our lips, and we could only stand and watch him with frightened glances, as if we were bewitched.

Old Grannie Duncan, the oldest and the kindest woman in the village, was the first to come to her senses. 'He may be a ghost, or a bogle, or a wraith,' she said; 'or he may only be a harmless brownie. It is beyond me to say; but this I know, that if he be an evil spirit, he will not dare to look on the Holy Book.' And with that she ran into her cottage, and brought out the great leather-bound Bible which always lay on her little table by the window.

She stood on the road, and held it out, right in front of the creature, but he took no more heed of it than if it had been an old song-book, and went slowly on, with his weary cry for work.

'He's just a brownie,' cried Grannie Duncan in triumph, 'a simple, kindly brownie. I've heard tell of such folk before, and many a long day's work will they do for the people who treat them well.'

Gathering courage from her words, we all crowded round the wee man, and now that we were close to him, we saw that his hairy face was kind and gentle, and his tiny eyes had a merry twinkle in them.

'Save us, and help us, creature!' said an old man reprovingly, 'but can ye no speak, and tell us what ye want, and where ye come from?'

For answer the brownie looked all round him, and gave such a groan, that we scattered and ran in all directions, and it was full five minutes before we could pluck up our courage and go close to him again.

But Grannie Duncan stood her ground, like the brave old woman that she was, and it was to her that the creature spoke.

'I cannot tell you whence I come,' he said. ' 'Tis a nameless land, and 'tis very different from this land of yours. For there we all learn to serve, while here everyone wishes to be served. And when there is no work for us to do at home, then we sometimes set out to visit your land, to see if there is any work which we may do here. I must seem strange to human eyes, that I know; but if you let me, I will stay in this place awhile. I need not that any should wait on me, for I seek neither wages, nor clothes, nor bedding. All I ask for is the corner of a barn to sleep in, and a cogful of brose set down on the floor at bedtime; and if no one meddles with me, I will be ready to help anyone who needs me. I'll gather your sheep betimes on the hill; I'll take in your harvest by moonlight. I'll sing the bairns to sleep in their cradles, and, though I doubt you'll not believe it, you'll find that the babes will love me. I'll churn your churns for you, goodwives, and I'll bake your bread on a busy day; while, as for the menfolk, they may find me useful when there is corn to thrash, or untamed colts in the stables, or when the waters are out in flood.'

No one quite knew what to say in answer to the creature's strange request. It was an unheard-of thing for anyone to come and offer their services for nothing, and the men began to whisper among themselves, and to say that it was not canny, and 'twere better to have nothing to do with him.

But up spoke old Grannie Duncan again. ' 'Tis but a brownie, I tell you,' she repeated, 'a poor, harmless brownie, and many a story have I heard in my young days about the work that a brownie can do, if he be well treated and let alone. Have we not been complaining all summer about bad times, and scant wages, and a lack of workmen to do the work? And now, when a workman comes ready to your hand, ye will have none of him, just because he is not bonnie to look on.'

Still the men hesitated, and the silly young wenches screwed their faces, and pulled their mouths. 'But, Grannie,' cried they, 'that is all very well, but if we keep such a creature in our village, no one will come near it, and then what shall we do for sweethearts?'

'Shame on ye,' cried Grannie impatiently, 'and on all you men for encouraging the silly things in their whimsies. It's time that ye were thinking o' other things than bonnie faces and sweethearts. "Handsome is that handsome does", is a good old saying; and what about the corn that stands rotting in the fields, and it's past Hallow-e'en already? I've heard that a brownie can stack a whole ten-acre field in a single night.'

That settled the matter. The miller offered the creature the corner of his barn to sleep in, and Grannie promised to boil the cogful of brose, and send her grandchild, wee Jeannie, down with it every evening, and then we all said good-night, and went into our houses, looking over our shoulders as we did so, for fear that the strange little man was following us.

But if we were afraid of him that night, we had a very different song to sing before a week was over. Whatever he was, or wherever he came from, he was the most wonderful worker that men had ever known. And the strange thing was that he did most of it at night. He had the corn safe into the stackyards and the stacks thatched in the clap of a hand, as the old folk say.

The village became the talk of the countryside, and folk came from all parts to see if they could catch a glimpse of our queer, hairy little visitor; but they were always unsuccessful, for he was never to be seen when one looked for him. One might go into the miller's barn twenty times a day, and twenty times a day find nothing but a heap of straw; and although the cog of brose was aye empty in the morning, no one knew when he came home, or when he supped it.

But wherever there was work to be done, whether it was a sickly bairn to be sung to, or a house to be tidied up; a churn that would not churn, or a batch of bread that would not rise; a flock of sheep to be gathered together on a stormy night, or a bundle to be carried home by some weary labourer; Aiken-Drum, as we learned to call him, always got to know of it, and appeared in the nick of time. It looked as if we had all got wishing-caps, for we had just to wish, and the work was done.

Many a time, some poor mother, who had been up with a crying babe all night, would sit down with it in her lap, in front of the fire, in the morning, and fall fast asleep, and when she awoke, she would find that Aiken-Drum had paid her a visit, for the floor would be washed, and the dishes too, and the fire made up, and the kettle put on to boil; but the little man would have slipped away, as if he were frightened of being thanked.

The bairns were the only ones who ever saw him idle, and oh, how they loved him! In the gloaming, or when the school was out, one could see them away down in some corner by the burn-side, crowding round the little dark-brown figure, with its kilt of rushes, and one would hear the sound of wondrous low sweet singing, for he knew all the songs that the little ones loved.

So by and by the name of Aiken-Drum came to be a household word amongst us, and although we so seldom saw him near at hand, we loved him like one of our ain folk.

And he might have been here still had it not been for a silly, senseless young wife who thought she knew better than everyone else, and who took some idle notion into her empty head that it was not right to make the little man work and give him no wage.

She dinned this into our heads, morning, noon, and night, and she would not believe us when we told her that Aiken-Drum worked for love, and love only.

Poor thing, she could not understand anyone doing that, so she made up her mind that she, at least, would do what was right, and set us all an example.

She did not mean any harm, she said afterwards, when the miller took her to task for it; but although she might not mean to do any harm, she did plenty, as senseless folk are apt to do when they cannot bear to take other people's advice, for she took a pair of her husband's old, mouldy, worn-out breeches, and laid them down one night beside the cogful of brose.

By my faith, if the village folk had not remembered so well what Aiken-Drum had said about wanting no wages, they would have found something better to give him than a pair of worn-out breeks.

Be that as it may, the long and the short of it was that the dear wee man's feelings were hurt because we would not take his services for nothing, and he vanished in the night, as brownies are apt to do, so Grannie Duncan says, if anyone tries to pay them; and we have never seen him from that day to this, although the bairns declare that they sometimes hear him singing down by the mill, as they pass it in the gloaming on their way home from school.

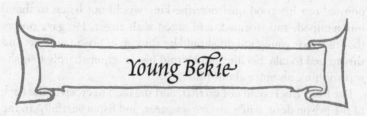

Young Bekie

It was the Court of France: the gayest, and the brightest, and the merriest court in the whole world. For there the sun seemed always to be shining, and the nobles, and the fair court ladies did not know what care meant.

In all the palace there was only one maiden who wore a sad and troubled look, and that was Burd Isbel, the king's only daughter. A year before she had been the lightest-hearted maiden in France. Her face had been like sunshine, and her voice like rippling music; but now all was changed. She crept about in silence, with pale cheeks, and clouded eyes, and the king, her father, was in deep distress.

He summoned all the great doctors, and offered them all manner of rewards if only they would give him back, once more, his light-hearted little daughter. But they shook their heads gravely; for although doctors can do many things, they have not yet found out the way to make heavy hearts light again.

All the same these doctors knew what ailed the princess, but they dared not say so. That would have been to mention a subject which nearly threw the king into a fit whenever he thought of it.

For just a year before, a brave young Scottish knight had come over to France to take service at the king's court. His name was Young Bekie, and he was so strong and so noble that at first the king had loved him like a son. But before long the young man had fallen in love with Burd Isbel, and of course Burd Isbel had fallen in love with him; and he had gone straight to the king, and asked him if he might marry her – and then the fat was in the fire.

For although the stranger seemed to be brave, and noble, and good, and far superior to any Frenchman, he was not of royal birth, and the king declared that it was a piece of gross impertinence on his part ever to think of marrying a king's daughter.

It was in vain that the older nobles, who had known Burd Isbel since she was a child, begged for pity for the young man, and pointed out his good qualities; the king would not listen to them, but stamped, and stormed, and raged with anger. He gave orders that the poor young knight should be shut up in prison at once, and threatened to take his life; and he told his daughter sharply that she was to think no more about him.

But Burd Isbel could not do that, and she used to creep to the back of the prison door, when no one was near, and listen wistfully, in the hope that she might hear her lover's voice. For a long time she was unsuccessful, but one day she heard him bemoaning his hard fate – to be kept a prisoner in a foreign land, with no chance of sending a message to Scotland of the straits that he was in.

'Oh,' he murmured piteously to himself, 'if only I could send word home to Scotland to my father, he would not leave me long in this vile prison. He is rich, and he would spare nothing for my ransom. He would send a trusty servant with a bag of good red gold, and another of bonnie white silver, to soften the cruel heart of the King of France.'

Then she heard him laugh bitterly to himself.

'There is little chance that I will escape,' he muttered, 'for who is likely to carry a message to Scotland for me? No, no, my bones will rot here; that is clear enough. And yet how willingly I would be a slave, if I could escape. If only some great lady needed a servant, I would gladly run at her horse's bridle if she could gain me my liberty. If only a widow needed a man to help her, I would promise to be a son to her, if she could obtain my freedom. Nay, if only some poor maiden would promise to wed me, and crave my pardon at the king's hand, I would in return carry her to Scotland, and dower her with all my wealth; and that is not inconsiderable, for am I not master of the forests and the lands and the Castle of Linnhe?'

Many a maiden would have been angry had she heard her lover speak these words; but Burd Isbel loved him too much to be offended at anything he said, so she crept away to her chamber with a determined look on her girlish face.

' 'Tis not for your lands or your castle,' she whispered, 'but for pure love of you. Love has made maidens brave ere now, and it will make them brave again.'

That night, when all the palace was quiet, Burd Isbel wrapped herself in a long grey cloak, and crept noiselessly from her room.

She might have been taken for a dark shadow, had it not been for her long plait of lint-white hair and her little bare feet, which peeped out and in beneath the folds of her cloak, as she stole down the great polished staircase.

Silently she crept across the hall, and peeped into the guardroom.

All the guards were asleep, and, on the wall above their heads hung the keys of the palace, and beside them a great iron key. That was the key of the prison. She stole across the floor on tiptoe, making no more noise than a mouse, and, stretching up her hand, she took down the heavy key, and hid it under her cloak. Then she sped quickly out of the guardroom, and through a turret door, into a dark courtyard where the prison was. She fitted the key in the lock. It took all her strength to turn it, but she managed it at last, and, shutting the door behind her, she went into the little cell where Young Bekie was imprisoned.

A candle flickered in its socket on the wall, and by its light she saw him lying asleep on the cold stone floor. She could not help giving a little scream when she saw him, for there were three mice and two great rats sitting on the straw at his head, and they had nibbled away nearly all his long yellow hair, which she had admired so much when first he came to court. His beard had grown long and rough too, for he had had no razors to shave with, and altogether he looked so strange that she hardly knew him.

At the sound of her voice he woke and started up, and the mice and the rats scampered away to their holes. He knew her at once, and in a moment he forgot his dreams of slaves, and widows, and poor maidens. He sprang across the floor, and knelt at her feet, and kissed her little white hands.

'Ah,' he said, 'now would I stay here for ever, if I might always have you for a companion.'

But Burd Isbel was a sensible maiden, and she knew that if her lover meant to escape, he must make haste, and not waste time in making pretty speeches. She knew also that if he went out of prison looking like a beggar or a vagabond, he would soon be taken captive again, so she hurried back to the palace, and went hither and thither noiselessly with her little bare feet, and presently she returned with her hands full of parcels.

She had brought a comb to comb the hair which the rats had left on his head, and a razor for him to shave himself with, and she had brought five hundred pounds of good red money, so that he might travel like a real knight.

Then, while he was making his toilet, she went into her father's stable, and led out a splendid horse, strong of limb and fleet of foot, and on it she put a saddle and a bridle which had been made for the king's own charger.

Finally, she went to the kennels, and, stooping down, she called softly, 'Hector, Hector.'

A magnificent black hound answered her call and came and crouched at her feet, fawning on them and licking them. After him came three companions, all the same size, and all of them big enough to kill a man.

These dogs belonged to Burd Isbel, and they were her special pets. A tear rolled down her face as she stooped and kissed their heads.

'I am giving you to a new master, darlings,' she said. 'See and guard him well.'

Then she led them to where the horse was standing, saddled and bridled; and there, beside him, stood Young Bekie. Now that his beard was trimmed, and his hair arranged, he looked as gallant, and brave, and noble as ever.

When Burd Isbel told him that the money, and the hounds, and the horse with its harness, were all his, he caught her in his arms, and swore that there had never been such a brave and generous maiden born before, and that he would serve her in life and death.

Then, as time was pressing, and the dawn was beginning to break, they had to say farewell; but before they did so, they vowed a solemn vow that they would be married to each other within three years. After this Burd Isbel opened the great gate, and her lover rode away, with money in his pocket, and hounds by his side, like the well-born knight that he was; and nobody who met him ever imagined that he was an escaped prisoner, set free by the courage of the king's daughter.

*   *   *

Alas, alas, for the faithfulness of men! Young Bekie was brave, and gentle, and courteous, but his will was not very strong, and he liked to be comfortable. And it came about that, after he had been back in Scotland for a year, the Scotch king had a daughter for whom he wanted to find a husband, and he made up his mind that Young Bekie would be the very man for her.

So he proposed that he should marry her, and was quite surprised and angry when the young man declined. 'It is an insult to my daughter,' he said, and he determined to force Bekie to do as he wanted, by using threats. So he told the knight that if he agreed to marry his daughter he would grow richer and richer, but, if he refused, he would lose all his lands, and the Castle of Linnhe.

Poor Young Bekie! I am afraid he was not a hero, for he chose to marry the princess and keep his lands, and he tried to put the thought of Burd Isbel and what she had done for him, and the solemn vow that he had made to her, out of his head.

Meanwhile Burd Isbel lived on at her father's court, and because her heart was full of faith and love, it grew light and merry again, and she began to dance and to sing as gaily as ever.

But early one morning she woke up with a start, and there, at the foot of her bed, stood the queerest little manikin that she had ever seen. He was only about a foot high, and he was dressed all in russet brown, and his face was just like a wrinkled apple.

'Who are you?' she cried, starting up, 'and what do you want?'

'My name is Billy Blin,' said the funny old man. 'I am a brownie, and I come from Scotland. My family all live there, and we are all very kind-hearted, and we like to help people. But it is no time to be talking of my affairs, for I have come to help you. I have just been wondering how you can lie there and sleep so peacefully when this is Young Bekie's wedding day. He is to be married at noon.'

'Oh, what shall I do? what shall I do?' cried poor Burd Isbel in deep distress. 'It is a long way from France to Scotland, and I can never be there in time.'

Billie Blin waved his little hand. 'I will manage it for you,' he said, 'if you will only do what I tell you. Go into your mother's chamber as fast as you can, and get two of your mother's maids-of-honour. And, remember, you must be careful to see that they are both called Mary. Then you must dress yourself in your most beautiful dress. You have a scarlet dress, I know, which becomes you well, for I have seen you wear it. Nay, be not surprised; we brownies can see people when they do not see us. Put that dress on, and let your Marys be dressed all in green. And in your father's treasury there are three jewelled belts, each of them worth an earl's ransom. These you must get, and clasp them round your waists, and steal down to the seashore, and there, on the water, you will see a beautiful Dutch boat. It will come to the shore for you, and you must step in, and greet the crew with a mystic greeting. Then your part is done. I will do the rest.'

The brownie vanished, and Burd Isbel made haste to do exactly what he had told her to do.

She ran to her mother's room, and called to two maids called Mary to come and help her to dress. Then she put on her lovely scarlet robe, and bade them attire themselves in green, and she took the jewelled girdles out of the treasury, and gave one to each of them to put on; and when they were dressed, they all went down to the seashore.

There, on the sea, as the brownie had promised, was a beautiful Dutch boat, with its sails spread. It came dancing over the water to them, and when Burd Isbel stepped on board, and greeted the sailors with a mystic greeting, they turned its prow towards Scotland, and Billy Blin appeared himself and took the helm.

Away, away, sailed the ship, until it reached the Firth of Tay, and there, high up among the hills, stood the Castle of Linnhe.

When Burd Isbel and her maidens went to the gate they heard beautiful music coming from within, and their hearts sank. They rang the bell, and the old porter appeared.

'What news, what news, old man?' cried Burd Isbel. 'We have heard rumours of a wedding here, and would fain know if they are true or no?'

'Certainly, madam, they are true,' he answered; 'for this very day, at noon, the master of this place, Young Bekie, will be married to the King of Scotland's daughter.'

Then Burd Isbel felt in her jewelled pouch, and drew out three merks. 'Take these, old man,' she said, 'and bid thy master speak to me at once.'

The porter did as he was bid, and went upstairs to the great hall, where all the wedding guests were assembled. He bent low before the king, and before the queen, and then he knelt before his young lord.

'I have served you these thirty and three years, sire,' he said, 'but never have I seen ladies come to the gate so richly attired as the three who wait without at this moment. There is one of them clad in scarlet, such scarlet as I have never seen, and two are clad in green, and they have girdles round their waists which might well pay an earl's ransom.'

When the Scottish princess heard these words, she tossed her head haughtily. She was tall and buxom, and she was dressed entirely in cloth of gold.

'Lack-a-day,' she said, 'what a to-do about three strangers! This old fool may think them finely dressed, but I warrant some of us here are every whit as fine as they.'

But Young Bekie sprang to his feet. He knew who it was, and the thought of his ingratitude brought the tears to his eyes.

'I'll wager my life 'tis Burd Isbel,' he cried, 'who has come over the sea to seek me.'

Then he ran downstairs, and sure enough it was Burd Isbel.

He clasped her in his arms, and kissed her, and now that he had her beside him, it seemed to him as if he had never loved anyone else.

But the wedding guests came trooping out, and when they heard the story they shook their heads.

'A likely tale,' they cried. 'Who is to believe it? If she be really the King of France's daughter, how came she here alone, save for those two maidens?'

But some of them looked at the jewelled girdles, and held their peace.

Then Burd Isbel spoke out clearly and simply. 'I rescued my love out of prison,' she said, 'and gave him horse and hounds. And if the hounds know me not, then am I proved false.' So saying she raised her voice. 'Hector, Hector,' she cried, and lo! the great black hound came bounding out of its kennel, followed by its companions, and lay down fawning at her feet, and licked them.

Then the wedding guests knew that she had told the truth, and they turned their eyes on Young Bekie, to see what he would do. He, on his part, was determined that he would marry Burd Isbel, let happen what might.

'Take home your daughter again,' he cried impatiently to the king, 'and my blessing go with her; but she sought me ere I sought her. This is my own true love; I can wed no other.'

'Nay,' answered the king, in angry astonishment, 'but this thing cannot be. Whoever heard of a maiden being sent home unwed, when the very wedding guests were assembled? I tell you it cannot be.'

In despair Young Bekie turned to the lady herself. 'Good lack, madam,' he cried, 'is there no one else whom you can marry? There is many a better and manlier man than I who goes seeking a wife. There, for instance, stands my cousin John. He is taller and stronger than I, a better fighter, and a right good man. Could you not accept him for a husband? If you could, I would pay him down five hundred pounds of good red gold on his wedding day.'

A murmur of displeasure ran through the crowd of wedding guests at this bold proposal, and the king grasped his sword in a rage. But, to everyone's amazement, the princess seemed neither displeased nor daunted. She blushed rosy red, and smiled softly.

'Keep your money to yourself, Bekie,' she answered. 'Your cousin John and I have no need of it. Neither does he require a bribe to make him willing to take me for his wife. To speak truth, we loved each other long ere I set eyes on you, and 'twas but the king, my father, who would have none of him. Perchance by now he has changed his mind.'

So there were two weddings in the Castle of Linnhe instead of one. Young Bekie married Burd Isbel, and his cousin John married the king's daughter, and they 'lived happy, happy, ever after'.

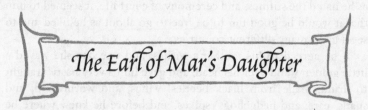

The Earl of Mar's Daughter

Long, long ago, in a country far away over the sea, there lived a queen who had an only son. She was very rich, and very great, and the only thing that troubled her was that her son did not want to get married in the very least.

In vain his mother gave grand receptions and court balls, to which she asked all the young countesses and baronesses, in the hope that the prince would take a fancy to one of them. He would talk to them, and dance with them, and be very polite, but when his mother hinted that it was time that he looked for a wife, he only shrugged his shoulders and said that there was not a pretty girl among them.

And perhaps there was some truth in his answer, for the maidens of that country were all fat, and little, and squat, and everyone of them waddled like a duck when she walked.

'If you can't find a wife to your liking at home,' the queen would say, 'go to other countries and see the maidens there; surely somewhere you would find one whom you could love.'

But Prince Florentine, for that was his name, only shook his head and laughed. 'And marry a shrew? For when the maidens heard my name, and knew for what purpose I had come, they would straightway smile their sweetest, and look their loveliest, and I would have no chance of knowing what manner of maidens they really were.'

Now the queen had a very wonderful gift. She could change a man's shape so that he would appear to be a hare, or a cat, or a bird; and at last she proposed to the prince that she should turn him into a dove, and then he could fly away to foreign countries, and go up and down until he saw some maiden whom he thought he could really love, and then he could go back to his real shape, and get to know her in the usual way.

This proposal pleased Prince Florentine very much. He would take good care not to fall in love with anyone, he told himself; but, as he hated the stiffness and ceremony of court life, it seemed to him that it would be good fun to be free to go about as he liked and to see a great many different countries.

So he agreed to his mother's wishes; and one day she waved a little golden wand over his head, and gave him a very nasty draught to drink, made from black beetles' wings, and wormwood, and snails' ears, and hedgehogs' spikes, and before he knew where he was, he was changed into a beautiful grey dove, with a white ring round its neck.

At first, when he saw himself in this changed guise, he was frightened; but his mother quickly tied a tiny charm round his neck, and hid it under his soft grey feathers, and taught him how to press it against his heart until a fragrant odour came from it, and as soon as he did this, he became once more a handsome young man.

Then he was very pleased, and kissed her, and said farewell, promising to return some day with a beautiful young bride; and after that he spread his wings, and flew away in search of adventure.

For a year and a day he wandered about, now visiting this country, now that, and he was so amused and interested in all the strange and wonderful things that he saw, that he never once wanted to turn himself into a man, and he completely forgot that his mother expected that he was looking out for a wife.

At last, one lovely summer's day, he found himself flying over broad Scotland, and as the sun was very hot, he looked round for somewhere to shelter from its rays. Just below him was a stately castle, surrounded by magnificent trees.

'This is just what I want,' he said to himself; 'I will rest here until the sun goes down.'

So he folded his wings, and sank gently down into the very heart of a wide-spreading oak tree, near which, as good fortune would have it, there was a field of ripening grain, which provided him with a hearty supper. Here, for many days, the prince took up his abode, partly because he was getting rather tired of flying about continually, and partly because he began to feel interested in a lovely young girl who came out of the castle every day at noon, and amused herself with playing at ball under the spreading branches of the great tree. Generally she was quite alone, but once or twice an old lady, evidently her governess, came with her, and sat on a root, which formed a comfortable seat, and worked at some fine embroidery while her pupil amused herself with her ball.

Prince Florentine soon found out that the maiden's name was Grizel, and that she was the only child of the Earl of Mar, a nobleman of great riches and renown. She was very beautiful, so beautiful, indeed, that the prince sat and feasted his eyes upon her all the time that she was at play, and then, when she had gone home, he could not sleep, but, sat with wide-open eyes, staring into the warm twilight, and wondering how he could get to know her. He could not quite make up his mind whether he should use his mother's charm, and take his natural shape, and walk boldly up to the castle and crave her father's permission to woo her, or fly away home, and send an ambassador with a train of nobles, and all the pomp that belonged to his rank, to ask for her hand.

The question was settled for him one day, however, and everything happened quite differently. On a very hot afternoon, Lady Grizel came out, accompanied by her governess, and, as usual, the old lady sat down to her embroidery and the girl began to toss her ball. But the sun was so very hot that by and by the governess laid down her needle and fell fast asleep, while her pupil grew tired of running backwards and forwards, and, sitting down, began to toss her ball right up among the branches. All at once it caught in a leafy bough, and when she was gazing up, trying to see where it was, she caught sight of a beautiful grey dove, sitting watching her. Now, as I have said, Lady Grizel was an only child, and she had had few playmates, and all her life she had been passionately fond of animals, and when she saw the bird, she stood up and called gently, 'Oh Coo-me-doo, come down to me, come down.' Then she whistled so softly and sweetly, and stretched out her white hands above her head so entreatingly, that Prince Florentine left his branch, and flew down and alighted gently on her shoulder.

The delight of the maiden knew no bounds. She kissed and fondled her new pet, which perched quite familiarly on her arm, and promised him a latticed silver cage, with bars of solid gold.

The bird allowed the girl to carry him home, and soon the beautiful cage was made, and hung up on the wall of her chamber, just inside the window, and Coo-me-doo, as the dove was named, placed inside.

He seemed perfectly happy, and grew so tame that soon he went with his mistress wherever she went, and all the people who lived near the castle grew quite accustomed to seeing the earl's daughter driving or riding with her tame dove on her shoulder.

When she went out to play at ball, Coo-me-doo would go with her, and perch up in his old place, and watch her with his bright dark eyes. One day when she was tossing the ball among the branches it rolled away, and for a long time she could not find it, and at last a voice behind her said, 'Here it is,' and, turning round, she saw to her astonishment a handsome young man dressed all in dove-grey satin, who handed her the ball with a stately bow.

Lady Grizel was frightened, for no strangers were allowed inside her father's park, and she could not think where he had come from; but just as she was about to call out for help, the young man smiled and said, 'Lady, do you not know your own Coo-me-doo?'

Then she glanced up into the branches, but the bird was gone, and as she hesitated (for the stranger spoke so kindly and courteously she did not feel very much alarmed), he took her hand in his.

' 'Tis true, my own love,' he said; 'but if you cannot recognise your favourite when his grey plumage is changed into grey samite, perhaps you will know him when the grey samite is once more changed into softest feathers;' and pressing to his heart a tiny gold locket which he wore, he vanished, and in his stead was her own grey dove, hovering down to his resting-place on her shoulder.

'Oh, I cannot understand it, I cannot understand it,' she cried, putting up her hand to stroke her pet; but the feathers seemed to slip from between her fingers, and once more the gallant stranger stood before her.

'Sit down and rest, sweetheart,' he said, leading her to the root where her governess was wont to sit and stretching himself on the turf at her feet, 'and I will explain the mystery to you.'

Then he told her all. How his mother was a great queen away in a far country, and how he was her only son. Lady Grizel's fears were all gone now, and she laughed merrily as he described the girls who lived in his own country, and told her how little and fat they were, and how they waddled when they walked; but when he told her how his mother had used her magic and turned him into a dove, in order that he might bring home a wife, her face grew grave and pale.

'My father has sworn a great oath,' she said, 'that I shall never wed with anyone who lives out of Scotland; so I fear we must part, and you must go elsewhere in search of a bride.'

But Prince Florentine shook his head.

'Nay,' he said; 'indeed, rather than part from you, I will live all my life as a dove in a cage, if I may only be near you, and talk to you when we are alone.'

'But what if my father should want me to wed with some Scottish lord?' asked the maiden anxiously; 'could you bear to sit in your cage and sing my wedding song?'

'That could I not,' answered Prince Florentine, drawing her closer to him; 'and in order to prevent such a terrible thing happening, sweetheart, we must find ways and means to be married at once, and then, come what may, no one can take you from me. This very evening I must go and speak to your father.'

Now the Earl of Mar was a violent man, and fear of him lay on all the countryside – even his only child was afraid of him – and when her lover made this suggestion she clung to him and begged him with tears in her eyes not to do this. She told him what a fiery temper the earl had, and how she feared that when he heard his story he would simply order him to be hanged on the nearest tree, or thrown into the dungeon to starve to death. So for a long time they sat and talked, now thinking of one plan, now of another, but none of them seemed of any use, and it seemed as though Prince Florentine must either remain in the shape of her pet dove, or go away altogether.

All at once Lady Grizel clapped her hands. 'I have it, I have it,' she cried; 'why cannot we be married secretly? Old Father John out at the chapel on the moor could marry us; he is so old and so blind, he would never recognise me if I went bare-headed and bare-footed like a gypsy girl; and you must go dressed as a woodman, with muddy shoes, and an axe over your arm. Then we can dwell together as we are doing now, and no one will suspect that the Earl of Mar's daughter is married to her tame pet dove, which sits on her shoulder, and goes with her wherever she goes. And if the worst comes to the worst, and some gallant Scotch wooer appears, why, then we must confess what we have done, and bear the consequences together.'

A few days later, in the early morning, when old Father John, the priest who served the little chapel which stood on the heather-covered moor, was preparing to say Mass, he saw a gypsy girl, bare-headed and bare-footed, steal into the chapel, followed by a stalwart young woodman, clad all in sober grey, with a bright wood-axe gleaming on his shoulder.

In a few words they told him the purpose for which they had come, and after he had said Mass the kindly old priest married them, and gave them his blessing, never doubting but that they were a couple of simple country lovers who would go home to some tiny cottage in the woods near by. Little did he think that only half a mile away a page boy, wearing the livery of the Earl of Mar, was patiently waiting with a white palfrey until his young mistress should return, accompanied by her grey dove, from visiting an old nurse, who, she told her governess, was 'teaching her how to spin'.

And little did her father, or her governess, or any of the servants at the castle, think that Lady Grizel was leading a double life, and that the grey dove which was always with her, and which she seemed to love more than any other of her pets, was a grey dove only when anyone else was by, but turned into a gallant young prince, who ate, and laughed, and talked with her the moment they were alone.

Strange to say, their secret was never found out for seven long years, even although every year a little son was born to them, and carried away under the grey dove's wing to the country far over the sea. At these times Lady Grizel used to cry and be very sad, for she dare not keep her babies beside her, but had to kiss them, and let them go, to be brought up by their grandmother whom she had never seen.

Every time Prince Florentine carried home a new baby, he brought back tidings to his wife how tall, and strong, and brave her other sons were growing, and tender messages from the queen, his mother, telling her how she hoped that one day she would be able to come home with her husband, and then they would be all together.

But year after year went by, and still the fierce old earl lived on, and there seemed little hope that poor Lady Grizel would ever be able to go and live in her husband's land, and she grew pale and thin. And year after year her father grew more and more angry with her, because he wanted her to marry one of the many wooers who came to crave her hand; but she would not.

'I love to dwell alone with my sweet Coo-me-doo,' she used to say, and the old earl would stamp his foot, and go out of her chamber muttering angry words in his vexation.

At last, one day, a very great and powerful nobleman arrived with his train to ask the earl's daughter to marry him. He was very rich, and owned four beautiful castles, and the earl said, 'Now, surely, my daughter will consent.'

But she only gave her old answer, 'I love best to live alone with my sweet Coo-me-doo.'

Then her father slammed the door in a rage, and went into the great hall, where all his men-at-arms were, and swore a mighty oath that on the morrow, before he broke his fast, he would wring the neck of the wretched bird which seemed to have bewitched his daughter.

Now just above his head, in the gallery, hung Coo-me-doo's cage with the golden bars, and he happened to be sitting in it, and when he heard this threat he flew away in haste to his wife's room and told her. 'I must fly home and crave help from my mother,' he said; 'maybe she will be able to aid us, for I shall certainly be no help to you here, if my neck is wrung tomorrow. For the moment, fall in with your father's wishes, and promise to marry this nobleman; only see to it that the wedding doesn't take place until three clear days are past.'

Then Lady Grizel opened the window, and he flew away, leaving her to act her part as best she might.

Now it chanced that next evening, in the far distant land over the sea, the queen was walking up and down in front of her palace, watching her grandsons playing at tennis, and thinking sadly of her only son and his beautiful wife whom she had never seen. She was so deep in thought that she was unaware that a grey dove had come sailing over the trees and perched itself on a turret of the palace, until it fluttered down, and her son, Prince Florentine, stood beside her.

She threw herself into his arms joyfully, and kissed him again and again; then she would have called for a feast to be set, and for her minstrels to play, as she always did on the rare occasions when he came home, but he held up his hand to stop her.

'I need neither feasting nor music, mother,' he said, 'but I need your help sorely. If your magic cannot help me, then my wife and I are undone, and in two days she will be forced to marry a man whom she hates,' and he told the whole story.

'And what would you like me to do?' asked the queen in great distress.

'Give me a score of men-at-arms to fly over the sea with me,' answered the prince, 'and my sons to help me in the fray.'

But the queen shook her head sadly. ' 'Tis beyond my power,' she said; 'but perhaps Astora, the old dame who lives by the seashore, might help me, for in good sooth your need is great. She has more skill in magic than I have.'

So she hurried away to a little hut near the seashore where the wise old woman lived, while her son waited anxiously for her return.

At last she appeared again, and her face was radiant. 'Dame Astora has given me a charm,' she said, 'which will turn four-and-twenty of my stout men-at-arms into storks, and your seven sons into white swans, and you yourself into a gay goshawk, the proudest of all birds.'

Now the Earl of Mar, full of joy at the disappearance of the grey dove, which seemed to have bewitched his daughter, had bade all the nobles throughout the length and breadth of fair Scotland to come and witness her wedding with the lover whom he had chosen for her, and there was feasting, and dancing, and great revelry at the castle. There had not been such doings since the marriage of the earl's great-grandfather a hundred years before. There were huge tables, covered with rich food, standing constantly in the hall, and even the common people went in and out as they pleased, while outside on the green there was music, and dancing, and games.

Suddenly, when the revelry was at its height, a flock of strange birds appeared on the horizon, and everyone stopped to look at them. On they came, flying all together in regular order, first a gay goshawk, then behind him seven snow-white swans, and behind the swans four-and-twenty large grey storks. When they drew near, they settled down among the trees which surrounded the castle green, and sat there, each on his own branch, like sentinels, watching the sport.

At first some of the people were frightened, and wondered what this strange sight might mean, but the Earl of Mar only laughed.

'They come to do honour to my daughter,' he said; ' 'tis well that there is not a grey dove among them, else he would have found an arrow in his heart, and that right speedily,' and he ordered the musicians to strike up a measure.

The Lady Grizel was amongst the throng, dressed in her bridal gown, but no one noticed how anxiously she glanced at the great birds which sat so still on the branches.

Then a strange thing happened. No sooner had the musicians begun to play, and the dancers begun to dance, than the twenty-four grey storks flew down, and each of them seized a nobleman, and tore him from his partner, and whirled him round and round as fast as he could, holding him so tightly with his great grey wings that he could neither draw his sword nor struggle. Then the seven white swans flew down and seized the bridegroom, and tied him fast to a great oak tree. Then they flew to where the gay goshawk was hovering over Lady Grizel, and they pressed their bodies so closely to his that they formed a soft feathery couch, on which the lady sat down, and in a moment the birds soared into the air, bearing their precious burden on their backs, while the storks, letting the nobles go, circled round them to form an escort; and so the strange army of birds flew slowly out of sight, leaving the wedding guests staring at one another in astonishment, while the Earl of Mar swore so terribly that no one dared go near him.

*   *   *

And although the story of this strange wedding is told in Scotland to this day, no one has ever been able to guess where the birds came from, or to what land they carried the beautiful Lady Grizel.

Hynde Horn

Once upon a time there was a king of Scotland called King Aylmer, who had one little daughter, whose name was Jean. She was his only daughter, and, as her mother was dead, he adored her. He gave her whatever she liked to ask for, and her nursery was so full of toys and games of all kinds, that it was a wonder that any little girl, even although she was a princess, could possibly find time to play with them all.

She had a beautiful white palfrey to ride on, and two piebald ponies to draw her little carriage when she wanted to drive; but she had no one of her own age to play with, and she felt very lonely, and she was always asking her father to bring her a companion.

'By my troth,' he would reply, 'that is no easy matter, for you are a royal princess, and it is not fitting that you should play with children of less noble blood.'

Then little Princess Jean would go back to her splendid nurseries with the tears rolling down her cheeks, wishing with all her heart that she had been born just an ordinary little girl.

King Aylmer had gone away on a hunting expedition one day, and Princess Jean was playing alone as usual, in her nursery, when she heard the sound of her father's horn outside the castle walls, and the old porter hurried across the courtyard to open the gate. A moment later the king's voice rang through the hall, calling loudly for old Elspeth, the nurse.

The old dame hurried down the broad staircase, followed by the little princess, who was surprised that her father had returned so early from his hunting, and what was her astonishment to see him standing, with all his nobles round him, holding a fair-haired boy in his arms.

The boy's face was very white, and his eyes were shut, and the little princess thought that he was dead, and ran up to a grey-haired baron, whose name was Athelbras, and hid her face against his rough hunting coat.

But old Elspeth hurried forward and took the boy's hand in hers, and laid her ear against his heart, and then she asked that he might be carried up into her own chamber, and that the housekeeper might be sent after them with plenty of blankets, and hot water, and red wine.

When all this had been done, King Aylmer noticed his little daughter, and when he saw how pale her cheeks were, he patted her head and said, 'Cheer up, child, the young cock-sparrow is not dead; 'tis but a swoon caused by the cold and wet, and I think when old Elspeth has put a little life into him, you may perhaps have found a playfellow.'

Then he called for his horse and rode away to hunt again, and Princess Jean was once more left alone. But this time she did not feel lonely.

Her father's wonderful words, 'You may perhaps have found a playfellow,' rang in her ears, and she was so busy thinking about them, sitting by herself in the dark by the nursery fire, that she started when old Elspeth opened the door of her room and called out, 'Come, princess, the young gentleman has had a sweet sleep, and would like to talk with you.'

The little princess went into the room on tiptoe, and there, lying on the great oak settle by the fire, was the boy whom she had seen in her father's arms. He seemed about four years older than she was, and he was very handsome, with long yellow hair, which hung in curls round his shoulders, and merry blue eyes, and rosy cheeks.

He smiled at her as she stood shyly in the doorway, and held out his hand. 'I am your humble servant, princess,' he said. 'If it had not been for your father's kindness, and for this old dame's skill, I would have been dead by now.'

Princess Jean did not know what to say; she had often wished for someone who was young enough to play with her, but now that she had found a real playmate, she felt as if someone had tied her tongue.

'What is your name, and where do you come from?' she asked at last.

The boy laughed, and pointed to a little stool which stood beside the settle. 'Sit down there,' he said, 'and I will tell you. I have often wished to have a little sister of my own, and now I will pretend that you are my little sister.'

Princess Jean did as she was bid, and went and sat down on the stool, and the stranger began his tale.

'My name is Hynde Horn,' he said, 'and I am a king's son.'

'And I am a king's daughter,' said the little princess, and then they both laughed.

Then the boy's face grew grave again.

'They called my father King Allof,' he said, 'and my mother's name was Queen Godyet, and they reigned over a beautiful country far away in the East. I was their only son, and we were all as happy as the day was long, until a wicked king, called Mury, came with his soldiers, and fought against my father, and killed him, and took his kingdom. My mother and I tried to escape, but the fright killed my mother – she died in a hut in the forest where we had hidden ourselves, and some soldiers found me weeping beside her body, and took me prisoner, and carried me to the wicked king.

'He was too cruel to kill me outright – he wanted me to die a harder death – so he bade his men tie my hands and my feet, and carry me down to the seashore, and put me in a boat, and push it out into the sea; and there they left me to die of hunger and thirst.

'At first the sun beat down on my face, and burned my skin, but by and by it grew dark, and a great storm arose, and the boat drifted on and on, and I grew so hungry, and then so thirsty – oh! I thought I would die of thirst – and at last I became unconscious, for I remember nothing more until I woke up to find yonder kind old dame bending over me.'

'The boat was washed up on our shore, just as his highness the king rode past,' explained old Elspeth, who was stirring some posset over the fire, and listening to the story.

'And what did you say your name was?' demanded the little princess, who had listened with eager attention to the story.

'Hynde Horn,' repeated the boy, whose eyes were wet with tears at the thought of all that he had gone through.

'Prince Hynde Horn,' corrected Princess Jean, who always liked to have her title used, and expected other people liked the same.

'Well, I suppose I ought to be King Horn now, were it not for that wicked king who hath taken my kingdom, as well as my father's life; but the people in my own land always called me Hynde Horn, and I like the old name best.'

'But what does it mean?' persisted the little princess.

The boy blushed and looked down modestly. 'It is an old word which in our language means "kind" or "courteous", but I am afraid that they flattered me, for I did not always deserve it.'

The little princess clapped her hands. 'We will call you by it,' she said, 'until you prove yourself unworthy of it.'

After this a new life opened up for the little girl.

King Aylmer, finding that the young prince who had been so unexpectedly thrown on his protection was both modest and manly, determined to befriend him, and to give him a home at his court until he was old enough to go and try to recover his kingdom, and avenge his parents' death, so he gave orders that a suite of rooms in the castle should be given to him, and arranged that Baron Athelbras, his steward, should train him in all knightly accomplishments, such as hawking and tilting at the ring. He soon found out too that Hynde Horn had a glorious voice, and sang like a bird, so he gave orders that old Thamile, the minstrel, should teach him to play the harp; and soon he could play it so well that the whole court would sit round him on the long winter evenings listening to his music.

He was so sweet-tempered, and lovable, that everyone said the people in his own land had done well to name him Hynde Horn.

To the little princess he was the most delightful companion, for he was never too busy or too tired to play with her. He taught her to ride as she had never ridden before, not merely to jog along the road on her fat palfrey, but to gallop alongside of him under the trees in the forest, and they used to be out all day, hunting and hawking, for he trained two dear little white falcons and gave them to her, and taught her to carry them on her wrist; and she grew so hale and rosy that everyone said it was a joyful day when Hynde Horn was washed up on the seashore in the boat.

But alas! people do not remain children for ever, and, as years went on, Hynde Horn grew into as goodly a young man as anyone need wish to see, and of course he fell in love with Princess Jean, and of course she fell in love with him. Everyone was quite delighted, and said, 'What is to hinder them from being married at once, and then when Princess Jean comes to be queen, we will be quite content to have Hynde Horn for our king?'

But wise King Aylmer would not agree to this. He knew that it is not good for any man to have no difficulties to overcome, and to get everything that he wants without any trouble.

'Nay,' he said, 'but the lad has to win his spurs first, and to show us of what stuff he is made. Besides, his father's Kingdom lies desolate, ruled over by an alien. He shall be betrothed to my daughter, and we will have a great feast to celebrate the event, and then I will give him a ship, manned by thirty sailors, and he shall go away to his own land in search of adventure, and when he has done great deeds of daring, and avenged his father's death, he shall come again, and my daughter will be waiting for him.'

So there was a splendid feast held at the castle, and all the great lords and barons came to it, and Princess Jean and Hynde Horn were betrothed amidst great rejoicing, for everyone was glad to think that their princess would wed someone whom they knew, and not a stranger.

But the hearts of the two lovers were heavy, and when the feast was over, and all the guests had gone away, they went out on a little balcony in front of the castle, which overlooked the sea. It was a lovely evening, the moon was full, and by its light they could see the white sails of the ship lying ready in the little bay, waiting to carry Hynde Horn far away to other lands. The roses were nodding their heads over the balcony railings and the honeysuckle was falling in clusters from the castle walls, but it might have been December for all that poor Princess Jean cared, and the tears rolled fast down her face as she thought of the parting.

'Alack, alack, Hynde Horn,' she said, 'if only I could go with you! How shall I live all these years, with no one to talk to or to ride with?'

Then he tried to comfort her with promises of how brave he would be, and how soon he would conquer his father's enemies and come back to her; but they both knew in their hearts that this was the last time that they would be together for long years to come.

At last Hynde Horn drew a slender case from his pocket, out of which he took a beautifully wrought silver wand, with three little silver larks sitting on the end of it. 'This,' he said, 'dear love, is for you; the sceptre is a token that you rule in my heart, as well as over broad Scotland, and the three singing laverocks are to remind you of me, for you have oft-times told me that my poor singing reminds you of a lark.'

Then Princess Jean drew from her finger a gold ring, set with three priceless diamonds. It was so small it would only go on the little finger of her lover's left hand. 'This is a token of my love,' she said gravely, 'therefore guard it well. When the diamonds are bright and shining, you shall know that my love for you is burning clear and true; but if ever they lose their lustre and grow pale and dim, then you shall know that some evil has befallen me. Either I am dead, or else someone tempts me to be untrue.'

Next morning the fair white ship spread her sails, and carried Hynde Horn far away over the sea. Princess Jean stood on the little balcony until the tallest mast had disappeared below the horizon, and then she threw herself on her bed, and wept as though her heart would break.

After this, for many a long day, there was nothing heard of Hynde Horn, not even a message came from him, and people began to say that he must be dead, and that it was high time that their princess forgot him, and listened to the suit of one of the many noble princes who came to pay court to her from over the sea. She would not listen to them, however, and year after year went by.

Now it happened that when seven years had passed, a poor beggar went up one day to the castle in the hope that one of the servants would see him, and give him some of the broken bread and meat that was always left from the hall table. The porter knew him by sight and let him pass into the courtyard, but although he loitered about for a whole hour, no one appeared to have time to speak to him. It seemed as if something unusual were going on, for there were horses standing about in the courtyard, held by grooms in strange liveries, and servants were hurrying along, as if they were so busy they hardly knew what to do first. The old beggarman spoke to one or two of them as they passed, but they did not pay any attention to him, so at last he thought it was no use waiting any longer, and was about to turn away, when a little scullery-maid came out of the kitchen, and began to wash some pots under a running tap. He went up to her, and asked if she could spare him any broken victuals.

She looked at him crossly. 'A pretty day to come for broken victuals,' she cried, 'when we all have so much to do that we would need twenty fingers on every hand, and four pairs of hands at the very least. Don't you know that an embassage has come from over the sea, seeking the hand of our Princess Jean for the young Prince of Eastnesse, he that is so rich that he could dine off diamonds every day, if it suited him, and they are all in the great hall now, talking it over with King Aylmer? Only 'tis said that the princess does not favour the thought; she is all for an old lover called Hynde Horn, whom everyone else holds to be dead this many a year. Be it as it may, I have no time to talk to the likes of you, for we have a banquet to cook for fifty guests, not counting the king and all his nobles. The like of it has not been seen since the day when Princess Jean and that Hynde Horn plighted their troth these seven years ago. But hark'ee, old man, it might be well worth your while to come back tomorrow; there will be plenty of pickings then.' And, flapping her dish-clout in the wind, she ran into the kitchen again.

The old beggar went away, intending to take her advice and return on the morrow; but as he was walking along the sands to a little cottage where he sometimes got a night's lodging, he met a gallant knight on horseback, who was very finely dressed, and wore a lovely scarlet cloak.

The beggar thought that he must be one of the king's guests, who had come out for a gallop on the smooth yellow sands, and he stood aside and pulled off his cap; but the knight drew rein, and spoke to him.

'God shield you, old man,' he said, 'and what may the news be in this country? I used to live here, but I have been in far-off lands these seven years, and I know not how things go on.'

'Sire,' answered the beggar, 'things have gone on much as usual for these few years back, but it seems as if changes are now in the air. I was but this moment at the castle, and 'twas told me that the young Prince Eitel, heir to the great Kingdom of Eastnesse, has sent to crave the hand of our princess; and although the young lady favours not his suit (she being true to an old love, one Hynde Horn, who is thought to be dead), the king her father is likely to urge her to it, for the King of Eastnesse is a valuable ally, and fabulously rich.'

Then a strange light came into the stranger's eyes, and to the beggar's astonishment, he sprang from his horse, and held out the rein to him. 'Will you do me a favour, friend?' he said. 'Will you give me your beggar's wallet, and staff, and cloak, if I give you my horse, and this cloak of crimson sarsenet? I have a mind to turn beggar.'

The beggar scratched his head, and looked at him in surprise. 'He has been in the East, I think,' he muttered, 'and the sun has touched his brain, but even so 'tis a fair exchange; that crimson cloak will sell for ten merks any day, and for the horse I can get twenty pounds,' and presently he cantered off, well pleased with the bargain, while the other – the beggar's wallet in his hand, his hat drawn down over his eyes and leaning on his staff – began to ascend the steep hill leading to the castle.

When he reached the great gate, he knocked boldly with the iron knocker, and the knock was so imperious that the porter hastened to open it at once. He expected to see some lordly knight waiting there, and when he saw no one but a weary-looking beggarman, he uttered an angry exclamation, and was about to shut the great gate in his face; but the beggar's voice was so wondrously sweet and low that he could not help listening to it.

'Good porter, for the sake of St Peter and St Paul, and for the sake of Him who died on the Holy Rood, give a cup of wine, and a little piece of bread, to a poor wayfarer.'

As the porter hesitated between pity and impatience, the pleading voice went on, 'And one more boon would I crave, kind man. Carry a message from me to the fair bride who is to be betrothed this day, and ask her if she will herself hand the bite and the sup to one who hath come from far?'

'Ask the bride! ask the Princess Jean to come and feed you with her own hands!' cried the man in astonishment. 'Nay, you are mad. Away with you; we want no madmen here,' and he would have thrust the beggar aside; but the stranger laid his hand on his shoulder, and said calmly, as if he were giving an order to a servant, 'Go, tell her it is for the sake of Hynde Horn.' And the old porter turned and went without a word.

Meanwhile all the guests in the castle were gathered at the banquet in the great banqueting hall. On a raised dais at the end of the room sat King Aylmer and the great ambassador who had come from Prince Eitel of Eastnesse, and between them sat Princess Jean, dressed in a lovely white satin dress, with a little circlet of gold on her head. The king and the ambassador were in high spirits, for they had persuaded the princess to marry Prince Eitel in a month and a day from that time; but poor Princess Jean looked pale and sad.

As all the lords and nobles who were feasting in the hall below stood up and filled their glasses, and drank to the health of Prince Eitel of Eastnesse and his fair bride, she had much ado to keep the tears from falling, as she thought of the old days when Hynde Horn and she went out hunting and hawking together.

Just at that moment the door opened, and the porter entered, and, without looking to the right hand or to the left, marched straight up the hall and along the dais, until he came to where Princess Jean sat; then he stooped down and whispered something to her.

In a moment the princess's pale face was like a damask rose, and, taking a glass full of ruby-red wine in one hand and a farl of cake in the other, she rose, and walked straight out of the hall.

'By my faith,' said King Aylmer, who was startled by the look on his daughter's face, 'something hath cropped up, I suspect, which may change the whole course of events,' and he rose and followed her, accompanied by the ambassador and all the great nobles.

At the head of the staircase they stopped and watched the princess as she went down the stairs and across the courtyard, her long white robe trailing behind her, with the glass of ruby-red wine in one hand and the farl of cake in the other.

When she came to the gateway, there was no one there but a poor old beggarman, and all the foreign noblemen looked at each other and shook their heads, and said, 'It's certainly doubtful whether this bride will please our young prince, if she is wont to disturb a court banquet in order to serve beggars with her own hands.'

But Princess Jean heard none of this. With trembling hands she held out the glass to the beggar. He raised the wine to his lips, and pledged the fair bride before he drank it, and when he handed the glass back to her, lo! in the bottom of it lay the gold ring which she had given to her lover Hynde Horn, seven long years before.

'Oh,' she cried breathlessly, snatching it out of the glass, 'tell me quickly, I pray you, where did you find this? Was it on the sea, or in a far-off land, and was the hand that it was taken from alive or dead?'

'Nay, noble lady,' answered the beggar, and at the sound of his voice Princess Jean grew pale again, 'I did not get it on the sea, or in a far-off land, but in this country, and from the hand of a fair lady. It was a pledge of love, noble princess, which I had given to me seven long years ago, and the diamonds were to be tokens of the brightness and constancy of that love. For seven long years they have gleamed and sparkled clearly, but now they are dim, and losing their brightness, so I fear me that my lady's love is waning and growing cold.'

Then Princess Jean knew all, and she tore the circlet of gold from her head and knelt on the cold stones at his feet, and cried, 'Hynde Horn, my own Hynde Horn, my love is not cold, neither is it dim; but you were so long in coming, and they said it was my duty to marry someone else. But now, even if you are a beggar, I will be a beggar's wife, and follow you from place to place, and we can harp and sing for our bread.'

Hynde Horn laughed a laugh that was pleasant to hear, and he threw off the beggar's cloak, and, behold, he was dressed as gaily as any gallant in the throng.

'There is no need of that, sweetheart,' he said. 'I did it but to try you. I have not been idle these seven years; I have killed the wicked king, and come into my own again, and I have fought and conquered the Saracens in the East, and I have gold enough and to spare.'

Then he drew her arm within his, and they crossed the courtyard together and began to ascend the stairs. Suddenly old Athelbras, the steward, raised his cap and shouted, 'It is Hynde Horn, our own Hynde Horn,' and then there was such a tumult of shouting and cheering that everyone was nearly deafened. Even the ambassador from Eastnesse and all his train joined in it, although they knew that now Princess Jean would never marry their prince; but they could not help shouting, for everyone looked so happy.

And the next day there was another great banquet prepared, and riders were sent all over the country to tell the people everywhere to rejoice, for their princess was being married, not to any stranger, but to her old lover, Hynde Horn, who had come back in time after all.

The Gay Goshawk

It was the beautiful month of June, and among the bevy of fair maidens who acted as maids-of-honour to Queen Margaret at Windsor there was none so fair as the Lady Katherine, the youngest of them all.

As she joined in a game of bowls in one of the long alleys under the elm trees, or rode out, hawk on wrist, in the great park near the castle, her merry face, with its rosy cheeks and sparkling blue eyes, was a pleasure to see. She had gay words for everyone, even for the sharp-tongued, grave-faced old baroness who acted as governess to the queen's maids, and kept a sharp lookout lest any of the young ladies under her charge should steal too shy glances at the pages and gentlemen-at-arms who waited on the king.

The old lady loved her in return, and pretended to be blind when she noticed, what every maid-of-honour had noticed for a fortnight, that there was one knight in particular who was always at hand to pick up Lady Katherine's balls for her, or to hold her palfrey's rein if she wanted to alight, when she was riding in the forest.

This gallant knight was not one of the king's gentlemen, but the son of a Scottish earl, who had been sent to Windsor with a message from the King of Scotland. Lord William, for that was his name, was so tall, and strong, and brave, and manly, it was no wonder that little Lady Katherine fell in love with him, and preferred him to all the young English lords who were longing to lay their hearts at her feet.

So things went merrily on, in the pleasant June weather, until one sunny afternoon, when Lady Katherine was riding slowly through the park, under the shady beech trees, with Lord William, as usual, by her side. He was telling her how much he loved her, a story which he had told her very often before, and describing the old ivy-covered grey castle, far away in the north, where he would take her to live some day, when a little page, clad all in Lincoln green, ran across the park and bowed as he stopped at the palfrey's side.

'Pardon, my lady,' he said breathlessly, 'but the Baroness Anne sent me to carry tidings to you that your mother, the duchess, has arrived, and would speak with you at once.'

Then the bright red roses faded from the poor little lady's cheeks, for she knew well that the duchess, who was not her real mother, but only her stepmother, wished her no good. Sorrowfully she rode up to the castle, Lord William at her side, and it seemed to both of them as if the little birds had stopped singing, and the sun had suddenly grown dim.

And it was indeed terrible tidings that the little maiden heard when she reached the room where her stern-faced stepmother awaited her. An old marquis, a friend of her father's, who was quite old enough to be her grandfather, had announced his wish to marry her, and, as she had five sisters at home, all waiting to get a chance to become maids-of-honour, and see a little of the world, her stepmother thought it was too good an opportunity to let slip, and she had come to fetch her home.

In vain poor Lady Katherine threw herself at the duchess's feet, and besought her to let her marry the gallant Scottish knight. Her ladyship only curled her lip and laughed. 'Marry a beggarly Scot!' she said. 'Not as long as I have any power in your father's house. No, no, wench, you don't know what's good for you. Where is your waiting-maid? Let her pack up your things at once; you have tarried here quite long enough.'

So Lady Katherine was carted off, bag and baggage, to the great turreted mansion on the borders of Wales, where her five sisters and her grandfatherly old lover were waiting for her, without ever having a chance of bidding Lord William farewell.

As for that noble youth, he mounted his horse, and called his men-at-arms together, and straightway rode away to Scotland, and never halted till he reached the old grey castle, three days' ride over the Border. When he arrived there he shut himself up in the great square tower where his own apartments were, and frightened his family by growing so pale and thin that they declared he must have caught some fever in England, and had come home to die. In vain the earl, his father, tried to persuade him to ride out with him to the chase; he cared for nothing but to be left alone to sit in the dim light of his own room, and dream of his lost love.

Now Lord William was fond of all living things – horses, and dogs, and birds; but one pet he had which he loved above all the others, and that was a gay goshawk which he had found caught in a snare one day, and had set free, and tamed, and which always sat on a perch by his window.

One evening, when he was sitting dreaming sadly of the days at Windsor, stroking his favourite's plumage meanwhile, he was startled to hear the bird begin to speak. 'What mischance has befallen you, my master,' it said, 'that you look so pale and unhappy? Have you been defeated in a tourney by some southern loon, or do you still mourn for that fair maiden, the lovely Lady Katherine? Can I not help you?'

Then a strange light shone in Lord William's eye, and he looked at the bird thoughtfully as it nestled closer to his heart.

'You shall help me, my gay goshawk,' he whispered, 'for, for this reason, I believe, you have received the gift of speech. Your wings are strong, and you can go where I cannot, and bring no harm to my love. You shall carry a letter to my dear one, and bring back an answer,' and in delight at the thought, the young man rose and walked up and down the room, the goshawk preening its wings on his shoulder, and crooning softly to itself.

'But how shall I recognise your love?' it said at last.

'Ah, that is easy,' answered Lord William. 'You must fly up and down the length of England, especially where any great mansion is, and you cannot mistake her. She is the fairest flower of all the fair flowers that that fair land contains. Her skin is white as milk, and the roses on her cheeks are red as blood. And, outside her chamber, by a little postern, there grows a nodding birch tree, the leaves of which dance in the slightest breeze, and you must perch thereon and sing your sweetest when she goes with her sisters and maids to hear Mass in the little chapel.'

That night, when all the country folk were asleep, a gay goshawk flew out from a window in the square tower, and sped swiftly through the quiet air, on and on, above lonely houses and sleeping towns, and when the sun rose it was still flying, hovering now and then over some great castle, or lordly manor house, but never resting long, never satisfied. Day and night it travelled, up and down the country, till at last it came one evening to a great mansion on the borders of

Wales, at one side of which was a tiny postern, with a high latticed window near it, and by the door grew a birch tree, whose branches nodded up and down against the panes.

'Ah,' said the goshawk to itself, 'I will rest here.' And it perched on a branch, and put its head under its wing, and slept till morning, for it was very tired. As soon as the sun rose, however, it was awake, with its bright eyes ready to see whatever was to be seen.

Nor had it long to wait.

Presently the bell at the tiny chapel down by the lake began to ring, and immediately the postern opened, and a bevy of fair maidens came laughing out, books in hand, on their way to the morning Mass. They were all beautiful, but the gay goshawk had no difficulty in telling which was his master's love, for the Lady Katherine was the fairest of them all, and, as soon as he saw her, he began to sing as though his little throat would burst, and all the maidens stood still for a moment and listened to his song.

When they returned from the little chapel he was still singing, and when Lady Katherine went up into her chamber the song sounded more beautiful than ever. It was a strange song too, quite unlike the song of any other bird, for first there came a long soft note, and then a clear distinct one, and then some other notes which were always the same, 'Your love cannot come here; your love cannot come here.' So they sounded over and over again, in Lady Katherine's ears, until the roses on her cheeks disappeared, and she was white and trembling.

'Go ahead to the dining-hall, maidens; don't wait for me,' she said suddenly. 'I would like to be alone to enjoy this lovely song.' And, as the fresh morning air had made them all hungry, they obeyed her without a moment's thought.

As soon as she was alone she ran to the window and opened it, and there, just outside, sat a gay goshawk, with the most beautiful plumage that she had ever seen.

'Oh,' she cried faintly, 'I cannot understand it; but something in my heart tells me that you have seen my own dear love.'

Then the gay goshawk put his head on one side, and whistled a merry tune; then he looked straight into her eyes and sang a low sweet one; then he pecked and pecked at one of his wings until the tender-hearted little lady took hold of him gently to see if he were hurt, and who can describe her delight and astonishment when she found a tiny letter from Lord William tied in a little roll under his wing.

The letter was very sad, and the tears came into her eyes as she read it. It told her how he had already sent her three letters which had never reached her, and how he felt as if he must soon die, he was so sick with longing for her.

When she had read it, she sat for a long time thinking, with her face buried in her hands, while the gay goshawk preened his feathers, and crooned to himself on the window sill. At last she sprang to her feet, her eyes flashing and her mouth set determinedly. Taking a beautiful ring from her hand, she tied it with trembling fingers under the bird's wing where the letter had been.

'Tell him that with the ring I send him my heart,' she whispered passionately, and the gay goshawk just gave one little nod with his head, and then sat quite still to hear the rest of her message. 'Tell him to set his bakers and his brewers to work,' she went on firmly, 'to bake rich bridal cake, and brew the wedding ale, and while they are yet fresh I will meet him at the Kirk o' St Mary, the church he has so often told me of.'

At these words the gay goshawk opened his eyes a shade wider. 'Beshrew me, lady,' he said to himself, 'but you talk as if you had wings!' but he knew his duty was to act and not to talk, so with one merry whistle he spread his wings, and flew away to the north.

That night, when all the people in the great house were asleep, the little postern opened very gently, and a grey-cloaked figure crept softly out. It went slowly in the shadow of the trees until it came to the little chapel by the lake; then it ran softly and lightly through the long grass until it reached a tiny little cottage under a spreading oak tree. It tapped three times on the window, and presently a quavering old voice asked who was there.

' 'Tis I, Dame Ursula; it is your nursling Katherine. Open to me, I pray you; I am in sore need of your help.'

A moment later the door was opened by a little old woman, with a white cap and a rosy face like a wrinkled apple.

'And what need drives my little lady to me at this time of night?' she asked.

Then the maiden told her story, and made her request.

The old woman listened, shaking her head, and laughing to herself

meanwhile. 'I can do it, I can do it,' she cried, 'and 'twere worth a
year's wages to see thy proud stepdame's face when thy brothers
return to tell the tale.' Then she drew Lady Katherine into her tiny
room, and set her down on a three-legged stool by the smouldering
fire, while she pottered about, and made up a draught, taking a few
drops of liquid from one bottle, and a few drops from another; for
this curious old woman seemed to keep quite a number of bottles, as
well as various bunches of herbs, on a high shelf at one end of her
kitchen.

At last she was finished, and turning to the maiden, she handed
her a little phial containing a deep-red mixture.

'Swallow it all at once,' she chuckled, 'when you require the spell
to work. 'Twill last three days, and then you will wake up as fresh as
a lark.'

Next morning the duke and his seven sons were going hunting,
and the courtyard rang with merry laughter as they came out to
mount the horses which the pages held ready for them. The ladies
were on the terrace waiting to wave them goodbye, when, just as the
duke was about to mount his horse, his eldest daughter, whom he
loved dearly, ran into the courtyard and knelt at his feet.

'A boon, a boon, dear father,' she cried, and she looked so lovely
with her golden hair waving in the wind, and her bright eyes looking
up into his, that he felt he could not refuse her anything.

'Ask what you will, my daughter,' he said kindly, laying his hand
on her head, 'and I will grant it you. Except permission to marry
that Scottish squire,' he added, laughing.

'That will I never ask, sire,' she said submissively; 'but though you
forbid me to think of him, my heart yearns for Scotland, the country
that he told me of, and if it is your will that I marry and live in
England, I would at least like to be buried in the north. And as I have
always had due reverence for the Holy Church, I pray that when that
day comes, as come it must some day, you will cause a Mass to be
sung at the first Scotch kirk we come to, and that the bells may toll
for me at the second kirk, and that at the third, at the Kirk o' St
Mary, you will deal out gold, and cause my body to rest there.'

Then the duke raised her to her feet. 'Talk not so, my little
Katherine,' he said kindly. 'The marquis is a goodly man, albeit not
too young, and you will be a happy wife and mother yet; but if 'twill

ease your heart, child, I will remember your fancy.' Then the kind old man rode away, and Katherine went back to her sisters.

'What were you asking, girl?' asked her jealous stepmother with a frown as she passed.

'That I may be buried in Scotland when my time comes to die,' said Katherine, bowing low, with downcast eyes, for in those days maidens had to order themselves lowly to their elders, even although they were Duke's daughters.

'And did he grant your strange request?' went on the duchess, looking suspiciously at the girl's burning cheeks.

'Yes, if it please you, madam,' answered her stepdaughter meekly, and then with another low curtsey she hurried off to her own room, not waiting to hear the lady's angry words: 'I wish, proud maiden, that I had had the giving of the answer, for, by my troth, I would have turned a deaf ear to your request. Buried in Scotland, indeed! You have a lover in Scotland, and it is he you are hankering after, and not a grave.'

Two hours afterwards, when the duke and his sons came back from hunting, they found the castle in an uproar. All the servants were running about, wringing their hands, and crying; and indeed it was little wonder, for had not Lady Katherine's waiting-woman, when she went into her young lady's room at noon, found her lying cold and white on her couch, and no one had been able to rouse her? When the poor old duke heard this, he rushed up to her chamber, followed by all his seven sons; and when he saw her lying there, so white, and still, he covered his face with his hands, and cried out that his little Katherine, his dearly loved daughter, was dead.

But the cruel stepmother shook her head and said nothing. Somehow she did not believe that Lady Katherine was really dead, and she determined to do a very cruel thing to find out the truth. When everyone had left the room she ordered her waiting-maid, a woman who was as wicked as herself, to melt some lead, and bring it to her in an iron spoon, and when it was brought she dropped a drop on the young girl's breast; but she neither started nor screamed, so the cruel duchess had at last to pretend to be satisfied that she was really dead, and she gave orders that she should be buried at once in the little chapel by the lake.

But the old duke remembered his promise, and vowed that it

should be kept. So Lady Katherine's seven brothers went into the great park, and cut down a giant oak tree, and out of the trunk of it they hewed a bier, and they overlaid it with silver; while her sisters sat in the turret room and sewed a beautiful gown of white satin, which they put on Lady Katherine, and laid her on the silver bier; and then eight of her father's men-at-arms took it on their shoulders, and her seven brothers followed behind, and so the procession set out for Scotland.

And it all fell out as the old duke had promised. At the first Scotch kirk which the procession came to, the priests sang a solemn Mass, and at the second, they caused the bells to toll mournfully, and at the third kirk, the Kirk o' St Mary, they thought to lay the maiden to rest.

But, as they came slowly up to it, what was their astonishment to find that it was surrounded by a row of spearmen, whose captain, a tall, handsome young man, stepped up to them as they were about to enter the kirk, and requested them to lay down the bier. At first Lady Katherine's seven brothers objected to this being done. What business of the stranger's was it? they asked, and they haughtily ordered the men-at-arms to proceed. But the young soldier gave a sign to his men, and in an instant they had crossed their spears across the doorway, and the rest surrounded the men who carried the bier, and compelled them to do as they were bid.

Then the young captain stepped forward to where Lady Katherine was lying in her satin gown, and knelt down and took hold of her hand.

Immediately the rosy colour began to come back to her cheeks, and she opened her eyes; and when they fell on Lord William – for it was he who had come to meet her at the Kirk o' St Mary, as she had bidden him – she smiled faintly and said, 'I pray you, my lord, give me one morsel of bread and a mouthful of your good red wine, for I have fasted for three days, ever since the draught which my old nurse Ursula gave me, began to do its work.'

When she had drunk the wine her strength came back, and she sprang up lightly, and a murmur of delight went round among Lord William's spearmen when they saw how lovely she was in the white satin gown which her sisters had made, and which would do beautifully for her wedding.

But her seven brothers were very angry at the trick which had been played on them, and if they had dared, they would have carried her back to England by force; but they dared not, because of all the spearmen who stood round.

'You will rue this yet, proud girl,' said her eldest brother; 'you might have been a marchioness in England, with land, and castles, and gold enough and to spare, instead of coming to this beggarly land and breaking your father's and your mother's hearts.'

Then the little lady put her hand in that of her lover, and answered quietly, 'Nay, but I had no mind to wed with one who was already in his dotage; little good the lands, and castles, and gold would have done me had I been obliged to spend my time in nursing an old man; and, as for my father, I know he will secretly rejoice when he hears that, after all, I shall wed my own true love, who, I would have him know, is an earl's son, although he may not be so rich as is my lord the marquis; and, as for my cruel stepmother, 'tis no matter what she thinks.'

Her brother stamped his foot in useless anger. 'Then,' said he, pointing to the silver bier lying forgotten on the grass, 'I swear that that bier on which you came hither shall be the only wedding portion that your husband will ever see of yours; maybe poverty will bring you to your senses.'

But his sister only laughed as she pressed closer to her bridegroom and said bravely, 'Happiness is more than gold, brother, and the contented heart better than the restless one which is ever seeking riches.'

So the seven brothers went back to England in a rage, while Lord William married his brave little bride in the old Kirk o' St Mary; and then they rode home to the grey ivy-covered castle, where the gay goshawk was waiting on the square tower to sing his very sweetest song to greet them.

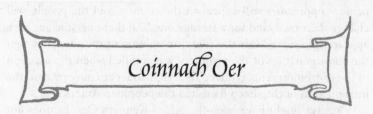

Coinnach Oer

Coinnach Oer, which means Dun Kenneth, was a celebrated man in his generation. He has been called the Isaiah of the North. The prophecies of this man are very frequently alluded to and quoted in various parts of the Highlands; although little is known of the man himself, except in Ross-shire. He was a smallholder in Strathpeffer, near Dingwall, and for many years of his life neither exhibited any talents, nor claimed any intelligence above his fellows. The manner in which he obtained the prophetic gift was told by himself in the following manner:

As he was one day at work in the hill casting peats, he heard a voice which seemed to call to him out of the air. It commanded him to dig under a little green knoll which was near, and to gather up the small white stones which he would discover beneath the turf. The voice informed him, at the same time, that while he kept these stones in his possession, he should be endued with the power of supernatural foreknowledge.

Kenneth, though greatly alarmed at this aerial conversation, followed the directions of his invisible instructor, and turning up the turf on the hillock, in a little time discovered the talismans. From that day forward, the mind of Kenneth was illuminated by gleams of unearthly light; and he made many predictions, of which the credulity of the people, and the coincidence of accident, often supplied confirmation; and he certainly became the most notable of the Highland prophets. The most remarkable and well known of his vaticinations is the following: 'Whenever a McLean with long hands, a Fraser with a black spot on his face, a McGregor with a black knee and a club-footed McLeod of Raga shall have existed; whenever there shall have been successively three McDonalds of the name of John, and three McKinnons of the same Christian name – oppressors will appear in the country and the people will change their own land for a strange one.' All these personages have appeared since; and it is the common opinion of the peasantry that the consummation of the prophecy was fulfilled when the exaction of the exorbitant rents reduced the Highlanders to poverty, and the introduction of the sheep banished the people to America.

Whatever might have been the gift of Kenneth Oer, he does not appear to have used it with an extraordinary degree of discretion; and the last time he exercised it, he was very near paying dear for his divination.

On this occasion he happened to be at some high festival of the McKenzies at Castle Braan. One of the guests was so exhilarated by the scene of gaiety that he could not forbear a eulogium on the gallantry of the feast, and the nobleness of the guests. Kenneth, it appears, had no regard for the McKenzies, and was so provoked by this sally in their praise that he not only broke out into a severe satire against their whole race, but gave vent to the prophetic denunciation of wrath and confusion upon their posterity. The guests being informed (or having overheard a part) of this rhapsody, instantly rose up with one accord to punish the contumely of the prophet. Kenneth, though he foretold the fate of others, did not in any manner look into that of himself; for this reason, being doubtful of debating the propriety of his prediction upon such unequal terms, he fled with the greatest precipitation. The McKenzies followed with infinite zeal; and more than one ball had whistled over the head of the seer before he reached Loch Ousie. The consequences of this prediction so disgusted Kenneth with any further exercise of his prophetic calling that, in the anguish of his flight, he solemnly renounced all communication with its power; and, as he ran along the margin of Loch Ousie, he took out the wonderful pebbles, and cast them in a fury into the water. Whether his evil genius had now forsaken him, or his condition was better than that of his pursuers, is unknown, but certain it is, Kenneth, after the sacrifice of the pebbles, outstripped his enraged enemies, and never, so far as I have heard, made any attempt at prophecy from the hour of his escape.

Kenneth Oer had a son, who was called Ian Dubh MacCoinnach (Black John, the son of Kenneth) and who lived in the village of Miltoun, near Dingwall. His chief occupation was brewing whisky;

and he was killed in a fray at Miltoun, early in the nineteenth century. His exit would not have formed the catastrophe of an epic poem, and appears to have been one of those events of which his father had no intelligence. Having fallen into a dispute with a man with whom he had previously been on friendly terms, he proceeded to trade blows with him; in the scuffle, the boy, the son of Ian's adversary, observing the two combatants locked in a close and firm embrace of eager contention, and being doubtful of the outcome, ran into the house and brought out the iron pot-crook, with which he saluted the head of the unfortunate Ian so severely that he not only relinquished his combat, but departed this life on the ensuing morning.

Canobie Dick and Thomas of Ercildoun

Now it chanced many years ago that there lived on the Borders a jolly rattling horse-dealer, who was remarkable for a reckless and fearless temper, which made him much admired and a little dreaded amongst his neighbours. One moonlight night, as he rode over Bowden Moor, on the west side of the Eildon Hills, the scene of Thomas the Rhymer's prophecies, and often mentioned in his history, having a brace of horses along with him which he had not been able to dispose of, he met a man of venerable appearance and singularly antique dress, who, to his great surprise, asked the price of his horses, and began to chaffer with him on the subject. To Canobie Dick, for so shall we call our Border dealer, a chap was a chap, and he would have sold a horse to the devil himself, without minding his cloven hoof, and would have probably cheated Old Nick into the bargain. The stranger paid the price they agreed on, and all that puzzled Dick in the transaction was that the gold which he received was in unicorns, bonnet-pieces and other ancient coins, which would have been invaluable to collectors, but were rather troublesome in modern currency. It was gold, however, and there-fore Dick contrived to get better value for the coin than he perhaps gave to his customer. By the command of so good a merchant, he brought horses to the same spot more than once; the purchaser only stipulating that he should always come by night and alone. I do not know whether it was from mere curiosity, or whether some hope of gain mixed with it, but after Dick had sold several horses in this way, he began to complain that dry bargains were unlucky, and to hint that since his chap must live in the neighbourhood, he ought, in the courtesy of dealing, to treat him to half a mutchkin.

'You may see my dwelling if you will,' said the stranger; 'but if you lose courage at what you see there, you will rue it all your life.'

Dickon, however, laughed the warning to scorn, and having alighted and secured his horse, he followed the stranger up a narrow footpath, which led them up the hills to the singular eminence stuck betwixt the most southern and the centre peaks, and called, from its resemblance to such an animal in its form, the Lucken Hare. At the foot of this eminence, which is almost as famous for witch-meetings as the neighbouring windmill of Kippilaw, Dick was somewhat startled to observe that his conductor entered the hillside by a passage or cavern, of which he himself, though well acquainted with the spot, had never seen nor heard.

'You may still return,' said his guide, looking ominously back upon him; but Dick scorned to show the white feather, and on they went. They entered a very long range of stables; in every stall stood a coal-black horse; by every horse lay a knight in coal-black armour, with a drawn sword in his hand; but all were as silent, hoof and limb, as if they had been cut out of marble. A great number of torches lent a gloomy lustre to the hall, which, like those of the Caliph Vathek, was of large dimensions. At the upper end, however, they at length arrived, where a sword and horn lay on an antique table.

'He that shall sound that horn and draw that sword,' said the stranger, who now intimated that he was the famous Thomas of Ercildoun, 'shall, if his heart fail him not, be king over all broad Britain. So speaks the tongue that cannot lie. But all depends on courage, and much on your taking the sword or horn first.'

Dick was much disposed to take the sword, but his bold spirit was quailed by the supernatural terrors of the hall, and he thought to unsheathe the sword first might be construed into defiance, and give offence to the powers of the mountain. He took the bugle with a trembling hand, and blew a feeble note, but loud enough to produce a terrible answer. Thunder rolled in stunning peals through the immense hall; horses and men started to life; the steeds snorted, stamped, ground their bits, and tossed their heads; the warriors sprang to their feet, clashed their armour, and brandished their swords. Dick's terror was extreme at seeing the whole army, which had been so lately silent as the grave, in uproar, and about to rush on him. He dropped the horn, and made a feeble attempt to seize the enchanted sword, but at the same moment a voice pronounced aloud the mysterious words:

'Woe to the coward, that ever he was born,
Who did not draw the sword before he blew the horn!'

At the same time a whirlwind of irresistible fury howled through the
long hall, bore the unfortunate horse-jockey clear out of the mouth
of the cavern, and precipitated him over a steep bank of loose stones,
where the shepherds found him the next morning, with just breath
sufficient to tell his fearful tale, after concluding which he expired.

Elphin Irving: The Fairies' Cupbearer

The lady kilted her kirtle green
A little aboon her knee,
The lady snooded her yellow hair
A little aboon her bree,
And she's gane to the good greenwood
As fast as she could hie.
And first she let the black steed pass,
And syne she let the brown,
And then she flew to the milk-white steed,
And pulled the rider down:
Syne out then sang the queen o' the fairies,
Frae midst a bank of broom,
She that has won him, young Tamlane,
Has gotten a gallant groom.

Old Ballad

The romantic Vale of Corriewater, in Annandale, is regarded by the inhabitants, a pastoral and unmingled people, as the last border refuge of those beautiful and capricious beings, the fairies. Many old people yet living imagine they have had intercourse of good words and good deeds with the 'good folk', and continue to tell that in the ancient days the fairies danced on the hill, and revelled in the glen, and showed themselves, like the mysterious children of the deity of old, among the sons and daughters of men. Their visits to the earth were periods of joy and mirth to mankind, rather than of sorrow and apprehension. They played on musical instruments of wonderful sweetness and variety of note, spread unexpected feasts, the supernatural flavour of which overpowered on many occasions the religious scruples of the Presbyterian shepherds, performed wonderful deeds of horsemanship, and marched in midnight processions, when the sound of their elfin minstrelsy charmed

youths and maidens into love for their persons and pursuits; and
more than one family of Corriewater have the fame of augmenting
the numbers of the elfin chivalry. Faces of friends and relatives,
long since doomed to the battle-trench or the deep sea, have been
recognised by those who dared to gaze on the fairy march. The
maid has seen her lost lover, and the mother her stolen child; and
the courage to plan and achieve their deliverance has been possessed
by at least one border maiden. In the legends of the people of
Corrievale, there is a singular mixture of elfin and human adventure,
and the traditional story of the Cupbearer to the Queen of the
Fairies appeals alike to our domestic feelings and imagination.

In one of the little green loops or bends on the banks of Corriewater, mouldered walls and a few stunted wild plum trees and
vagrant roses still point out the site of a cottage and garden. A well
of pure spring water leaps out from an old tree-root before the
door; and here the shepherds, shading themselves in summer from
the influence of the sun, tell to their children the wild tale of Elphin
Irving and his sister Phemie; and, singular as the story seems, it has
gained full credence among the people where the scene is laid.

When Elphin Irving and his sister Phemie were in their sixteenth
year, for tradition says they were twins, their father was drowned in
Corriewater attempting to save his sheep from a sudden swell, to
which all mountain streams are liable; and their mother, on the day
of her husband's burial, laid down her head on the pillow from
which, on the seventh day, it was lifted to be dressed for the same
grave. The inheritance left to the orphans may be briefly described:
seventeen acres of plough and pasture land, seven milk cows and
seven pet sheep (many old people take delight in odd numbers); and
to this may be added seven bonnet-pieces of Scottish gold, and a
broadsword and spear, which their ancestor had wielded with such
strength and courage in the battle of Dryfe Sands, that the minstrel
who sang of that deed of arms ranked him only second to the Scotts
and Johnstones.

The youth and his sister grew in stature and in beauty. The fine
bright brow, the clear blue eye and frank and blithe deportment of
the former gave him some influence among the young women of the
valley; while the latter was no less the admiration of the young men,
and at fair and dance, and at bridal, happy was he who touched but

her hand or received the benediction of her eye. Like all other Scottish beauties, she was the theme of many a song; and while tradition is yet busy with the singular history of her brother, song has taken all the care that rustic minstrelsy can of the gentleness of her spirit and the charms of her person.

But minstrel skill and true love-tale seemed to want their usual influence when they sought to win her attention; she was only observed to pay most respect to those youths who were most beloved by her brother; and the same hour that brought these twins to the world seemed to have breathed through them a sweetness and an affection of heart and mind which nothing could divide. If, like the virgin queen of the immortal poet, she walked 'in maiden meditation fancy free', her brother Elphin seemed alike untouched with the charms of the fairest virgins in Corrie. He ploughed his field, he reaped his grain, he leaped, he ran and wrestled, and danced, and sang, with more skill and life and grace than all other youths of the district; but he had no twilight and stolen interviews; when all other young men had their loves by their side, he was single, though not unsought, and his joy seemed never perfect save when his sister was near him. If he loved to share his time with her, she loved to share her time with him alone, or with the beasts of the field, or the birds of the air. She watched her little flock late, and she tended it early; not for the sordid love of the fleece, unless it was to make mantles for her brother, but with the look of one who had joy in its company. The very wild creatures, the deer and the hares, seldom sought to shun her approach, and the bird forsook not its nest, nor stinted its song, when she drew nigh; such is the confidence which maiden innocence and beauty inspire.

It happened one summer, about three years after they became orphans, that rain had been for a while withheld from the earth, the hillsides began to parch, the grass in the vales to wither and the stream of Corrie was diminished between its banks to the size of an ordinary rill. The shepherds drove their flocks to moorlands, and marsh and tarn had their reeds invaded by the scythe to supply the cattle with food. The sheep of his sister were Elphin's constant care; he drove them to the moistest pastures during the day, and he often watched them at midnight, when flocks, tempted by the sweet dewy grass, are known to browse eagerly, that he might guard them from the fox, and lead them to the choicest herbage. In these nocturnal watchings he sometimes drove his little flock over the water of Corrie, for the fords were hardly ankle-deep; or permitted his sheep to cool themselves in the stream, and taste the grass which grew along the brink. All this time not a drop of rain fell, nor did a cloud appear in the sky.

One evening, during her brother's absence with the flock, Phemie sat at her cottage-door, listening to the bleatings of the distant folds and the lessened murmur of the water of Corrie, now scarcely audible beyond its banks. Her eyes, weary with watching along the accustomed line of road for the return of Elphin, were turned on the pool beside her, in which the stars were glimmering fitful and faint. As she looked she imagined the water grew brighter and brighter; a wild illumination presently shone upon the pool, and leaped from bank to bank, and suddenly changing into a human form, ascended the margin, and, passing her, glided swiftly into the cottage. The visionary form was so like her brother in shape and air, that, starting up, she flew into the house, with the hope of finding him in his customary seat. She found him not, and, impressed with the terror which a wraith or apparition seldom fails to inspire, she uttered a shriek so loud and so piercing as to be heard at Johnstone Bank, on the other side of the Vale of Corrie.

It is hardly known how long Phemie Irving continued in a state of insensibility. The morning was far advanced, when a neighbouring maiden found her seated in an old chair, as white as monumental marble; her hair, about which she had always been solicitous, loosened from its curls, and hanging disordered over her neck and bosom, her hands and forehead. The maiden touched the one, and kissed the other; they were as cold as snow; and her eyes, wide open, were fixed on her brother's empty chair, with the intensity of gaze of one who had witnessed the appearance of a spirit. She seemed insensible of anyone's presence, and sat fixed and still and motionless. The maiden, alarmed at her looks, thus addressed her: 'Phemie, lass, Phemie Irving! Dear me, but this be awful! I have come to tell ye that seven of your pet sheep have escaped drowning in the water; for Corrie, sae quiet and sae gentle yestreen, is rolling and dashing frae bank to bank this morning. Dear me, woman, dinna let the loss of the world's gear bereave ye of your senses. I would rather make ye a present of a dozen mug-ewes of the Tinwald brood myself; and now I think on 't, if ye'll send over Elphin, I will help him hame with them in the gloaming myself. So, Phemie, woman, be comforted.'

At the mention of her brother's name she cried out, 'Where is he? Oh, where is he?' gazed wildly round, and, shuddering from head to foot, fell senseless on the floor. Other inhabitants of the valley, alarmed by the sudden swell of the river, which had augmented to a torrent, deep and impassable, now came in to enquire if any loss had been sustained, for numbers of sheep and bales of hay had been observed floating down about the dawn of the morning. They assisted in reclaiming the unhappy maiden from her swoon; but insensibility was joy compared to the sorrow to which she awakened. 'They have ta'en him away, they have ta'en him away,' she chanted, in a tone of delirious pathos; 'him that was whiter and fairer than the lily on Lyddal Lee. They have long sought, and they have long sued, and they had the power to prevail against my prayers at last. They have ta'en him away; the flower is plucked from among the weeds, and the dove is slain amid a flock of ravens. They came with shout, and they came with song, and they spread the charm, and they placed the spell, and the baptised brow has been bowed down to the unbaptised hand. They have ta'en him away, they have ta'en him away; he was too lovely, and too good, and too noble, to bless us with his continuance on earth; for what are the sons of men compared to him? – the light of the moonbeam to the morning sun, the glowworm to the eastern star. They have ta'en him away, the invisible dwellers of the earth. I saw them come on him with shouting and with singing, and they charmed him where he sat, and away they bore him; and the horse he rode was never shod with iron, nor owned before the mastery of human hand. They have ta'en him away over the water, and over the wood, and over the hill. I got but one look of his bonnie blue eye, but one; one look. But as I have endured what never maiden endured, so will I undertake what never maiden undertook, I will win him from them all. I know the invisible ones of the earth; I have heard their wild and wondrous music in the wild woods, and there shall a christened maiden seek him, and achieve his deliverance.' She paused, and glancing around a circle of condoling faces, down which the tears were dropping like rain, said, in a calm and altered but still delirious tone: 'Why do you weep, Mary Halliday? and why do you weep, John Graeme? Ye think that Elphin Irving – oh, it's a bonnie, bonnie name, and dear to many a maiden's heart, as well as mine – ye think he is drowned in Corrie; and ye will seek in the deep, deep pools for the bonnie, bonnie corse, that ye may weep over it, as it lies in its last linen, and lay it, amid weeping and wailing in the dowie kirkyard. Ye may seek, but ye shall never find; so leave me to trim up my hair, and prepare my dwelling, and make myself ready to watch for the hour of his return to upper earth.' And she resumed her household labours with an alacrity which lessened not the sorrow of her friends.

Meanwhile the rumour flew over the vale that Elphin Irving was drowned in Corriewater. Matron and maid, old man and young, collected suddenly along the banks of the river, which now began to subside to its natural summer limits, and commenced their search; interrupted every now and then by calling from side to side, and from pool to pool, and by exclamations of sorrow for this misfortune. The search was fruitless: five sheep, pertaining to the flock which he conducted to pasture, were found drowned in one of the deep eddies; but the river was still too brown, from the soil of its moorland sources, to enable them to see what its deep shelves, its pools and its overhanging and hazelly banks concealed. They remitted further search till the stream should become pure; and old man taking old man aside, began to whisper about the mystery of the youth's disappearance; old women laid their lips to the ears of their coevals, and talked of Elphin Irving's fairy parentage, and his having been dropped by an unearthly hand into a Christian cradle. The young men and maids conversed on other themes; they grieved for the loss of the friend and the lover, and while the former thought that a heart so kind and true was not left in the vale, the latter thought, as maidens will, on his handsome person, gentle manners and merry blue eye, and speculated with a sigh on the time when they might have hoped a return for their love. They were soon joined by others who had heard the wild and delirious language of his sister: the old belief was added to the new assurance, and both again commented upon by minds full of superstitious feeling, and hearts full of supernatural fears, till the youths and maidens of Corrievale held no more love trysts for seven days and nights, lest, like Elphin Irving, they should be carried away to augment the ranks of the unchristened chivalry.

It was curious to listen to the speculations of the peasantry. 'For my part,' said a youth, 'if I were sure that poor Elphin escaped from that perilous water, I would not give the fairies a pound of hiplock wool for their chance of him. There has not been a fairy seen in the land since Donald Cargil, the Cameronian, conjured them into the Solway for playing on their pipes during one of his nocturnal preachings on the hip of the Burnswark Hill.'

'Preserve me, bairn,' said an old woman, justly exasperated at the incredulity of her nephew, 'if ye winna believe what I both heard and saw at the moonlight end of Craigyburnwood on a summer night, rank after rank of the fairy folk, ye'll at least believe a douce man and a ghostly professor, even the late minister of Tinwaldkirk. His only son – I mind the lad weel, with his long yellow locks and his bonnie blue eyes – when I was but a gilpie of a lassie, *he* was stolen away from off the horse at his father's elbow as they crossed that false and fearsome water, even Locherbriggflow, on the night of the midsummer fair of Dumfries. Ay, ay, who can doubt the truth of that? Have not the godly inhabitants of Almsfieldtown and Tinwaldkirk seen the sweet youth riding at midnight, in the midst of the unhallowed troop, to the sound of flute and of dulcimer, and though meikle they prayed, naebody tried to achieve his deliverance?'

'I have heard it said by douce folk and sponsible,' interrupted another, 'that every seven years the elves and fairies make an offering of one of their children to the grand enemy of salvation, and that they are permitted to purloin one of the children of men to present to the fiend – a more acceptable offering, I'll warrant, than one of their own infernal brood that are Satan's sib allies and drink a drop of the deil's blood every May morning. And touching this lost lad, ye all ken his mother was a hawk of an uncanny nest, a second cousin of Kate Kimmer, of Barfloshan, as rank a witch as ever rode on ragwort. Ay, sirs, what's bred in the bone is ill to come out of the flesh.'

On these and similar topics, which a peasantry full of ancient tradition and enthusiasm and superstition readily associate with the commonest occurrences of life, the people of Corrievale continued to converse till the fall of evening, when each, seeking their home, renewed again the wondrous subject, and illustrated it with all that popular belief and poetic imagination could so abundantly supply.

The night which followed this melancholy day was wild with wind and rain; the river came down broader and deeper than before, and the lightning, flashing by fits over the green woods of Corrie, showed the ungovernable and perilous flood sweeping above its banks. It happened that a farmer, returning from one of the border fairs, encountered the full swing of the storm; but mounted on an excellent horse, and mantled from chin to heel in a good grey plaid, beneath which he had the further security of a thick greatcoat, he sat dry in his saddle, and proceeded in the anticipated joy of a subsided tempest and a glowing morning sun. As he entered the long grove, or rather the remains of the old Galwegian forest, which lines for some space the banks of the Corriewater, the storm began to abate, the wind sighed milder and milder among the trees, and here and there a star, twinkling momentarily through the sudden rack of the clouds, showed the river raging from bank to brae. As he shook the moisture from his clothes, he was not without a wish that the day would dawn, and that he might be preserved on a road which his imagination beset with greater perils than the raging river; for his superstitious feeling let loose upon his path elf and goblin, and the current traditions of the district supplied very largely to his apprehension the ready materials of fear.

Just as he emerged from the wood, where a fine sloping bank, covered with short greensward, skirts the limit of the forest, his horse made a full pause, snorted, trembled and started from side to side, stooped his head, erected his ears, and seemed to scrutinise every tree and bush. The rider, too, it may be imagined, gazed round and round, and peered warily into every suspicious-looking place. His dread of a supernatural visitation was not much allayed when he observed a female shape seated on the ground at the root of a huge old oak tree, which stood in the centre of one of those patches of verdant sward known by the name of 'fairy rings', and avoided by all peasants who wish to prosper. A long thin gleam of eastern daylight enabled him to examine accurately the being who, in this wild place and unusual hour, gave additional terror to this haunted spot. She was dressed in white from the neck to the knees;

her arms, long and round and white, were perfectly bare; her head, uncovered, allowed her long hair to descend in ringlet succeeding ringlet, till the half of her person was nearly concealed in the fleece. Amidst the whole, her hands were constantly busy in shedding aside the tresses which interposed between her steady and uninterrupted gaze down a line of old road which wound among the hills to an ancient burial-ground.

As the traveller continued to gaze, the figure suddenly rose, and, wringing the rain from her long locks, paced round and round the tree, chanting in a wild and melancholy manner an equally wild and delirious song.

'The small bird's head is under its wing,
The deer sleeps on the grass;
The moon comes out, and the stars shine down,
The dew gleams like the glass:
There is no sound in the world so wide,
Save the sound of the smitten brass,
With the merry cittern and the pipe
Of the fairies as they pass.
But oh! the fire maun burn and burn,
And the hour is gone, and will never return.

The green hill cleaves, and forth, with a bound,
Comes elf and elfin steed;
The moon dives down in a golden cloud,
The stars grow dim with dread;
But a light is running along the earth,
So of heaven's they have no need:
O'er moor and moss with a shout they pass,
And the word is spur and speed –
But the fire maun burn, and I maun quake,
And the hour is gone that will never come back.

And when they came to Craigyburnwood,
The Queen of the Fairies spoke:
"Come, bind your steeds to the rushes so green,
And dance by the haunted oak:
I found the acorn on Heshbon Hill,

In the nook of a palmer's poke,
A thousand years since; here it grows!"
And they danced till the greenwood shook.
But oh! the fire, the burning fire,
The longer it burns, it but blazes the higher.

"I have won me a youth," the Elf Queen said,
"The fairest that earth may see;
This night I have won young Elph Irving
My cupbearer to be.
His service lasts but seven sweet years,
And his wage is a kiss of me."
And merrily, merrily, laughed the wild elves
Round Corris's greenwood tree.
But oh! the fire it glows in my brain,
And the hour is gone, and comes not again.

The Queen she has whispered a secret word,
"Come hither, my Elphin sweet,
And bring that cup of the charméd wine,
Thy lips and mine to weet."
But a brown elf shouted a loud, loud shout,
"Come, leap on your coursers fleet,
For here comes the smell of some baptised flesh,
And the sounding of baptised feet."
But oh! the fire that burns, and maun burn;
For the time that is gone will never return.

On a steed as white as the new-milked milk,
The Elf Queen leaped with a bound,
And young Elphin a steed like December snow
'Neath him at the word he found.
But a maiden came, and her christened arms
She linked her brother around,
And called on God, and the steed with a snort
Sank into the gaping ground.
But the fire maun burn, and I maun quake,
And the time that is gone will no more come back.

And she held her brother, and lo! he grew
A wild bull waked in ire;
And she held her brother, and lo! he changed
To a river roaring higher;
And she held her brother, and he became
A flood of the raging fire;
She shrieked and sank, and the wild elves laughed
Till the mountain rang and mire.
But oh! the fire yet burns in my brain,
And the hour is gone, and comes not again.

"O maiden, why waxed thy faith so faint,
Thy spirit so slack and slaw?
Thy courage kept good till the flame waxed wud,
Then thy might begun to thaw;
Had ye kissed him with thy christened lip,
Ye had wan him frae 'mang us a'.
Now bless the fire, the elfin fire,
That made thee faint and fa';
Now bless the fire, the elfin fire,
The longer it burns it blazes the higher." '

At the close of this unusual strain, the figure sat down on the grass,
and proceeded to bind up her long and disordered tresses, gazing
along the old and unfrequented road.

'Now God be my helper,' said the traveller, who happened to be
the laird of Johnstone Bank, 'can this be a trick of the fiend, or can it
be bonnie Phemie Irving who chants this dolorous song? Something
sad has befallen that makes her seek her seat in this eerie nook amid
the darkness and tempest; through might from aboon I will go on
and see.' And the horse, feeling something of the owner's reviving
spirit in the application of spur-steel, bore him at once to the foot of
the tree.

The poor delirious maiden uttered a yell of piercing joy as she
beheld him, and, with the swiftness of a creature winged, linked her
arms round the rider's waist, and shrieked till the woods rang. 'Oh, I
have ye now, Elphin, I have ye now,' and she strained him to her
bosom with a convulsive grasp.

'What ails ye, my bonnie lass?' said the laird of Johnstone Bank, his fears of the supernatural vanishing when he beheld her sad and bewildered look. She raised her eyes at the sound, and seeing a strange face, her arms slipped their hold, and she dropped with a groan on the ground.

The morning had now fairly broke; the flocks shook the rain from their sides, the shepherds hastened to inspect their charges, and a thin blue smoke began to stream from the cottages of the valley into the brightening air. The laird carried Phemie Irving in his arms, till he observed two shepherds ascending from one of the loops of Corriewater, bearing the lifeless body of her brother. They had found him whirling round and round in one of the numerous eddies, and his hands, clutched and filled with wool, showed that he had lost his life in attempting to save the flock of his sister. A plaid was laid over the body, which, along with the unhappy maiden in a half-lifeless state, was carried into a cottage, and laid in that apartment distinguished among the peasantry by the name of the chamber.

While the peasant's wife was left to take care of Phemie, old man and matron and maid had collected around the drowned youth, and each began to relate the circumstances of his death – when the door suddenly opened, and his sister, advancing to the corpse, with a look of delirious serenity, broke out into a wild laugh and said: 'Oh, it is wonderful, it's truly wonderful! That bare and death-cold body, dragged from the darkest pool of Corrie, with its hands filled with fine wool, wears the perfect similitude of my own Elphin! I'll tell ye – the spiritual dwellers of the earth, the fairyfolk of our evening tale, have stolen the living body and fashioned this cold and in-animate clod to mislead your pursuit. In common eyes this seems all that Elphin Irving would be, had he sunk in Corriewater; but so it seems not to me. Ye have sought the living soul, and ye have found only its garment. But oh, if ye had beheld him, as I beheld him tonight, riding among the elfin troop, the fairest of them all; had you clasped him in your arms, and wrestled for him with spirits and terrible shapes from the other world, till your heart quailed and your flesh was subdued, then would ye yield no credit to the semblance which this cold and apparent flesh bears to my brother. But hearken! On Hallowmass Eve, when the spiritual people are let loose on earth for a season, I will take my stand in the burial-ground of Corrie; and when my Elphin and his unchristened troop come past, with the sound of all their minstrelsy, I will leap on him and win him, or perish for ever.'

All gazed aghast on the delirious maiden, and many of her auditors gave more credence to her distempered speech than to the visible evidence before them. As she turned to depart, she looked round, and suddenly sank upon the body, with tears streaming from her eyes, and sobbed out, 'My brother! Oh, my brother!' She was carried out insensible, and again recovered; but relapsed into her ordinary delirium, in which she continued till the Hallow Eve after her brother's burial. She was found seated in the ancient burial-ground, her back against a broken gravestone, her locks white with frost-rime, watching with intensity of look the road to the kirkyard; but the spirit which gave life to the fairest form of all the maids of Annandale was fled for ever.

Such is the singular story which the peasants know by the name of 'Elphin Irving, the Fairies' Cupbearer'; and the title, in its fullest and most supernatural sense, still obtains credence among the industrious and virtuous dames of the romantic Vale of Corrie.

The Ghosts of Craig-Aulnaic

Two celebrated ghosts existed, once on a time, in the wilds of Craig-Aulnaic, a romantic place in the district of Strathdown, Banffshire. The one was a male and the other a female. The male was called Fhuna Mhoir Ben Baynac, after one of the mountains of Glenavon, where at one time he resided; and the female was called Clashnichd Aulnaic, from her having had her abode in Craig-Aulnaic. But although the great ghost of Ben Baynac was bound by the common ties of nature and of honour to protect and cherish his weaker companion, Clashnichd Aulnaic, yet he often treated her in the most cruel and unfeeling manner. In the dead of night, when the surrounding hamlets were buried in deep repose, and when nothing else disturbed the solemn stillness of the midnight scene, oft would the shrill shrieks of poor Clashnichd burst upon the slumberer's ears, and awake him to anything but pleasant reflections.

But of all those who were incommoded by the noisy and unseemly quarrels of these two ghosts, James Gray, the tenant of the farm of Balbig of Delnabo, was the greatest sufferer. From the proximity of his abode to their haunts, it was the misfortune of himself and family to be the nightly audience of Clashnichd's cries and lamentations, which they considered anything but agreeable entertainment.

One day as James Gray was on his rounds looking after his sheep, he happened to fall in with Clashnichd, the ghost of Aulnaic, with whom he entered into a long conversation. In the course of it he took occasion to remonstrate with her on the very disagreeable disturbance she caused himself and family by her wild and unearthly cries – cries which, he said, few mortals could relish in the dreary hours of midnight. Poor Clashnichd, by way of apology for her conduct, gave James Gray a sad account of her usage, detailing at full length the series of cruelties committed upon her by Ben Baynac. From this account, it appeared that her living with the latter was by no means a matter of choice with Clashnichd; on the contrary, it seemed that she had, for a long time, lived apart with much comfort, residing in a snug dwelling, as already mentioned, in the wilds of Craig-Aulnaic; but Ben Baynac having unfortunately taken into his head to pay her a visit, took a fancy, not to herself, but her dwelling, of which, in his own name and authority, he took immediate possession, and soon after he expelled poor Clashnichd, with many stripes, from her natural inheritance. Not satisfied with invading and depriving her of her just rights, he was in the habit of following her into her private haunts, not with the view of offering her any endearments, but for the purpose of inflicting on her person every torment which his brain could invent.

Such a moving relation could not fail to affect the generous heart of James Gray, who determined from that moment to risk life and limb in order to vindicate the rights and avenge the wrongs of poor Clashnichd, the ghost of Craig-Aulnaic. He, therefore, took good care to interrogate his new *protégée* touching the nature of her oppressor's constitution, whether he was of that *killable* species of ghost that could be shot with a silver sixpence, or if there was any other weapon that could possibly accomplish his annihilation. Clashnichd informed him that she had occasion to know that Ben Baynac was wholly invulnerable to all the weapons of man, with the exception of a large mole on his left breast, which was no doubt penetrable by silver or steel; but that, from the specimens she had of his personal prowess and strength, it were vain for mere man to attempt to combat him. Confiding, however, in his expertness as an archer – for he was allowed to be the best marksman of the age – James Gray told Clashnichd he did not fear him with all his might – that *he* was a man; and desired her, moreover, next time the ghost chose to repeat his incivilities to her, to apply to him, James Gray, for redress.

It was not long ere he had an opportunity of fulfilling his promises. Ben Baynac having one night, for the want of better amusement, entertained himself by inflicting an inhuman castigation on Clashnichd, she lost no time in waiting on James Gray, with a full and particular account of it. She found him smoking his *cutty*, for it was night when she came to him; but, notwithstanding the inconvenience of the hour, James needed no great persuasion to induce him to proceed directly along with Clashnichd to hold a communing with their friend, Ben Baynac, the great ghost. Clashnichd was stout and sturdy, and understood the knack of travelling much better than our women do. She expressed a wish that, for the sake of expedition, James Gray would suffer her to bear him along, a motion to which the latter agreed; and a few minutes brought them close to the scene of Ben Baynac's residence. As they approached his haunt, he came forth to meet them, with looks and gestures which did not at all indicate a cordial welcome. It was a fine moonlight night, and they could easily observe his actions. Poor Clashnichd was now sorely afraid of the great ghost. Apprehending instant destruction from his fury, she exclaimed to James Gray that they would be both dead people, and that immediately, unless James Gray hit with an arrow the mole which covered Ben Baynac's heart. This was not so difficult a task as James had hitherto apprehended it. The mole was as large as a common bonnet, and yet nowise disproportioned to the natural size of the ghost's body, for he certainly was a great and a mighty ghost. Ben Baynac cried out to James Gray that he would soon make eagle's meat of him; and certain it is, such was his intention, had not the shepherd so effectually stopped him from the execution of it. Raising his bow to his eye when within a few yards of Ben Baynac, he took deliberate aim: the arrow flew – it hit – a yell from Ben Baynac announced the result. A hideous howl re-echoed from the surrounding mountains, responsive to the groans of a thousand ghosts; and Ben Baynac, like the smoke of a shot, vanished into air.

Clashnichd, the ghost of Aulnaic, now found herself delivered from the most abject state of slavery, and restored to freedom and liberty, through the invincible courage of James Gray. Overpowered with gratitude, she fell at his feet, and vowed to devote the whole of her time and talents towards his service and prosperity. Meanwhile, being anxious to have her remaining goods and furniture removed to her former dwelling, whence she had been so iniquitously expelled by Ben Baynac, the great ghost, she requested of her new master the use of his horses to remove them. James observing on the adjacent hill a flock of deer, and wishing to have a trial of his new servant's sagacity or expertness, told her those were his horses – she was welcome to the use of them; desiring that when she had done with them, she would enclose them in his stable. Clashnichd then proceeded to make use of the horses, and James Gray returned home to enjoy his night's rest.

Scarce had he reached his armchair and reclined his cheek on his hand to ruminate over the bold adventure of the night, when Clash–nichd entered, with her 'breath in her throat', and venting the bitterest complaints at the unruliness of his horses, which had broken one-half of her furniture, and caused her more trouble in the stabling of them than their services were worth.

'Oh! they are stabled, then?' enquired James Gray. Clashnichd replied in the affirmative. 'Very well,' rejoined James, 'they shall be tame enough tomorrow.'

From this specimen of Clashnichd the ghost of Craig-Aulnaic's expertness, it will be seen what a valuable acquisition her service proved to James Gray and his young family. They were, however, speedily deprived of her assistance by a most unfortunate accident. From the sequel of the story, from which the foregoing is an extract, it appears that poor Clashnichd was deeply addicted to propensities which at that time rendered her kin so obnoxious to their human neighbours. She was constantly in the habit of visiting her friends much oftener than she was invited, and, in the course of such visits, was never very scrupulous in making free with any eatables which fell within the circle of her observation.

One day, while engaged on a foraging expedition of this description, she happened to enter the mill of Delnabo, which was inhabited in those days by the miller's family. She found his wife engaged in roasting a large gridiron of fine savoury fish, the agreeable smell proceeding from which perhaps occasioned her visit. With the usual enquiries after the health of the miller and his family, Clashnichd proceeded with the greatest familiarity and good-humour to make herself comfortable at their expense. But the miller's wife, enraged at the loss of her fish, and not relishing such unwelcome familiarity, punished the unfortunate Clashnichd rather too severely for her freedom. It happened that there was at the time a large cauldron of boiling water suspended over the fire, and this caldron the enraged wife overturned in Clashnichd's bosom!

Scalded beyond recovery, she fled up the wilds of Craig-Aulnaic, uttering the most melancholy lamentations, nor has she been ever heard of since.

Whippety Stourie

There was once a gentleman that lived in a very grand house, and he married a young lady that had been delicately brought up. In her husband's house she found everything that was fine – fine tables and chairs, fine looking-glasses and fine curtains; but then her husband expected her to be able to spin twelve hanks of thread every day, besides attending to her house; and, to tell the even-down truth, the lady could not spin a bit. This made her husband glunchy with her, and, before a month had passed, she found herself very unhappy.

One day the husband went away upon a journey, after telling her that he expected her, before his return, to have not only learned to spin, but to have spun a hundred hanks of thread. Quite downcast, she took a walk along the hillside, till she came to a big flat stone, and there she sat down and wept. By and by she heard a strain of fine music, coming as it were from beneath the stone, and on turning it up, she saw a cave below, where there were sitting six wee ladies in green gowns, each one of them spinning on a little wheel, and singing,

'Little kens my dame at hame
That Whippety Stourie is my name.'

The lady walked into the cave, and was kindly asked by the wee bodies to take a chair and sit down, while they still continued their spinning. She observed that each one's mouth was drawn away to one side, but she didn't venture to enquire the reason. They asked why she looked so unhappy, and she told them that it was because she was expected by her husband to be a good spinner, when the plain truth was that she could not spin at all, and found herself quite unable for it, having been so delicately brought up; neither was there any need for it, as her husband was a rich man.

'Oh, is that all?' said the little wifies, speaking out of their cheeks alike.

'It's quite enough for me!' said the lady, her heart like to burst with distress.

'We could easily quit ye o' that trouble,' said the wee women. 'Just ask us all to dinner for the day when your husband is to come back. We'll then let you see how we'll manage him.'

So the lady asked them all to dine with herself and her husband on the day when he was to come back.

When the goodman came home, he found the house so occupied with preparations for dinner that he had no time to ask his wife about her thread; and, before ever he had once spoken to her on the subject, the company was announced at the hall door. The six ladies all came in a coach-and-six, and were as fine as princesses, but still wore their gowns of green. The gentleman was very polite, and showed them up the stair with a pair of wax candles in his hand. And so they all sat down to dinner, and conversation went on very pleasantly, till at length the husband, becoming familiar with them, said – 'Ladies, if it be not an uncivil question, I should like to know how it happens that all your mouths are turned away to one side?'

'Oh,' said one at once, 'it's with our constant *spin-spin-spinning*.'

'Is that the case?' cried the gentleman; 'then, John, Tam and Dick, fie, go haste and burn every rock and reel and spinning-wheel in the house, for I'll not have my wife to spoil her bonnie face with *spin-spin-spinning*.'

And so the lady lived happily with her goodman all the rest of her days.

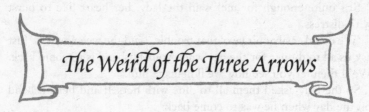

The Weird of the Three Arrows

Sir James Douglas, the companion of Bruce, and well known by his appellation of the 'Black Douglas', was once, during the hottest period of the exterminating war carried on by him and his colleague Randolph against the English, stationed at Linthaughlee, near Jedburgh. He was resting, himself and his men after the toils of many days' fighting-marches through Teviotdale; and, according to his custom, had walked round the tents, previous to retiring to the unquiet rest of a soldier's bed. He stood for a few minutes at the entrance to his tent contemplating the scene before him, rendered more interesting by a clear moon, whose silver beams fell, in the silence of a night without a breath of wind, calmly on the slumbers of mortals destined to mix in the mêlée of dreadful war, perhaps on the morrow. As he stood gazing, irresolute whether to retire to rest or indulge longer in a train of thought not very suitable to a warrior who delighted in the spirit-stirring scenes of his profession, his eye was attracted by the figure of an old woman, who approached him with a trembling step, leaning on a staff, and holding in her left hand three English cloth-shaft arrows.

'You are he who is ca'ed the guid Sir James?' said the old woman.

'I am, good woman,' replied Sir James. 'Why have you wandered from the sutler's camp?'

'I dinna belang to the camp o' the hoblers,' answered the woman. 'I hae been a residenter in Linthaughlee since the day when King Alexander passed the door o' my cottage wi' his bonny French bride, wha was terrified awa' frae Jedburgh by the death's-head whilk appeared to her on the day o' her marriage. What I hae suffered sin' that day' (looking at the arrows in her hand) 'lies between me an' heaven.'

'Some of your sons have been killed in the wars, I presume?' said Sir James.

'Ye hae guessed a pairt o' my waes,' replied the woman. 'That arrow' (holding out one of the three) 'carries on its point the bluid o' my first born; that is stained wi' the stream that poured frae the heart o' my second; and that is red wi' the gore in which my youngest weltered, as he gae up the life that made me childless. They were a' shot by English hands, in different armies, in different battles. I am an honest woman, and wish to return to the English what belongs to the English; but that in the same fashion in which they were sent. The Black Douglas has the strongest arm an' the surest ee in auld Scotland; an' wha can execute my commission better than he?'

'I do not use the bow, good woman,' replied Sir James. 'I love the grasp of the dagger or the battle-axe. You must apply to some other individual to return your arrows.'

'I canna tak' them hame again,' said the woman, laying them down at the feet of Sir James. 'Ye'll see me again on St James's E'en.'

The old woman departed as she said these words.

Sir James took up the arrows, and placed them in an empty quiver that lay among his baggage. He retired to rest, but not to sleep. The figure of the old woman and her strange request occupied his thoughts, and produced trains of meditation which ended in nothing but restlessness and disquietude. Getting up at daybreak, he met a messenger at the entrance of his tent, who informed him that Sir Thomas de Richmont, with a force of ten thousand men, had crossed the Borders, and would pass through a narrow defile, which he mentioned, where he could be attacked with great advantage. Sir James gave instant orders to march to the spot; and, with that genius for scheming, for which he was so remarkable, commanded his men to twist together the young birch trees on either side of the passage to prevent the escape of the enemy. This finished, he concealed his archers in a hollow way, near the gorge of the pass.

The enemy came on; and when their ranks were embarrassed by the narrowness of the road, and it was impossible for the cavalry to act with effect, Sir James rushed upon them at the head of his horsemen; and the archers, suddenly revealing themselves, poured in a flight of arrows on the confused soldiers, and put the whole army to flight. In the heat of the onset, Douglas killed Sir Thomas de Richmont with his dagger.

Not long after this, Edmund de Cailon, a knight of Gascony and Governor of Berwick, who had been heard to vaunt that he had sought the famous Black Knight but could not find him, was returning to England loaded with plunder, the fruit of an inroad on Teviotdale. Sir James thought it a pity that a Gascon's vaunt should be heard unpunished in Scotland, and made long forced marches to satisfy the desire of the foreign knight, by giving him a sight of the dark countenance he had made a subject of reproach. He soon succeeded in gratifying both himself and the Gascon. Coming up in his terrible manner, he called to Cailon to stop, and before he proceeded into England, receive the respects of the Black Knight he had come to find but hitherto had not met. The Gascon's vaunt was now changed; but shame supplied the place of courage, and he ordered his men to receive Douglas's attack. Sir James assiduously sought his enemy. He at last succeeded; and a single combat ensued, of a most desperate character. But who ever escaped the arm of Douglas when fairly opposed to him in single conflict? Cailon was killed; he had met the Black Knight at last.

'So much,' cried Sir James, 'for the vaunt of a Gascon!'

Similar in every respect to the fate of Cailon, was that of Sir Ralph Neville. He, too, on hearing the great fame of Douglas's prowess from some of Cailon's fugitive soldiers, openly boasted that he would fight with the Scottish knight if he would come and show his banner before Berwick. Sir James heard the boast and rejoiced in it. He marched to that town, and caused his men to ravage the country in front of the battlements, and burn the villages. Neville left Berwick with a strong body of men; and, stationing himself on high ground, waited till the rest of the Scots should disperse to plunder; but Douglas called in his detachment and attacked the knight. After a desperate conflict, in which many were slain, Douglas, as was his custom, succeeded in bringing the leader to a personal encounter, and the skill of the Scottish knight was again successful. Neville was slain, and his men utterly discomfited.

Having retired one night to his tent to take some rest after so much pain and toil, Sir James Douglas was surprised by the re-appearance of the old woman whom he had seen at Linthaughlee.

'This is the feast o' St James,' said she, as she approached him. 'I said I would see ye again this nicht, an' I'm as guid's my word. Hae ye returned the arrows I left wi' ye to the English wha sent them to the hearts o' my sons?'

'No,' replied Sir James. 'I told ye I did not fight with the bow. Wherefore do ye importune me thus?'

'Give me back the arrows then,' said the woman.

Sir James went to bring the quiver in which he had placed them. On taking them out, he was surprised to find that they were all broken through the middle.

'How has this happened?' said he. 'I put these arrows in this quiver entire, and now they are broken.'

'The weird is fulfilled!' cried the old woman, laughing eldrichly, and clapping her hands. 'That broken shaft cam' frae a soldier o' Richmont's; that frae ane o' Cailon's, and that frae ane o' Neville's. They are a' dead, an' I am revenged!'

The old woman then departed, scattering as she went the broken fragments of the arrows on the floor of the tent.

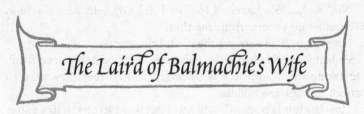

The Laird of Balmachie's Wife

In the olden times, when it was the fashion for gentlemen to wear swords, the Laird of Balmachie went one day to Dundee, leaving his wife at home ill in bed. Riding home in the twilight, he had occasion to leave the high road, and when crossing between some little romantic knolls, called the Cur Hills, in the neighbourhood of Carlungy, he encountered a troop of fairies supporting a kind of litter, upon which some person seemed to be borne. Being a man of dauntless courage, and, as he said, impelled by some internal impulse, he pushed his horse close to the litter, drew his sword, laid it across the vehicle, and in a firm tone exclaimed, 'In the name of God, release your captive.'

The tiny troop immediately disappeared, dropping the litter on the ground. The laird dismounted, and found that it contained his own wife, dressed in her nightclothes. Wrapping his coat around her, he placed her on the horse before him, and, having only a short distance to ride, arrived safely at home.

Placing her in another room, under the care of an attentive friend, he immediately went to the chamber where he had left his wife in the morning, and there to all appearance she still lay, very sick of a fever. She was fretful, discontented, and complained much of having been neglected in his absence, at all of which the laird affected great concern, and pretending much sympathy, insisted upon her rising to have her bed made. She said that she was unable to rise, but her husband was peremptory, and having ordered a large wood fire to warm the room, he lifted the impostor from the bed, and bearing her across the floor as if to a chair, which had been previously prepared, he threw her on the fire, from which she bounced like a skyrocket, and went through the ceiling, and out at the roof of the house, leaving a hole among the slates. He then brought in his own wife, a little recovered from her alarm, who said that sometime after sunset, the nurse having left her for the purpose of preparing a little caudle, a multitude of elves came in at the window, thronging like bees from a hive. They filled the room, and having lifted her from the bed carried her through the window, after which she recollected nothing further, till she saw her husband standing over her on the Cur Hills, at the back of Carlungy. The hole in the roof, by which the female fairy made her escape, was mended, but could never be kept in repair: a tempest of wind happened always once a year, which uncovered that particular spot, without injuring any other part of the roof.

The Minister and the Fairy

Not long since, a pious clergyman was returning home, after administering spiritual consolation to a dying member of his flock. It was late of the night, and he had to pass through a good deal of *uncanny* land. He was, however, a good and a conscientious minister of the Gospel, and feared not all the spirits in the country. On his reaching the end of a lake which stretched along the roadside for some distance, he was a good deal surprised at hearing the most melodious strains of music. Overcome by pleasure and curiosity, the minister coolly sat down to listen to the harmonious sounds, and try what new discoveries he could make with regard to their nature and source. He had not sat many minutes before he could distinguish the approach of the music, and also observe a light in the direction from whence it proceeded gliding across the lake towards him. Instead of taking to his heels, as any faithless wight would have done, the pastor fearlessly determined to await the issue of the phenomenon. As the light and music drew near, the clergyman could at length distinguish an object resembling a human being walking on the surface of the water, attended by a group of diminutive musicians, some of them bearing lights, and others instruments of music, from which they continued to evoke those melodious strains which first attracted his attention. The leader of the band dismissed his attendants, landed on the beach, and afforded the minister the amplest opportunities of examining his appearance. He was a little primitive-looking grey-headed man, clad in the most grotesque habit the clergyman had ever seen, and such as led him at once to suspect his real character. He walked up to the minister, whom he saluted with great grace, offering an apology for his intrusion. The pastor returned his compliments, and, without hesitation, invited the mysterious stranger to sit down by his side. The invitation was complied with, upon which the minister proposed the following question: 'Who are you, stranger, and from whence?'

To this question the fairy, with downcast eye, replied that he was one of those sometimes called Doane Shee, or men of peace, or good men, though the reverse of this title was a more fit appellation for them. Originally angelic in his nature and attributes, and once a sharer of the indescribable joys of the regions of light, he was seduced by Satan to join him in his mad conspiracies; and, as a punishment for his transgression, he was cast down from those regions of bliss, and was now doomed, along with millions of fellow-sufferers, to wander through seas and mountains, until the coming of the Great Day. What their fate would be then they could not divine, but they apprehended the worst. 'And,' continued he, turning to the minister, with great anxiety, 'the object of my present intrusion on you is to learn your opinion, as an eminent divine, as to our final condition on that dreadful day.'

Here the venerable pastor entered upon a long conversation with the fairy, touching the principles of faith and repentance. Receiving rather unsatisfactory answers to his questions, the minister desired the 'sheech' to repeat after him the Paternoster, in attempting to do which, it was not a little remarkable that he could not repeat the word 'art' but said '*wert*' in heaven. Inferring from every circumstance that their fate was extremely precarious, the minister resolved not to puff the fairies up with presumptuous and perhaps groundless expectations. Accordingly, addressing himself to the unhappy fairy, who was all anxiety to know the nature of his sentiments, the reverend gentleman told him that he could not take it upon him to give them any hopes of pardon, as their crime was of so deep a hue as scarcely to admit of it. On this the unhappy fairy uttered a shriek of despair, plunged headlong into the loch, and the minister resumed his course to his home.

The Fisherman and the Merman

Of mermen and merwomen many strange stories are told in the Shetland Isles. Beneath the depths of the ocean, according to these stories, an atmosphere exists adapted to the respiratory organs of certain beings, resembling, in form, the human race, possessed of surpassing beauty, of limited supernatural powers and liable to the incident of death. They dwell in a wide territory of the globe, far below the region of fishes, over which the sea, like the cloudy canopy of our sky, loftily rolls, and they possess habitations constructed of the pearl and coral productions of the ocean. Having lungs not adapted to a watery medium, but to the nature of atmospheric air, it would be impossible for them to pass through the volume of waters that intervenes between the submarine and supramarine world, if it were not for the extraordinary power they inherit of entering the skin of some animal capable of existing in the sea, which they are enabled to occupy by a sort of demoniacal possession. One shape they put on is that of an animal human above the waist yet terminating below in the tail and fins of a fish, but the most favourite form is that of the larger seal or haaf-fish, for, in possessing an amphibious nature, they are enabled not only to exist in the ocean but to land on some rock, where they frequently lighten themselves of their sea-dress, resume their proper shape, and with much curiosity examine the nature of the upper world belonging to the human race. Unfortunately, however, each merman or merwoman possesses but one skin, enabling the individual to ascend the seas, and if, on visiting the abode of man, the garb be lost, the hapless being must unavoidably become an inhabitant of the earth.

A story is told of a boat's crew who landed for the purpose of attacking the seals lying in the hollows of the crags at one of the stacks. The men stunned a number of the animals, and while they were in this state stripped them of their skins, with the fat attached to them. Leaving the carcasses on the rock, the crew were about to set off for the shore of Papa Stour, when such a tremendous swell arose that everyone flew quickly to the boat. All succeeded in entering it except one man, who had imprudently lingered behind. The crew were unwilling to leave a companion to perish on the skerries, but the surge increased so fast that after many unsuccessful attempts to bring the boat close in to the stack the unfortunate wight was left to his fate. A stormy night came on, and the deserted Shetlander saw no prospect before him but that of perishing from cold and hunger, or of being washed into the sea by the breakers which threatened to dash over the rocks. At length, he perceived many of the seals, who in their flight had escaped the attack of the boatmen, approach the skerry, disrobe themselves of their amphibious hides, and resume the shape of the sons and daughters of the ocean. Their first object was to assist in the recovery of their friends, who having been stunned by clubs, had, while in that state, been deprived of their skins. When the flayed animals had regained their sensibility, they assumed their proper form of mermen or merwomen, and began to lament in a mournful lay, wildly accompanied by the storm that was raging around, the loss of their seadress, which would prevent them from again enjoying their native azure atmosphere and the coral mansions that lay below the deep waters of the Atlantic. But their chief lamentation was for Ollavitinus, the son of Gioga, who, having been stripped of his seal's skin, would be for ever parted from his mates, and condemned to become an outcast inhabitant of the upper world. Their song was at length broken off at the sight of one of their enemies viewing, with shivering limbs and looks of comfortless despair, the wild waves that dashed over the stack. Gioga immediately conceived the idea of turning to the advantage of the son the perilous situation of the man.

She addressed him with mildness, proposing to carry him safe on her back across the sea to Papa Stour, on condition of receiving the seal-skin of Ollavitinus. A bargain was struck, and Gioga clad herself in her amphibious garb; but the Shetlander, alarmed at the sight of the stormy main that he was to ride through, prudently begged leave of the matron, for his better preservation, that he might be allowed to cut a few holes in her shoulders and flanks, in order to procure, between the skin and the flesh, a better fastening for his hands and feet. The request being complied with, the man grasped the neck of

the seal, and committing himself to her care, found himself landed
safely at Acres Gio in Papa Stour; from which place he immediately
repaired to a skeo at Hamna Voe, where the skin was deposited, and
honourably fulfilled his part of the contract by affording Gioga the
means whereby her son could again revisit the ethereal space over
which the sea spread its green mantle.

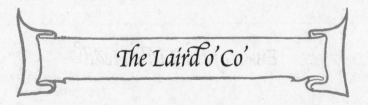

The Laird o' Co'

In the days of yore, the proprietors of Colzean, in Ayrshire (ancestors of the Marquis of Ailsa), were known in that country by the title of Lairds o' Co', a name bestowed on Colzean from some co's (or coves) in the rock beneath the castle.

One morning, a very little boy, carrying a small wooden can, addressed the laird near the castle gate, begging for a little ale for his mother, who was sick. The laird directed him to go to the butler and get his can filled; so away he went as ordered. The butler had a barrel of ale on tap, still about half full, out of which he proceeded to fill the boy's can; but to his extreme surprise he emptied the cask, and still the little can was not nearly full. The butler was unwilling to broach another barrel, but the little fellow insisted on the fulfilment of the laird's order, and reference was made to the laird by the butler, who stated the miraculous capacity of the tiny can, and received instant orders to fill it if it took all the ale in the cellar. Obedient to this command, he broached another cask, but had scarcely drawn a drop when the can was full, and the boy, who was in reality a dwarf, departed with expressions of gratitude.

Some years afterwards the laird being at the wars in Flanders was taken prisoner, and for some reason or other (probably as a spy) condemned to die a felon's death. The night prior to the day for his execution, he was confined in a dungeon which was strongly barricaded. Suddenly the doors flew open, and the dwarf reappeared, saying: 'Laird o' Co', rise an' go!' a summons too welcome to require repetition.

On their emerging from prison, the boy caused him to mount on his shoulders, and in a short time set him down at his own gate, on the very spot where they had formerly met, saying – 'Ae gude turn deserves anither – Take ye that for being sae kind to my auld mither,' and vanished.

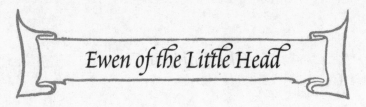

Ewen of the Little Head

About three hundred years ago, Ewen Maclaine of Lochbuy, on the Island of Mull, having been engaged in a quarrel with a neighbouring chief, fixed a day for determining the affair by the sword. Lochbuy, before the day arrived, consulted a celebrated witch as to the result of the feud. The witch declared that if Lochbuy's wife should on the morning of that day give him and his men food unasked, he would be victorious, but if not, the result would be the reverse. This was a disheartening response for the unhappy votary, his wife being a noted shrew.

The fatal morning arrived, and the hour for meeting the enemy approached, but there appeared no symptoms of refreshment for Lochbuy and his men. At length the unfortunate man was compelled to ask his wife to supply them with food. She set down before them curds, but without spoons. When the husband enquired how they were to eat them, she replied they should assume the bills of hens. The men ate the curds, as well as they could, with their hands; but Lochbuy himself ate none. After behaving with the greatest bravery in the bloody conflict which ensued, he fell, covered with wounds, leaving his wife to the execration of the people. She is still known in that district under the appellation of Corr-dhu, or the Black Crane.

But the miseries brought on the luckless Lochbuy by his wife did not end with his life, for he died fasting, and his ghost is frequently seen to this day riding the very horse on which he was mounted when he was killed. It was a small, but very neat and active pony, dun or mouse-coloured, to which the laird was much attached, and on which he had ridden for many years before his death. Its appearance is as accurately described on the Island of Mull as any steed is at Newmarket. The prints of its shoes are discerned by connoisseurs, and the rattling of its curb is recognised on the darkest night. It is not particular with regard to roads, for it goes up hill and down dale with equal velocity. Its hard-fated rider still wears the same green cloak which covered him in his last battle; and he is particularly distinguished by the small size of his head, a peculiarity which, we suspect, the learned disciples of Spurzheim have never yet had the sagacity to discover is indicative of an extraordinary talent and incomparable perseverance in horsemanship.

It is now above three hundred years since Ewen-a-chin-vig, aka Hugh of the Little Head, fell in the field of honour; but neither the vigour of the horse nor of the rider is yet diminished. His mournful duty has always been to attend the dying moments of every member of his own tribe, and to escort the departed spirit on its long and arduous journey. He has been seen in the remotest of the Hebrides; and he has found his way to Ireland on these occasions long before steam navigation was invented. About a century ago he took a fancy for a young man of his own race, and frequently did him the honour of placing him behind himself on horseback. He entered into conversation with him, and foretold many circumstances connected with the fate of his successors which have undoubtedly since come to pass.

Many a long winter night have I listened to the feats of Ewen-a-chin-vig, the faithful and indefatigable guardian of his ancient family in the hour of their last and greatest trial, affording an example worthy the imitation of every chief – perhaps not beneath the notice of Glengarry himself.

About a dozen years since some symptoms of Ewen's decay gave very general alarm to his friends. He accosted one of his own people (indeed he never has been known to notice any other), and shaking him cordially by the hand, he attempted to place him on the saddle behind him; but the uncourteous dog declined the honour. Ewen struggled hard, but the clown was a great, strong, clumsy fellow, and stuck to the earth with all his might. He candidly acknowledged, however, that his chief would have prevailed had it not been for a birch tree which stood by and which he got within the fold of his left arm. The contest became very warm indeed, and the tree was certainly twisted like an osier, as thousands can testify who saw it as well as myself. At length, however, Ewen lost his seat for the first time, and the instant the pony found he was his own master, he set off with the fleetness of lightning. Ewen immediately pursued his steed, and the wearied rustic sped his way homeward. It was the

general opinion that Ewen found considerable difficulty in catching
the horse; but I am happy to learn that he has been lately seen riding
the old mouse-coloured pony without the least change in either the
horse or the rider. Long may he continue to do so!

Those who from motives of piety or curiosity have visited the
sacred Island of Iona must remember to have seen the guide point
out the tomb of Ewen, with his figure on horseback, very elegantly
sculptured in *alto-relievo*, and many of the above facts are on such
occasions related.

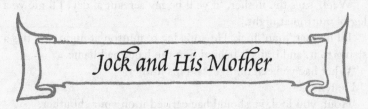

Jock and His Mother

Ye see, there was a wife had a son, and they called him Jock; and she said to him, 'You are a lazy fellow; ye maun gang awa' and do something for to help me.'

'Weel,' says Jock, 'I'll do that.'

So awa' he gangs, and fa's in wi' a packman.

Says the packman, 'If you carry my pack a' day, I'll gie you a needle at night.'

So he carried the pack, and got the needle; and as he was gaun awa' hame to his mither, he cuts a burden o' brackens, and put the needle into the heart o' them. Awa' he gaes hame.

Says his mither, 'What hae ye made o' yoursel' the day?'

Says Jock, 'I fell in wi' a packman, and carried his pack a' day, and he gae me a needle for't, and ye may look for it amang the brackens.'

'Hout,' quo' she, 'ye daft gowk, you should hae stuck it into your bonnet, man.'

'I'll mind that again,' quo' Jock.

Next day he fell in wi' a man carrying plough socks.

'If ye help me to carry my socks a' day, I'll gie ye ane to yersel' at night.'

'I'll do that,' quo' Jock. Jock carried them a' day, and got a sock, which he stuck in his bonnet. On the way hame, Jock was dry, and gaed away to take a drink out o' the burn; and wi' the weight o' the sock, his bonnet fell into the river, and gaed out o' sight.

He gaed hame, and his mither says, 'Weel, Jock, what hae you been doing a' day?'

And then he tells her.

'Hout,' quo' she, 'you should hae tied the string to it, and trailed it behind you.'

'Weel,' quo' Jock, 'I'll mind that again.'

Awa' he sets, and he fa's in wi' a flesher.

'Weel,' says the flesher, 'if ye'll be my servant a' day, I'll gie ye a leg o' mutton at night.'

'I'll be that,' quo' Jock. He got a leg o' mutton at night. He ties a string to it, and trails it behind him the hale road hame.

'What hae ye been doing?' said his mither.

He tells her.

'Hout, you fool, ye should hae carried it on your shouther.'

'I'll mind that again,' quo' Jock.

Awa' he gaes next day, and meets a horse-dealer. He says, 'If you will help me wi' my horses a' day, I'll give you ane to yoursel' at night.'

'I'll do that,' quo' Jock.

So he served him, and got his horse, and he ties its feet; but as he was not able to carry it on his back, he left it lying on the roadside. Hame he comes, and tells his mither.

'Hout, ye daft gowk, ye'll ne'er turn wise! Could ye no hae loupen on it, and ridden it?'

'I'll mind that again,' quo' Jock.

Aweel, there was a grand gentleman, wha had a daughter wha was very subject to melancholy; and her father gae out that whaever should mak' her laugh would get her in marriage.

So it happened that she was sitting at the window ae day, musing in her melancholy state, when Jock, according to the advice o' his mither, cam' flying up on a cow's back, wi' the tail over his shouther. And she burst out into a fit o' laughter.

When they made enquiry wha made her laugh, it was found to be Jock riding on the cow. Accordingly, Jock was sent for to get his bride. Weel, Jock was married to her, and there was a great supper prepared. Amongst the rest o' the things, there was some honey, which Jock was very fond o'.

After supper, they all retired, and the auld priest that married them sat up a' night by the kitchen fireside. So Jock waukens in the night-time, and says, 'Oh, wad ye gie me some o' yon nice sweet honey that we got to our supper last night?'

'Oh ay,' says his wife, 'rise and gang into the press, and ye'll find a pig fou o't.'

Jock rose, and thrust his hand into the honey-pig for a nievefu' o't, and he could not get it out.

So he cam' awa' wi' the pig in his hand, like a mason's mell, and says, 'Oh, I canna get my hand out.'

'Hoot,' quo' she, 'gang awa' and break it on the cheek-stane.'

By this time, the fire was dark, and the auld priest was lying snoring wi' his head against the chimney-piece, wi' a huge white wig on.

Jock gaes awa', and gae him a whack wi' the honey-pig on the head, thinking it was the cheek-stane, and knocks it a' in bits.

The auld priest roars out, 'Murder!'

Jock tak's doun the stair as hard as he could bicker, and hides himsel' amang the bees' skeps.

That night, as luck wad have it, some thieves cam' to steal the bees' skeps, and in the hurry o' tumbling them into a large grey plaid, they tumbled Jock in alang wi' them. So aff they set, wi' Jock and the skeps on their backs.

On the way, they had to cross the burn where Jock lost his bonnet. Ane o' the thieves cries, 'Oh, I hae fand a bonnet!' and Jock, on hearing that, cries out, 'Oh, that's mine!'

They thocht they had got the deil on their backs. So they let a' fa' in the burn; and Jock, being tied in the plaid, couldna get out; so he and the bees were a' drowned thegither.

If a' tales be true, that's nae lee.

St Columba

Soon after St Columba established his residence in Iona, tradition says that he paid a visit to a great seminary of Druids, then in the vicinity, at a place called Camusnan Ceul, or Bay of Cells, in the district of Ardnamurchan. Several remains of Druidical circles are still to be seen there, and on that bay and in the neighbourhood many places are still named after their rites and ceremonies, such as Ardintibert, the Mount of Sacrifice, and others. The fame of the saint had been for some time well known to the people, and his intention of instructing them in the doctrines of Christianity was announced to them. The ancient priesthood made every exertion to dissuade the inhabitants from hearing the powerful eloquence of Columba, and in this they were seconded by the principal man then in that country whose name was Donald, a son of Connal.

The saint had no sooner made his appearance, however, than he was surrounded by a vast multitude, anxious to hear so celebrated a preacher; and after the sermon was ended, many persons expressed a desire to be baptised, in spite of the remonstrances of the Druids. Columba had made choice of an eminence centrally situated for performing worship; but there was no water near the spot, and the son of Connal threatened with punishment any who should dare to procure it for his purpose. The saint stood with his back leaning on a rock; after a short prayer, he struck the rock with his foot, and a stream of water issued forth in great abundance. The miracle had a powerful effect on the minds of his hearers, and many became converts to the new religion. This fountain is still distinguished by the name of Columba, and is considered of superior efficacy in the cure of diseases. When the Catholic form of worship prevailed in that country it was greatly resorted to, and old persons yet remember to have seen offerings left at the fountain in gratitude for benefits received from the benignant influence of the saint's blessing on the water. At length it is said that a daughter of Donald, the son of

Connal, expressed a wish to be baptised, and the father restrained her by violence. He also, with the aid of the Druids, forced Columba to take refuge in his boat, and the holy man departed for Iona, after warning the inhospitable Caledonian to prepare for another world, as his life would soon terminate.

The saint was at sea during the whole night, which was stormy; and when the boat was approaching the shores of his own sacred island the following morning, a vast number of ravens were observed flying overhead, chasing another of extraordinary large size. The croaking of the ravens awoke the saint, who had been sleeping, and he instantly exclaimed that the son of Connal had just expired, which was afterwards ascertained to be true.

A very large Christian establishment appears to have been afterwards formed in the Bay of Cells; and the remains of a chapel, dedicated to St Kiaran, are still to be seen there. It is the favourite place of interment among the Catholics to this day. Indeed, Columba and many of his successors seem to have adopted the policy of engrafting their institutions on those which had formerly existed in the country. Of this there are innumerable instances, at least we observe the ruins of both still visible in many places; even in Iona we find the burying-ground of the Druids known at the present day. This practice may have had advantages at the time, but it must have been ultimately productive of many corruptions; and, in a great measure, accounts for many superstitious and absurd customs which prevailed among that people to a very recent period, and which are not yet entirely extinct. In a very ancient family in that country two round balls of coarse glass have been carefully preserved from time immemorial, and to these have been ascribed many virtues – among others, the cure of any extraordinary disease among cattle. The balls were immersed in cold water for three days and nights, and the water was afterwards sprinkled over all the cattle; this was expected to cure those affected, and to prevent the disease in the rest. From the names and appearance of these balls, there is no doubt that they had been symbols used by the Archdruids.

Within a short distance of the Bay of Cells there is a cave very remarkable in its appearance, and still more so from the purposes to which it has been appropriated. St Columba, on one of his many voyages among the Hebrides, was benighted on this rocky coast, and the mariners were alarmed for their own safety. The saint assured them that neither he nor his crew would ever be drowned. They unexpectedly discovered a light at no great distance, and to that they directed their course. Columba's boat consisted of a frame of osiers, which was covered with hides of leather, and it was received into a very narrow creek close to this cave. After returning thanks for their escape, the saint and his people had great difficulty in climbing up to the cave, which is elevated considerably above the sea. They at length got sight of the fire which had first attracted their attention. Several persons sat around it, and their appearance was not much calculated to please the holy man. Their aspects were fierce, and they had on the fire some flesh roasting over the coals. The saint gave them his benediction; and he was invited to sit down among them and to share their hurried repast, with which he gladly complied. They were freebooters, who lived by plunder and robbery, and this Columba soon discovered. He advised them to forsake that course, and to be converted to his doctrines, to which they all assented, and in the morning they accompanied the saint on his voyage homeward. This circumstance created a high veneration for the cave among the disciples and successors of Columba, and that veneration still continues, in some degree. In one side of it there was a cleft in the rock where lay the water with which the freebooters had been baptised; and this was afterwards formed by art into a basin, which is supplied with water by drops from the roof of the cave. It is alleged never to be empty or to overflow, and the most salubrious qualities are ascribed to it. To obtain the benefit of it, however, the votaries must undergo a very severe ordeal. They must be in the cave before daylight; they must stand on the spot where the saint first landed his boat, and nine waves must dash over their heads; they must afterwards pass through nine openings in the walls of the cave; and, lastly, they must swallow nine mouthfuls out of the holy basin. After invoking the aid of the saint, the votaries within three weeks are either relieved by death or by recovery. Offerings are left in a certain place appropriated for that purpose; and these are sometimes of considerable value, nor are they ever abstracted. Strangers are always informed that a young man, who had wantonly taken away some of these not many years since, broke his leg before he got home, and this affords the property of the saint ample protection.

The Fiddler and the Bogle of Bogandoran

Late one night, as my grand-uncle, Lachlan Dhu Macpherson, who was well known as the best fiddler of his day, was returning home from a ball, at which he had acted as a musician, he had occasion to pass through the once-haunted Bog of Torrans. Now, it happened at that time that the bog was frequented by a huge bogle or ghost, who was of a most mischievous disposition, and took particular pleasure in abusing every traveller who had occasion to pass through the place betwixt the twilight at night and the cock crowing in the morning. Suspecting much that he would also come in for a share of his abuse, my grand-uncle made up his mind, in the course of his progress, to return the ghost any 'civilities' which he might think meet to offer him. On arriving on the spot, he found his suspicions were only too well grounded, for whom did he see but the ghost of Bogandoran apparently ready waiting for him, and seeming by his ghastly grin not a little overjoyed at the meeting. Marching up to my grand-uncle, the bogle clapped a huge club into his hand, and furnishing himself with one of the same dimensions, he spat into his own hand and deliberately commenced the combat. My grand-uncle returned the salute with equal spirit, and so ably did both parties ply their batons that for a while the issue of the combat was extremely doubtful. At length, however, the fiddler could easily see that his opponent's vigour was much in the flagging order. Picking up renewed courage in consequence, he plied the ghost with renewed force, and after a stout resistance, in the course of which both parties were seriously handled, the ghost of Bogandoran thought it prudent to give up the night.

At the same time, filled no doubt with great indignation at this signal defeat, it seems the ghost resolved to re-engage my grand-uncle on some other occasion, under more favourable circumstances. Not long after, as my grand-uncle was returning home quite unattended from another ball in the Braes of the country, he had just

entered the hollow of Auldichoish, well known for its 'eerie' pro-
perties, when, lo! who presented himself to his view on the adjacent
eminence but his old friend of Bogandoran, advancing as large as
the gable of a house, and putting himself in the most threatening
and fighting attitudes.

Looking at the very dangerous nature of the ground where they
had met, and feeling no inclination for a second encounter with a
combatant of his weight, in a situation so little desirable, the fiddler
would have willingly deferred the settlement of their differences till
a more convenient season. He, accordingly, assuming the most sub-
missive aspect in the world, endeavoured to pass by his champion
in peace, but in vain. Longing, no doubt, to retrieve the disgrace of
his late discomfiture, the bogle instantly seized the fiddler, and
attempted with all his might to pull the latter down the precipice,
with the diabolical intention, it is supposed, of drowning him in
the River Avon below. In this pious design the bogle was happily
frustrated by the intervention of some trees which grew on the
precipice, and to which my unhappy grand-uncle clung with the zeal
of a drowning man. The enraged ghost, finding it impossible to
extricate him from those friendly trees, and resolving, at all events,
to be revenged upon him, fell upon maltreating the fiddler with his
hands and feet in the most inhuman manner.

Such gross indignities my worthy grand-uncle was not accustomed
to, and being incensed beyond all measure at the liberties taken by
Bogandoran, he resolved again to try his mettle, whether life or
death should be the consequence. Having no other weapon where-
with to defend himself but his dagger, which, considering the nature
of his opponent's constitution, he suspected would be of little avail
to him – as I say, in the absence of any other weapon, he sheathed
the dagger three times in the ghost of Bogandoran's body. And what
was the consequence? Why, to the great astonishment of my
courageous forefather, the ghost fell down cold dead at his feet, and
was never more seen or heard of.

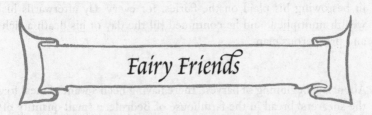

Fairy Friends

It is a good thing to befriend the fairies, as the following stories show: There have been from time immemorial at Hawick, during the two or three last weeks of the year, markets once a week, for the disposal of sheep for slaughter, at which the greater number of people, both in the middle and poorer classes of life, have been accustomed to provide themselves with their mutton. A poor man from Jedburgh who was on his way to Hawick for the purpose of attending one of these markets, as he was passing over that side of Rubislaw which is nearest the Teviot, was suddenly alarmed by a frightful and unaccountable noise. The sound, as he supposed, proceeded from an immense number of female voices, but no signs of whence it could come were visible. Amidst howling and wailing were mixed shouts of mirth and jollity, but he could gather nothing articulate except the following words: 'O there's a bairn born, but there's naething to pit on 't.'

The occasion of this elfish concert, it seemed, was the birth of a fairy child, at which the fairies, with the exception of two or three who were discomposed at having nothing to cover the little innocent with, were enjoying themselves with that joviality usually character-istic of such an event. The astonished rustic finding himself among a host of invisible beings, in a wild moorland place, and far from any human assistance, should assistance be required, full of the greatest consternation, immediately on hearing this expression again and again vociferated, stripped off his plaid and threw it on the ground. It was instantly snatched up by an invisible hand, and the wailings immediately ceased, but the shouts of mirth were continued with increased vigour. Being of opinion that what he had done had satisfied his invisible friends, he lost no time in making off, and proceeded on his road to Hawick, musing on his singular adventure. He purchased a sheep, which turned out a remarkably good bargain, and returned to Jedburgh. He had no cause to regret his generosity in bestowing his plaid on the fairies, for every day afterwards his wealth multiplied, and he continued till the day of his death a rich and prosperous man.

*　　*　　*

About the beginning of harvest, there having been a want of meal for the shearers' bread in the farmhouse of Bedrule, a small quantity of barley (being all that was yet ripe) was cut down and converted into meal. Mrs Buckham, the farmer's wife, rose early in the morning to bake the bread, and while she was engaged in baking, a little woman in green costume came in, and with much politeness, asked for a loan of a capful of meal. Mrs Buckham thought it prudent to comply with her request. A short time afterwards the woman in green returned with an equal quantity of meal, which Mrs Buckham put into the meal-bin. This meal had such a lasting quality that from it alone the goodwife of Bedrule baked as much bread as served her own family and the reapers throughout the harvest, and when harvest was over it was not exhausted.

The Fairies of Merlin's Craig

Early in the seventeenth century, John Smith, a barn-man at a farm, was sent by his master to cast divots on the green immediately behind Merlin's Craig. After having laboured for a considerable time, there came round from the front of the rock a little woman, about eighteen inches in height, clad in a green gown and red stockings, with long yellow hair hanging down to her waist, who asked the astonished operator how he would feel were she to send her husband to uncover his house, at the same time commanding him to place every divot he had cast back where he found it. John obeyed with fear and trembling, and, returning to his master, told what had happened. The farmer laughed at his credulity, and anxious to cure him of such idle superstition, ordered him to take a cart and fetch home the divots immediately.

John obeyed, although with much reluctance. Nothing happened to him in consequence till that day twelve months, when he left his master's work at the usual hour in the evening, with a small jug of milk in his hand, but he did not reach home, nor was he ever heard of for years (I have forgotten how many), when, upon the anniversary of that unfortunate day, John walked into his house at the usual hour, with the milk-jug in his hand.

The account that he gave of his captivity was that, on the evening of that eventful day, returning home from his labour, when passing Merlin's Craig, he felt himself suddenly taken ill and sat down to rest a little. Soon after he fell asleep, and awoke, as he supposed, about midnight, to find a troop of male and female fairies dancing round him. They insisted upon his joining in the sport, and gave him the finest girl in the company as a partner. She took him by the hand; they danced three times round in a fairy ring, after which he became so happy that he felt no inclination to leave his new associates. Their amusements were protracted till he heard his master's cock crow, when the whole troop immediately rushed forward to the front of the craig, hurrying him along with them. A door opened to receive them, and he continued a prisoner until the evening on which he returned, when the same woman who had first appeared to him when he was casting divots came and told him that the grass was again green on the roof of her house, which he had uncovered, and if he would swear an oath, which she dictated, never to reveal what he had seen in fairyland, he should be at liberty to return to his family.

John took the oath, and observed it most religiously, although sadly teased and questioned by his helpmate, particularly about the 'bonnie lassie' with whom he danced on the night of his departure. He was also observed to walk a mile out of his way rather than pass Merlin's Craig when the sun was below the horizon.

On a subsequent occasion the tiny inhabitants of Merlin's Craig surprised a shepherd who was watching his fold at night; he was asleep, and his bonnet had fallen off and rolled to some little distance. He was awakened by the fairies dancing round him in a circle, and was induced to join them; but, recollecting the fate of John Smith, he would not allow his female companion to take hold of his hands. In the midst of their gambols they came close to the hillock where the shepherd's bonnet lay; thereupon, he affected to stumble and fell upon his bonnet, which he immediately seized, clapping it on his head and causing the whole troop to vanish instantly. This exorcism was produced by the talismanic power of a Catechism, containing the Lord's Prayer and the Apostles' Creed, which the shepherd most fortunately recollected was deposited in the crown of his bonnet.

The Haunted Ships

Though my mind's not
Hoodwinked with rustic marvels, I do think
There are more things in the grove, the air, the flood,
Yea, and the charnelled earth, than what a wise man,
Who walks so proud as if his form alone
Filled the wide temple of the universe,
Will let a frail mind say. I'd write i' the creed
O' the sagest head alive, that fearful forms,
Holy or reprobate, do page men's heels;
That shapes, too horrid for our gaze, stand o'er
The murderer's dust, and for revenge glare up,
Even till the stars weep fire for very pity.

Along the sea of Solway – romantic on the Scottish side, with its woodland, its bays, its cliffs and headlands; and interesting on the English side, with its many beautiful towns with their shadows on the water, rich pastures, safe harbours and numerous ships – there still linger many traditional stories of a maritime nature, most of them connected with superstitions singularly wild and unusual. To the curious these tales afford a rich fund of entertainment, from the many diversities of the same story; some dry and barren and stripped of all the embellishments of poetry; others dressed out in all the riches of a superstitious belief and haunted imagination. In this they resemble the inland traditions of the peasants; but many of the oral treasures of the Galwegian or the Cumbrian coast have the stamp of the Dane and the Norseman upon them, and claim but a remote or faint affinity with the legitimate legends of Caledonia. Something like a rude prosaic outline of several of the most noted of the northern ballads, the adventures and depredations of the old ocean kings, still lends life to the evening tale; and, among others, the story of the Haunted Ships is still popular among the maritime peasantry.

One fine harvest evening I went on board the shallop of Richard Faulder of Allanbay, and, committing ourselves to the waters, we allowed a gentle wind from the east to waft us at its pleasure towards the Scottish coast. We passed the sharp promontory of Siddick, and, skirting the land within a stonecast, glided along the shore till we came within sight of the ruined Abbey of Sweetheart. The green mountain of Criffel ascended beside us; and the bleat of the flocks from its summit, together with the winding of the evening horn of the reapers, came softened into something like music over land and sea. We pushed our shallop into a deep and wooded bay, and sat silently looking on the serene beauty of the place. The moon glimmered in her rising through the tall shafts of the pines of Caerlaverock; and the sky, with scarce a cloud, showered down on wood and headland and bay the twinkling beams of a thousand stars, rendering every object visible. The tide, too, was coming in with that swift and silent swell observable when the wind is gentle; the woody curves along the land were filling with the flood, till it touched the green branches of the drooping trees; while in the centre current the roll and the plunge of a thousand pellocks told to the experienced fisherman that salmon were abundant.

As we looked, we saw an old man emerging from a path that wound to the shore through a grove of doddered hazel; he carried a halve-net on his back, while behind him came a girl, bearing a small harpoon, with which the fishers are remarkably dexterous in striking their prey. The senior seated himself on a large grey stone which overlooked the bay, laid aside his bonnet, and submitted his bosom and neck to the refreshing sea breeze, and, taking his harpoon from his attendant, sat with the gravity and composure of a spirit of the flood, with his ministering nymph behind him. We pushed our shallop to the shore and soon stood at their side.

'This is old Mark Macmoran the mariner, with his granddaughter Barbara,' said Richard Faulder, in a whisper that had something of fear in it; 'he knows every creek and cavern and quicksand in Solway; has seen the Spectre Hound that haunts the Isle of Man; has heard him bark, and at every bark has seen a ship sink; and he has seen, too, the Haunted Ships in full sail; and, if all tales be true, he has sailed in them himself – he's an awful person.'

Though I perceived in the communication of my friend something of the superstition of the sailor, I could not help thinking that common rumour had made a happy choice in singling out old Mark to maintain its intercourse with the invisible world. His hair, which seemed to have refused all intercourse with the comb, hung matted upon his shoulders; a kind of mantle, or rather blanket, pinned with a wooden skewer round his neck, fell mid-leg down, concealing all his nether garments as far as a pair of hose, darned with yarn of all conceivable colours, and a pair of shoes, patched and repaired till nothing of the original structure remained and clasped on his feet with two massy silver buckles. If the dress of the old man was rude and sordid, that of his granddaughter was gay, and even rich. She wore a bodice of fine wool, wrought round the bosom with alternate leaf and lily, and a kirtle of the same fabric, which, almost touching her white and delicate ankle, showed her snowy feet, so fairy-light and round that they scarcely seemed to touch the grass where she stood. Her hair, a natural ornament which woman seeks much to improve, was of bright glossy brown, and encumbered rather than adorned with a snood, set thick with marine productions, among which the small clear pearl found in the Solway was conspicuous. Nature had not trusted to a handsome shape and a sylphlike air for young Barbara's influence over the heart of man, but had bestowed a pair of large bright blue eyes, swimming in liquid light, so full of love and gentleness and joy that all the sailors from Annanwater to far St Bees acknowledged their power, and sang songs about the bonnie lass of Mark Macmoran. She stood holding a small gaff-hook of polished steel in her hand, and seemed not dissatisfied with the glances I bestowed on her from time to time, and which I held more than requited by a single glance of those eyes which retained so many capricious hearts in subjection.

The tide, though rapidly augmenting, had not yet filled the bay at our feet. The moon now streamed fairly over the tops of Caerlaverock pines and showed the expanse of ocean dimpling and swelling, on which sloops and shallops came dancing and displaying at every turn their extent of white sail against the beam of the moon. I looked on old Mark the mariner, who, seated motionless on his grey stone, kept his eye fixed on the increasing waters with a look of seriousness and sorrow, in which I saw little of the calculating spirit of a mere fisherman. Though he looked on the coming tide, his eyes seemed to dwell particularly on the black and decayed hulls of two vessels, which, half immersed in the quicksand, still addressed to every heart a tale of shipwreck and desolation. The tide wheeled and foamed around them, and, creeping inch by inch up the side, at last fairly threw its waters over the top, and a long and hollow eddy showed the resistance which the liquid element received.

The moment they were fairly buried in the water, the old man clasped his hands together, and said: 'Blessed be the tide that will break over and bury ye for ever! Sad to mariners and sorrowful to maids and mothers has the time been you have choked up this deep and bonnie bay. For evil were you sent, and for evil have you continued. Every season finds from you its song of sorrow and wail, its funeral processions and its shrouded corses. Woe to the land where the wood grew that made ye! Cursed be the axe that hewed ye on the mountains, the hands that joined ye together, the bay that ye first swam in, and the wind that wafted ye here! Seven times have ye put my life in peril, three fair sons have ye swept from my side, and two bonnie grand-bairns; and now, even now, your waters foam and flash for my destruction, did I venture my infirm limbs in quest of food in your deadly bay. I see by that ripple and that foam, and hear by the sound and singing of your surge, that ye yearn for another victim; but it shall not be me nor mine.'

Even as the old mariner addressed himself to the wrecked ships, a young man appeared at the southern extremity of the bay, holding his halve-net in his hand and hastening into the current. Mark rose and shouted, and waved him back from a place which, to a person unacquainted with the dangers of the bay, real and superstitious, seemed sufficiently perilous; his granddaughter, too, added her voice to his, and waved her white hands; but the more they strove, the faster advanced the peasant, till he stood to his middle in the water, while the tide increased every moment in depth and strength. 'Andrew, Andrew,' cried the young woman, in a voice quavering with emotion, 'turn, turn, I tell you! Oh, the Ships, the Haunted Ships!' But the appearance of a fine run of fish had more influence with the peasant than the voice of bonnie Barbara, and forward he dashed, net in hand. In a moment he was borne off his feet and mingled like foam with the water and hurried towards the fatal eddies which whirled and roared round the sunken ships. But he was a powerful young man, and an expert swimmer; he seized on one of the projecting ribs of the nearest hulk, and clinging to it with the grasp of despair, uttered yell after yell, sustaining himself against the prodigious rush of the current.

From a shieling of turf and straw, within the pitch of a bar from the spot where we stood, came out an old woman bent with age, and leaning on a crutch. 'I heard the voice of that lad Andrew Lammie; can the chield be drowning that he skirls sae uncannily?' said the old woman, seating herself on the ground, and looking earnestly at the water. 'Ou, ay,' she continued, 'he's doomed, he's doomed; heart and hand can never save him; boats, ropes, and man's strength and wit, all vain! vain! – he's doomed, he's doomed!'

By this time I had thrown myself into the shallop, followed reluctantly by Richard Faulder, over whose courage and kindness of heart superstition had great power, and with one push from the shore, and some exertion in sculling, we came within a quoitcast of the unfortunate fisherman. He stayed not to profit by our aid; for, when he perceived us near, he uttered a piercing shriek of joy, and bounded towards us through the agitated element the full length of an oar. I saw him for a second on the surface of the water, but the eddying current sucked him down; and all I ever beheld of him again was his hand held above the flood, and clutching in agony at some imaginary aid. I sat gazing in horror on the vacant sea before us; but a breathing-time before, a human being, full of youth and strength and hope, was there; his cries were still ringing in my ears, and echoing in the woods; and now nothing was seen or heard save the turbulent expanse of water, and the sound of its chafing on the shores. We pushed back our shallop, and resumed our station on the cliff beside the old mariner and his descendant.

'Wherefore sought ye to peril your own lives fruitlessly,' said Mark, 'in attempting to save the doomed? Whoso touches those infernal ships never survives to tell the tale. Woe to the man who is found nigh them at midnight, when the tide has subsided and they arise in their former beauty, with forecastle, and deck, and sail, and pennon, and shroud! Then is seen the streaming of lights along the water from their cabin windows, and then is heard the sound of mirth and the clamour of tongues and the infernal whoop and halloo and song ringing far and wide. Woe to the man who comes nigh them!'

To all this my Allanbay companion listened with a breathless attention. I felt strangely touched with a superstition to which I partly believed I had seen one victim offered up; and I enquired of the old mariner, 'How and when came these Haunted Ships there? To me they seem but the melancholy relics of some unhappy voyagers, and much more likely to warn people to shun destruction than entice and delude them to it.'

'And so,' said the old man with a smile, which had more of sorrow in it than of mirth; 'and so, young man, these black and shattered hulks seem to the eye of the multitude. But things are not what they seem: that water, a kind and convenient servant to the wants of man, which seems so smooth and so dimpling and so gentle, has swallowed up a human soul even now; and the place which it covers, so fair and so level, is a faithless quicksand, out of which none escape. Things are otherwise than they seem. Had you lived as long as I have had the sorrow to live; had you seen the storms, and braved the perils, and endured the distresses which have befallen me; had you sat gazing out on the dreary ocean at midnight on a haunted coast; had you seen comrade after comrade, brother after brother, and son after son, swept away by the merciless ocean from your very side; had you seen the shapes of friends, doomed to the wave and the quicksand, appearing to you in the dreams and visions of the night, then would your mind have been prepared for crediting the maritime legends of mariners; and the two haunted Danish ships would have had their terrors for you, as they have for all who sojourn on this coast.

'Of the time and the cause of their destruction,' continued the old man, 'I know nothing certain; they have stood as you have seen them for uncounted time; and while all other ships wrecked on this unhappy coast have gone to pieces, and rotted and sunk away in a few years, these two haunted hulks have neither sunk in the quick-sand nor has a single spar or board been displaced. Maritime legend says that two ships of Denmark having had permission, for a time, to work deeds of darkness and dolour on the deep, were at last condemned to the whirlpool and the sunken rock and were wrecked in this bonnie bay as a sign to seamen to be gentle and devout. The night when they were lost was a harvest evening of uncommon mildness and beauty: the sun had newly set; the moon came brighter and brighter out; and the reapers, laying their sickles at the root of the standing corn, stood on rock and bank, looking at the increasing magnitude of the waters, for sea and land were visible from St Bees to Barnhourie. The sails of two vessels were soon seen bent for the Scottish coast; and, with a speed outrunning the swiftest ship, they approached the dangerous quicksands and headland of Borranpoint. On the deck of the foremost ship not a living soul was seen, nor any shape, unless something in darkness and form resembling a human shadow could be called a shape, which flitted from extremity to extremity of the ship with the appearance of trimming the sails and directing the vessel's course. But the decks of its companion were crowded with human shapes: the captain and mate, and sailor and cabin-boy, all seemed there; and from them the sound of mirth and minstrelsy echoed over land and water. The coast which they skirted along was one of extreme danger, and the reapers shouted to warn them to beware of sandbank and rock; but of this friendly counsel no notice was taken, except that a large and famished dog, which sat on the prow, answered every shout with a long, loud and melancholy howl. The deep sandbank of Carsethorn was expected to arrest the career of these desperate navigators; but they passed, with the celerity of waterfowl, over an obstruction which had wrecked many pretty ships.

'Old men shook their heads and departed, saying, "We have seen the fiend sailing in a bottomless ship; let us go home and pray;" but one young and wilful man said, "Fiend! I'll warrant it's nae fiend, but douce Janet Withershins, the witch, holding a carouse with some of her Cumberland cummers, and mickle red wine will be spilt atween them. Dod I would gladly have a toothful! I'll warrant it's nane o' your cauld sour slae-water like a bottle of Bailie Skrinkie's port, but right drap-o'-my-heart's-blood stuff, that would waken a body out of their last linen. I wonder where the cummers will anchor their craft?" "And I'll vow," said another rustic, "the wine they quaff is none of your visionary drink, such as a drouthie body has dished out to his lips in a dream; nor is it shadowy and unsubstantial, like the vessels they sail in, which are made out of a cockel-shell or a cast-off slipper or the paring of a seaman's right thumbnail. I once got a hansel out of a witch's quaigh myself – auld Marion Mathers, of Dustiefoot, whom they tried to bury in the old kirkyard of

Dunscore; but she raised herself up as fast as they laid her down, and naewhere else would she lie but in the bonnie green kirkyard of Kier, among douce and sponsible fowk. So I'll vow that the wine of a witch's cup is as fell liquor as ever did a kindly turn to a poor man's heart; and be they fiends, or be they witches, if they have red wine asteer, I'll risk a drouket sark for ae glorious tout on't."

' "Silence, ye sinners," said the minister's son of a neighbouring parish, who united in his own person his father's lack of devotion with his mother's love of liquor. "Whist! – speak as if ye had the fear of something holy before ye. Let the vessels run their own way to destruction: who can stay the eastern wind, and the current of the Solway sea? I can find ye Scripture warrant for that; so let them try their strength on Blawhooly rocks, and their might on the broad quicksand. There's a surf running there would knock the ribs together of a galley built by the imps of the pit and commanded by the Prince of Darkness. Bonnily and bravely they sail away there, but before the blast blows by they'll be wrecked; and red wine and strong brandy will be as rife as dyke-water, and we'll drink the health of bonnie Bell Blackness out of her left-foot slipper."

'The speech of the young profligate was applauded by several of his companions, and away they flew to the Bay of Blawhooly, from whence they never returned. The two vessels were observed all at once to stop in the bosom of the bay, on the spot where their hulls now appear; the mirth and the minstrelsy waxed louder than ever, and the forms of maidens, with instruments of music and wine-cups in their hands, thronged the decks. A boat was lowered; and the same shadowy pilot who conducted the ships made it start towards the shore with the rapidity of lightning, and its head knocked against the bank where the four young men stood who longed for the unblest drink. They leaped in with a laugh, and with a laugh were they welcomed on deck; wine-cups were given to each, and as they raised them to their lips the vessels melted away beneath their feet, and one loud shriek, mingled with laughter still louder, was heard over land and water for many miles. Nothing more was heard or seen till the morning, when the crowd who came to the beach saw with fear and wonder the two Haunted Ships, such as they now seem, masts and tackle gone; nor mark, nor sign, by which their name, country or destination could be known, was left remaining. Such is the tradition of the mariners; and its truth has been attested by many families whose sons and whose fathers have been drowned in the haunted Bay of Blawhooly.'

'And trow ye,' said the old woman, who, attracted from her hut by the drowning cries of the young fisherman, had remained an auditor of the mariner's legend, – 'And trow ye, Mark Macmoran, that the tale of the Haunted Ships is done? I can say no to that. Mickle have mine ears heard; but more mine eyes have witnessed since I came to dwell in this humble home by the side of the deep sea. I mind the night weel; it was on Hallowmas Eve; the nuts were cracked, and the apples were eaten, and spell and charm were tried at my fireside; till, wearied with diving into the dark waves of futurity, the lads and lasses fairly took to the more visible blessings of kind words, tender clasps and gentle courtship. Soft words in a maiden's ear, and a kindly kiss o' her lips were old-world matters to me, Mark Macmoran; though I mean not to say that I have been free of the folly of daunering and daffin with a youth in my day, and keeping tryst with him in dark and lonely places. However, as I say, these times of enjoyment were passed and gone with me – the mair's the pity that pleasure should fly sae fast away – and as I couldna make sport I thought I should not mar any; so out I sauntered into the fresh cold air, and sat down behind that old oak, and looked abroad on the wide sea. I had my ain sad thoughts, ye may think, at the time: it was in that very bay my blithe goodman perished, with seven more in his company; and on that very bank where ye see the waves leaping and foaming, I saw seven stately corses streeked, but the dearest was the eighth. It was a woeful sight to me, a widow, with four bonnie boys, with nought to support them but these twa hands, and God's blessing, and a cow's grass. I have never liked to live out of sight of this bay since that time; and mony's the moonlight night I sit looking on these watery mountains and these waste shores; it does my heart good, whatever it may do to my head. So ye see it was Hallowmas Night, and looking on sea and land sat I; and my heart wandering to other thoughts soon made me forget my youthful company at hame. It might be near the howe hour of the night. The tide was making, and its singing brought strange old-world stories with it, and I thought on the dangers that sailors endure, the fates they meet with, and the fearful forms they see. My own blithe goodman had seen sights that made him grave enough at times, though he aye tried to laugh them away.

'Aweel, atween that very rock aneath us and the coming tide, I saw, or thought I saw – for the tale is so dreamlike that the whole might pass for a vision of the night – I saw the form of a man; his plaid was grey, his face was grey, and his hair, which hung low down till it nearly came to the middle of his back, was as white as the white sea-foam. He began to howk and dig under the bank; an' God be near me, thought I, this maun be the unblessed spirit of auld Adam Gowdgowpin the miser, who is doomed to dig for shipwrecked treasure, and count how many millions are hidden for ever from man's enjoyment. The form found something which in shape and hue seemed a left-foot slipper of brass; so down to the tide he marched, and, placing it on the water, whirled it thrice round, and the infernal slipper dilated at every turn, till it became a bonnie barge with its sails bent, and on board leaped the form and scudded swiftly away. He came to one of the Haunted Ships, and striking it with his oar, a fair ship, with mast and canvas and mariners, started up; he touched the other Haunted Ship, and produced the like transformation; and away the three spectre ships bounded, leaving a track of fire behind them on the billows which was long unextinguished. Now wasna that a bonnie and fearful sight to see beneath the light of the Hallowmas moon? But the tale is far frae finished, for mariners say that once a year, on a certain night, if ye stand on the Borran Point, ye will see the infernal shallops coming snoring through the Solway; ye will hear the same laugh and song and mirth and minstrelsy which our ancestors heard; see them bound over the sandbanks and sunken rocks like seagulls, cast their anchor in Blawhooly Bay, while the shadowy figure lowers down the boat, and augments their numbers with the four unhappy mortals to whose memory a stone stands in the kirkyard, with a sinking ship and a shoreless sea cut upon it. Then the spectre ships vanish, and the drowning shriek of mortals and the rejoicing laugh of fiends are heard, and the old hulls are left as a memorial that the old spiritual kingdom has not departed from the earth. But I maun away, and trim my little cottage fire, and make it burn and blaze up bonnie, to warm the crickets and my cold and crazy bones that maun soon be laid aneath the green sod in the eerie kirkyard.' And away the old dame tottered to her cottage, secured the door on the inside, and soon the hearth-flame was seen to glimmer and gleam through the keyhole and window.

'I'll tell ye what,' said the old mariner, in a subdued tone, and with a shrewd and suspicious glance of his eye after the old sibyl, 'it's a word that may not very well be uttered, but there are many mistakes made in evening stories if old Moll Moray there, where she lives, knows not mickle more than she is willing to tell of the Haunted Ships and their unhallowed mariners. She lives cannily and quietly; no one knows how she is fed or supported; but her dress is aye whole, her cottage ever smokes, and her table lacks neither of wine, white and red, nor of fowl and fish, and white bread and brown. It was a dear scoff to Jock Matheson, when he called old Moll the uncanny carline of Blawhooly: his boat ran round and round in the centre of the Solway – everybody said it was enchanted – and down it went head foremost; and hadna Jock been a swimmer equal to a sheldrake, he would have fed the fish. But I'll warrant it sobered the lad's speech; and he never reckoned himself safe till he made old Moll the present of a new kirtle and a stone of cheese.'

'O father!' said his granddaughter Barbara, 'ye surely wrong poor old Mary Moray; what use could it be to an old woman like her, who has no wrongs to redress, no malice to work out against mankind, and nothing to seek of enjoyment save a canny hour and a quiet grave – what use could the fellowship of fiends and the communion of evil spirits be to her? I know Jenny Primrose puts rowan tree above the door-head when she sees old Mary coming; I know the good-wife of Kittlenaket wears rowan-berry leaves in the headband of her blue kirtle, and all for the sake of averting the unsonsie glance of Mary's right ee; and I know that the auld Laird of Burntroutwater drives his seven cows to their pasture with a wand of witch-tree, to keep Mary from milking them. But what has all that to do with haunted shallops, visionary mariners and bottomless boats? I have heard myself as pleasant a tale about the Haunted Ships and their unworldly crews as anyone would wish to hear in a winter evening. It was told me by young Benjie Macharg, one summer night, sitting on Arbigland Bank: the lad intended a sort of love meeting; but all that he could talk of was about smearing sheep

and shearing sheep, and of the wife which the Norway elves of the
Haunted Ships made for his uncle Sandie Macharg. And I shall tell
ye the tale as the honest lad told it to me.

'Alexander Macharg, besides being the laird of three acres of
peatmoss, two kale gardens, and the owner of seven good milch
cows, a pair of horses and six pet sheep, was the husband of one of
the handsomest women in seven parishes. Many a lad sighed the day
he was brided; and a Nithsdale laird and two Annandale moorland
farmers drank themselves to their last linen, as well as their last
shilling, through sorrow for her loss. But married was the dame; and
home she was carried, to bear rule over her home and her husband,
as an honest woman should. Now ye maun ken that though the
flesh-and-blood lovers of Alexander's bonnie wife all ceased to love
and to pursue her after she became another's, there were certain
admirers who did not consider their claim at all abated, or their
hopes lessened by the kirk's famous obstacle of matrimony. Ye have
heard how the devout minister of Tinwald had a fair son carried
away and wedded against his liking to an unchristened bride, whom
the elves and the fairies provided; ye have heard how the bonnie
bride of the drunken Laird of Soukitup was stolen by the fairies out
at the back-window of the bridal chamber, the time the bridegroom
was groping his way to the chamber door; and ye have heard – but
why need I multiply cases? Such things in the ancient days were as
common as candlelight. So ye'll no hinder certain water elves and
sea fairies, who sometimes keep festival and summer mirth in these
old haunted hulks, from falling in love with the weel-favoured wife
of Laird Macharg; and to their plots and contrivances they went
how they might accomplish to sunder man and wife; and sundering
such a man and such a wife was like sundering the green leaf from
the summer or the fragrance from the flower.

'So it fell on a time that Laird Macharg took his halve-net on his
back, and his steel spear in his hand, and down to Blawhooly Bay
gaed he, and into the water he went right between the two haunted
hulks, and placing his net awaited the coming of the tide. The night,
ye maun ken, was mirk, and the wind lowne, and the singing of the
increasing waters among the shells and the peebles was heard for
sundry miles. All at once light began to glance and twinkle on board
the two Haunted Ships from every hole and seam, and presently the

sound as of a hatchet employed in squaring timber echoed far and wide. But if the toil of these unearthly workmen amazed the laird, how much more was his amazement increased when a sharp shrill voice called out, "Ho, brother! what are you doing now?" A voice still shriller responded from the other haunted ship, "I'm making a wife to Sandie Macharg!" And a loud quavering laugh running from ship to ship and from bank to bank told the joy they expected from their labour.

'Now the laird, besides being a devout and a God-fearing man, was shrewd and bold; and in plot and contrivance, and skill in conducting his designs, was fairly an overmatch for any dozen land elves; but the water elves are far more subtle; besides their haunts and their dwellings being in the great deep, pursuit and detection is hopeless if they succeed in carrying their prey to the waves. But ye shall hear. Home flew the laird, collected his family around the hearth, spoke of the signs and the sins of the times, and talked of mortification and prayer for averting calamity; and, finally, taking his father's Bible, all brass clasps, black print and covered with calf-skin, from the shelf, he proceeded without let or stint to perform domestic worship. I should have told ye that he bolted and locked the door, shut up all inlet to the house, threw salt into the fire, and proceeded in every way like a man skilful in guarding against the plots of fairies and fiends. His wife looked on all this with wonder; but she saw something in her husband's looks that hindered her from intruding either question or advice, and a wise woman was she.

'Near the mid-hour of the night the rush of a horse's feet was heard, and the sound of a rider leaping from its back, and a heavy knock came to the door, accompanied by a voice, saying, "The cummer drink's hot, and the knave bairn is expected at Laird Laurie's tonight; sae mount, good-wife, and come."

' "Preserve me!" said the wife of Sandie Macharg, "that's news indeed; who could have thought it? The laird has been heirless for seventeen years! Now, Sandie, my man, fetch me my skirt and hood."

'But he laid his arm round his wife's neck, and said, "If all the lairds in Galloway go heirless, over this threshold shall you not stir tonight; and I have said, and I have sworn it; seek not to know why or wherefore – but, Lord, send us thy blessed morning light."

'The wife looked for a moment in her husband's eyes, and desisted from further entreaty. "But let us send a civil message to the gossips, Sandie; and hadna ye better say I am sair laid with a sudden sickness? though it's sinful-like to send the poor messenger a mile agate with a lie in his mouth without a glass of brandy."

' "To such a messenger, and to those who sent him, no apology is needed," said the austere laird; "so let him depart." And the clatter of a horse's hoofs was heard, and the muttered imprecations of its rider on the churlish treatment he had experienced.

' "Now, Sandie, my lad," said his wife, laying an arm particularly white and round about his neck as she spoke, "are you not a queer man and a stern? I have been your wedded wife now these three years; and, beside my dower, have brought you three as bonnie bairns as ever smiled aneath a summer sun. For sure, you are a douce man, and fitter to be an elder than even Willie Greer himself, I have the minister's ain word for 't, to put on these hard-hearted looks, and gang waving your arms that way, as if ye said, 'I winna take the counsel of sic a hempie as you;' I'm your ain leal wife, and will and maun have an explanation."

'To all this Sandie Macharg replied, "It is written, 'Wives, obey your husbands'; but we have been stayed in our devotion, so let us pray," and down he knelt; his wife knelt also, for she was as devout as bonnie; and beside them knelt their household, and all lights were extinguished.

' "Now this beats a'," muttered his wife to herself; "however, I shall be obedient for a time; but if I dinna ken what all this is for before the morn by sunket-time, my tongue is nae langer a tongue, nor my hands worth wearing."

'The voice of her husband in prayer interrupted this mental soliloquy; and ardently did he beseech to be preserved from the wiles of the fiends and the snares of Satan; from witches, ghosts, goblins, elves, fairies, spunkies and water-kelpies; from the spectre shallop of Solway; from spirits visible and invisible; from the Haunted Ships and their unearthly tenants; from maritime spirits that plotted against godly men, and fell in love with their wives –

' "Nay, but His presence be near us!" said his wife, in a low tone of dismay. "God guide my goodman's wits: I never heard such a prayer from human lips before. But, Sandie, my man, Lord's sake, rise. What fearful light is this? Barn and byre and stable maun be in a blaze; and Hawkie and Hurley, Doddie and Cherrie and Damson-plum will be smoored with reek and scorched with flame."

'And a flood of light, but not so gross as a common fire, which ascended to heaven and filled all the court before the house, amply justified the good-wife's suspicions. But to the terrors of fire Sandie was as immovable as he was to the imaginary groans of the barren wife of Laird Laurie; and he held his wife and threatened the weight of his right hand – and it was a heavy one – to all who ventured abroad, or even unbolted the door. The neighing and prancing of horses, and the bellowing of cows, augmented the horrors of the night; and to anyone who only heard the din, it seemed that the whole onstead was in a blaze, and horses and cattle perishing in the flames. All wiles, common or extraordinary, were put in practice to entice or force the honest farmer and his wife to open the door; and when the like success attended every new stratagem, silence for a little while ensued and a long, loud and shrilling laugh wound up the dramatic efforts of the night. In the morning, when Laird Macharg went to the door, he found standing against one of the pilasters a piece of black ship oak, rudely fashioned into something like human form; and this, skilful people declared, would have been clothed with seeming flesh and blood and palmed off upon him for his wife had he admitted his visitants. A synod of wise men and women sat upon the woman of timber, and she was finally ordered to be devoured by fire, and that in the open air. A fire was soon made, and into it the elfin sculpture was tossed from the prongs of two pairs of pitchforks. The blaze that arose was awful to behold; and hissings and burstings and loud cracklings and strange noises were heard in the midst of the flame; and when the whole sank into ashes, a drinking-cup of some precious metal was found; and this cup, fashioned no doubt by elfin skill, but rendered harmless by the purification of fire, the sons and daughters of Sandie Macharg and his wife drink out of to this very day. Bless all bold men, say I, and obedient wives!'

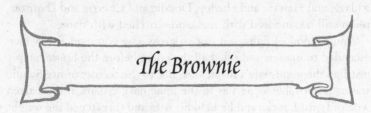

The Brownie

The Scottish brownie formed a class of being distinct in habit and disposition from the freakish and mischievous elves. He was meagre, shaggy and wild in his appearance. Thus Cleland, in his satire against the Highlanders, compares them to

> Faunes, or brownies, if ye will,
> Or satyres come from Atlas Hill.

In the daytime he lurked in remote recesses of the old houses which he delighted to haunt, and in the night sedulously employed himself in discharging any laborious task which he thought might be acceptable to the family to whose service he had devoted himself. But the brownie does not drudge from the hope of recompense. On the contrary, so delicate is his attachment that the offer of reward, but particularly of food, infallibly occasions his disappearance for ever.

It is told of a brownie, who haunted a Border family now extinct, that the lady having fallen unexpectedly ill, and the servant who was ordered to ride to Jedburgh for the *sage-femme* showing no great alertness in setting out, the familiar spirit slipped on the greatcoat of the lingering domestic, rode to the town on the laird's best horse and returned with the midwife *en croupe*. During the short space of his absence, the Tweed, which they must necessarily ford, rose to a dangerous height. The brownie, who transported his charge with all the rapidity of the ghostly lover of Lenore, was not to be stopped by the obstacle. He plunged in with the terrified old lady, and landed her in safety where her services were wanted. Having put the horse into the stable (where it was afterwards found in a woeful plight), he proceeded to the room of the servant, whose duty he had discharged, and finding him just in the act of drawing on his boots, he administered to him a most merciless drubbing with his own horsewhip. Such an important service excited the

gratitude of the laird, who, understanding that the brownie had
been heard to express a wish to have a green coat, ordered a
vestment of the colour to be made and left in his haunts. The
brownie took away the green coat, but was never seen more. We
may suppose that, tired of his domestic drudgery, he went in his
new livery to join the fairies.

The last brownie known in Ettrick Forest resided in Bodsbeck, a
wild and solitary spot, near the head of Moffat Water, where he
exercised his functions undisturbed, till the scrupulous devotion of
an old lady induced her to 'hire him away', as it was termed, by
placing in his haunt a porringer of milk and a piece of money. After
receiving this hint to depart, he was heard the whole night to howl
and cry, 'Farewell to bonnie Bodsbeck!' which he was compelled to
abandon for ever.

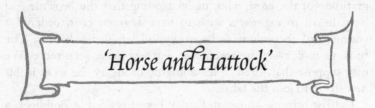

'Horse and Hattock'

The power of the fairies was not confined to unchristened children alone; it was supposed frequently to be extended to full-grown people, especially such as in an unlucky hour were devoted to the devil by the execrations of parents and of masters; or those who were found asleep under a rock, or on a green hill, belonging to the fairies, after sunset; or, finally, to those who unwarily joined their orgies.

A tradition existed, during the seventeenth century, concerning an ancestor of the noble family of Duffers, who, walking abroad in the fields near to his own house, was suddenly carried away, and found the next day in Paris, in the French king's cellar, with a silver cup in his hand. Being brought into the king's presence, and questioned by him as to who he was and how he came thither, he told his name, his country and the place of his residence, and that on such a day of the month, which proved to be the day immediately preceding, being in the fields, he heard a noise of a whirlwind, and of voices crying 'Horse and hattock!' (this is the word which the fairies are said to use when they move on from any place); whereupon he cried 'Horse and hattock!' also, and was immediately caught up and transported through the air by the fairies to that place, where, after he had drunk heartily, he fell asleep, and before he woke the rest of the company were gone and had left him in the posture wherein he was found. It is said the king gave him the cup which was found in his hand, and dismissed him. The tradition affirms that the cup was still preserved and was known by the name of the fairy cup. Mr Steward, tutor to the then Lord Duffers, remembered that when he was a boy at the school of Forres, he and his schoolfellows were once upon a time whipping their tops in the churchyard, before the door of the church, when, though the day was calm, they heard a noise of a wind, and at some distance saw the small dust begin to rise and turn round, which motion continued advancing till it came to the place where they were, whereupon they began to bless themselves; but one of their number being, it seems, a little more bold and confident than his companions, said, 'Horse and hattock with my top!' and immediately they all saw the top lifted up from the ground, but could not see which way it was carried, by reason of a cloud of dust which was raised at the same time. They sought for the top all about the place where it was taken up, but in vain; and it was found afterwards in the churchyard, on the other side of the church.

The Fairy Boy of Leith

About fifteen years since, having business that detained me for some time at Leith, which is near Edinburgh, in the kingdom of Scotland, I often met some of my acquaintance at a certain house there, where we used to drink a glass of wine for our refection. The woman who kept the house was of honest reputation among the neighbours, which made me give the more attention to what she told me one day about a fairy boy (as they called him) who lived about that town. She had given me so strange an account of him that I desired her I might see him at the first opportunity, which she promised; and not long after, passing that way, she told me there was the fairy boy, but a little before I came by; and, casting her eye into the street, said, 'Look you, sir, yonder he is, at play with those other boys,' and she pointed him out to me. I went and by smooth words, and a piece of money, got him to come into the house with me; where, in the presence of divers people, I demanded of him several astrological questions, which he answered with great subtlety; and, through all his discourse, carried it with a cunning much above his years, which seemed not to exceed ten or eleven.

He seemed to make a motion like drumming upon the table with his fingers, upon which I asked him whether he could beat a drum? To which he replied, 'Yes, sir, as well as any man in Scotland; for every Thursday night I beat all points to a sort of people that used to meet under yonder hill' (pointing to the great hill between Edinburgh and Leith). 'How, boy?' quoth I, 'what company have you there?' 'There are, sir,' said he, 'a great company both of men and women, and they are entertained with many sorts of music besides my drum; they have, besides, plenty of variety of meats and wine, and many times we are carried into France or Holland in the night, and return again, and while we are there, we enjoy all the pleasures the country doth afford.' I demanded of him how they got under that hill? To which he replied that there was a great pair of gates that opened to them, though they were invisible to others, and that within there were brave large rooms, as well accommodated as most in Scotland. I then asked him how I should know what he said to be true? Upon which he told me he would read my fortune, saying I should have two wives, and that he saw the forms of them over my shoulders; and both would be very handsome women.

The woman of the house told me that all the people in Scotland could not keep him from the rendezvous on Thursday night; upon which, by promising him some more money, I got a promise from him to meet me at the same place in the afternoon of the Thursday following, and so dismissed him at that time. The boy came again at the place and time appointed, and I had prevailed with some friends to continue with me (if possible) to prevent his moving that night. He was placed between us, and answered many questions, until, about eleven of the clock, he was got away unperceived by the company; but I, suddenly missing him, hastened to the door, and took hold of him, and so returned him into the same room. We all watched him, and, of a sudden, he was again got out of doors; I followed him close, and he made a noise in the street, as if he had been set upon, and from that time I could never see him.

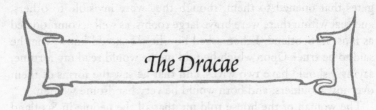

The Dracae

These are a sort of water-spirits who inveigle women and children into the recesses which they inhabit, beneath lakes and rivers, by floating past them, on the surface of the water, in the shape of gold rings or cups. The women thus seized are employed as nurses, and after seven years are permitted to revisit earth. Gervase mentions one woman in particular who had been allured by observing a wooden dish, or cup, float by her, while she was washing clothes in the river. Being seized as soon as she reached the depths, she was conducted into one of the subterranean recesses, which she described as very magnificent, and employed as nurse to one of the brood of the hag who had allured her. During her residence in this capacity having accidentally touched one of her eyes with an ointment of serpent's grease, she perceived, at her return to the world, that she had acquired the faculty of seeing the dracae when they intermingle themselves with men. Of this power she was, however, deprived by the touch of her ghostly mistress, whom she had one day incautiously addressed.

It is a curious fact that this story, in almost all its parts, is current in both the Highlands and Lowlands of Scotland, with no other variation than the substitution of fairies for dracae, and the cavern of a hill for that of a river. Indeed many of the vulgar account it extremely dangerous to touch anything which they may happen to find without blessing it first, the snares of the enemy being notorious and well attested. A pool-woman of Teviotdale having been fortunate enough, as she thought herself, to find a wooden beetle, at the very time when she needed such an implement, seized it without pronouncing a proper blessing, and, carrying it home, laid it above her bed to be ready for employment in the morning. At midnight the window of her cottage opened, and a loud voice was heard calling up someone within by a strange and uncouth name. The terrified cottager ejaculated a prayer, which, we may suppose,

ensured her personal safety; while the enchanted implement of
housewifery, tumbling from the bedhead, departed by the window
with no small noise and precipitation.

In a humorous fugitive tract, Dr Johnson has been introduced as
disputing the authenticity of an apparition, merely because the spirit
assumed the shape of a teapot and a shoulder of mutton. No doubt,
a case so much in point as that we have now quoted would have
removed his incredulity.

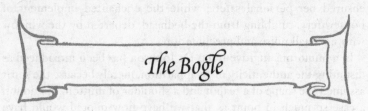

The Bogle

This is a freakish spirit who delights rather to perplex and frighten mankind than either to serve or seriously hurt them. The *Esprit Follet* of the French, Shakespeare's Puck or Robin Goodfellow, and Shellycoat, a spirit who resides in the waters, and has given his name to many a rock and stone on the Scottish coast, belong to the class of bogles.

One of Shellycoat's pranks is thus narrated: Two men on a very dark night, approaching the banks of the Ettrick, heard a doleful voice from its waves repeatedly exclaim, 'Lost! lost!' They followed the sound, which seemed to be the voice of a drowning person, and, to their astonishment, found that it ascended the river; still they continued to follow the cry of the malicious sprite, and, arriving before dawn at the very source of the river, were consternated to hear the voice descending the opposite side of the mountain. The fatigued and deluded travellers now relinquished the pursuit, and had no sooner done so than they heard Shellycoat applauding, in loud bursts of laughter, his successful roguery.

Daoine Shie or the Men of Peace

They are, though not absolutely malevolent, believed to be a peevish, repining and envious race, who enjoy, in the subterranean recesses, a kind of shadowy splendour. The Highlanders are at all times unwilling to speak of them, but especially on Friday, when their influence is supposed to be particularly extensive. As they are supposed to be invisibly present, they are at all times to be spoken of with respect. The fairies of Scotland are represented as a diminutive race of beings, of a mixed or rather dubious nature, capricious in their dispositions and mischievous in their resentment. They inhabit the interior of green hills, chiefly those of a conical form, in Gaelic termed *sighan*, on which they lead their dances by moonlight, impressing upon the surface the marks of circles, which sometimes appear yellow and blasted, sometimes of a deep-green hue, and within which it is dangerous to sleep or to be found after sunset. The removal of those large portions of turf, which thunderbolts sometimes scoop out of the ground with singular regularity, is also ascribed to their agency. Cattle which are suddenly seized with the cramp, or some similar disorder, are said to be elf-shot, and the approved cure is to chafe the parts affected with a blue bonnet, which, it may be readily believed, often restores the circulation. The triangular flints frequently found in Scotland, with which the ancient inhabitants probably barbed their shafts, are supposed to be the weapons of fairy resentment, and are termed elf arrowheads. The rude brazen battleaxes of the ancients, commonly called 'celts', are also ascribed to their manufacture. But, like the Gothic duergar, their skill is not confined to the fabrication of arms; for they are heard sedulously hammering in linns, precipices and rocky or cavernous situations, where, like the dwarfs of the mines mentioned by George Agricola, they busy themselves in imitating the actions and the various employments of men. The Brook of Beaumont, for example, which passes in its course by numerous linns and caverns, is notorious for being haunted by the fairies; and the perforated and rounded stones which are formed by trituration in its channels are termed by the vulgar fairy cups and dishes.

A beautiful reason is assigned by Fletcher for the fays frequenting streams and fountains. He tells us of

> A virtuous well, about whose flowery banks
> The nimble-footed fairies dance their rounds
> By the pale moonshine, dipping oftentimes
> Their stolen children, so to make them free
> From dying flesh and dull mortality.

It is sometimes accounted unlucky to pass such places without performing some ceremony to avert the displeasure of the elves. There is upon the top of Minchmuir, a mountain in Peeblesshire, a spring called the Cheese Well, because, anciently, those who passed that way were wont to throw into it a piece of cheese as an offering to the fairies, to whom it was consecrated.

Like the *feld elfen* of the Saxons, the usual dress of the fairies is green; though on the moors they have been sometimes observed in heath-brown, or in weeds dyed with the stone-raw or lichen. They often ride in invisible procession, when their presence is advertised by the shrill ringing of their bridles. On these occasions they sometimes borrow mortal steeds, and when such are found at morning, panting and fatigued in their stalls, with their manes and tails dishevelled and entangled, the grooms, I presume, often find this a convenient excuse for their situation, as the common belief of the elves quaffing the choicest liquors in the cellars of the rich might occasionally cloak the delinquencies of an unfaithful butler.

The fairies, besides their equestrian processions, are addicted, it would seem, to the pleasures of the chase. A young sailor, travelling by night from Douglas, in the Isle of Man, to visit his sister residing in Kirk Merlugh, heard a noise of horses, the holloa of a huntsman and the sound of a horn. Immediately afterwards, thirteen horsemen, dressed in green and gallantly mounted, swept past him. Jack was so much delighted with the sport that he followed them, and enjoyed the sound of the horn for some miles, and it was not till he arrived at his sister's house that he learned the danger which he had incurred. I must not omit to mention that these little personages are expert jockeys, and scorn to ride the little Manx ponies, though apparently well suited to their size. The exercise, therefore, falls heavily upon the English and Irish horses brought into the Isle of Man. Mr Waldron was assured by a gentleman of Ballafletcher that he had lost three or four capital hunters by these nocturnal excursions. From the same author we learn that the fairies sometimes take more legitimate modes of procuring horses. A person of the utmost integrity informed him that, having occasion to sell a horse, he was accosted among the mountains by a little gentleman plainly dressed, who priced his horse, cheapened him, and, after some chaffering, finally purchased him. No sooner had the buyer mounted and paid the price than he sank through the earth, horse and man, to the astonishment and terror of the seller, who experienced, however, no inconvenience from dealing with so extraordinary a purchaser.

The Death 'Bree'

There was once a woman, who lived in the Camp-del-more of Strathavon, whose cattle were seized with a murrain, or some such fell disease, which ravaged the neighbourhood at the time, carrying off great numbers of them daily. All the forlorn fires and hallowed waters failed of their customary effects, and she was at length told by the wise people, whom she consulted on the occasion, that it was evidently the effect of some infernal agency, the power of which could not be destroyed by any other means than the never-failing specific, the death 'bree' – the juice of a dead head from the church-yard – a nostrum certainly very difficult to be procured, considering that the head must needs be abstracted from the grave at the hour of midnight. Being, however, a woman of a stout heart and strong faith, native feelings of delicacy towards the sanctuary of the dead had more weight than had fear in restraining her for some time from resorting to this desperate remedy. At length, seeing that her stock would soon be annihilated by the destructive career of the disease, the wife of Camp-del-more resolved to put the experiment in practice, whatever the result might be.

Accordingly, having with considerable difficulty engaged a neighbouring woman as her companion in this hazardous expedition, she set out in her company a little before midnight for the parish churchyard, distant about a mile and a half from her residence, to execute her determination. On arriving at the churchyard her companion, whose courage was not so notable, appalled by the gloomy prospect before her, refused to enter among the habitations of the dead. She, however, agreed to remain at the gate till her friend's business was accomplished. This circumstance, however, did not stagger the wife's resolution. She, with the greatest coolness and intrepidity, proceeded towards what she supposed an old grave, took up her spade, and commenced her operations. After a good deal of toil she arrived at the object of her labour. Raising the first head, or rather skull, that came in her way, she was about to make it her own property, when a hollow, wild, sepulchral voice exclaimed, 'That is my head; let it alone!' Not wishing to dispute the claimant's title to this head, and supposing she could be otherwise provided, she very good-naturedly returned it and took up another. 'That is my father's head,' bellowed the same voice. Wishing, if possible, to avoid disputes, the wife of Camp-del-more took up a third head, when the same voice instantly started a claim to it as his grandfather's head. 'Well,' replied the wife, nettled at her disappointments, 'although it were your grandmother's head, you shan't get it till I am done with it.' 'What do you say, you limmer?' says the ghost, starting up in his awry habiliments in a great rage. 'By the great oath, you had better leave my grandfather's head.' Upon matters coming this length, the wily wife of Camp-del-more thought it proper to assume a more conciliatory aspect. Telling the claimant the whole particulars of the predicament in which she was placed, she promised faithfully that if his honour would only allow her to carry off his grandfather's skull or head in a peaceable manner, she would restore it again when done with. Here, after some communing, they came to an understanding; and she was allowed to take the head along with her, on condition that she should restore it before dawn, under the heaviest penalties.

On coming out of the churchyard and looking for her companion, she had the mortification to find her 'without a mouthful of breath in her body'; for, on hearing the dispute between her friend and the guardian of the grave, and suspecting much that she was likely to share the unpleasant punishments with which he threatened her friend, at the bare recital of them she fell down in a faint, from which it was no easy matter to recover her. This proved no small inconvenience to Camp-del-more's wife, as there were not above two hours to elapse ere she had to return the head according to her agreement. Taking her friend upon her back, she carried her up a steep bank to the nearest adjoining house, where she left her for the night; then repaired home with the utmost speed, made the death bree of the head ere the appointed time, restored the skull to its guardian and placed the grave in its former condition. It is needless to add that, as a reward for her exemplary courage, the bree had its desired effect. The cattle speedily recovered, and, so long as she retained any of it, all sorts of diseases were of short duration.

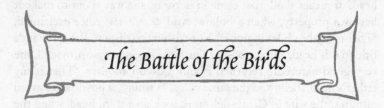

The Battle of the Birds

I will tell you a story about the wren. There was once a farmer who was seeking a servant, and the wren met him and said: 'What are you seeking?'

'I am seeking a servant,' said the farmer to the wren.

'Will you take me?' said the wren.

'You, you poor creature, what good would you do?'

'Try me,' said the wren.

So he engaged him, and the first work he set him to do was threshing in the barn. The wren threshed (What did he thresh with? Why a flail to be sure!), and he knocked off one grain. A mouse came out and she ate that.

'I'll trouble you not to do that again,' said the wren.

He struck again, and he struck off two grains. Out came the mouse and she ate them. So they arranged a contest to see who was strongest, and the wren brought his twelve birds, and the mouse her tribe.

'You have your tribe with you,' said the wren.

'As well as yourself,' said the mouse, and she struck out her leg proudly. But the wren broke it with his flail, and there was a pitched battle on a set day.

When every creature and bird was gathering to battle, the son of the King of Tethertown said that he would go to see the battle, and that he would bring sure word home to his father the king, who would be king of the creatures this year. The battle was over before he arrived all but one fight, between a great black raven and a snake. The snake was twined about the raven's neck, and although the raven held the snake's throat in his beak, it seemed as if the snake would get the victory over the raven. When the king's son saw this he helped the raven, and with one blow took the head off the snake. When the raven had taken breath, and saw that the snake was dead, he said, 'For your kindness to me this day, I will reward you. Come up now on the root of my two wings.' The king's son put his hands about the raven before his wings, and the bird took him over nine bens and nine glens and nine mountain moors.

'Now,' said the raven, 'see you that house yonder? Go now to it. It is a sister of mine that makes her dwelling in it; and I will go bail that you are welcome. And if she asks you, "Were you at the battle of the birds?" say you were. And if she asks, "Did you see anyone like me," say you did, but be sure that you meet me tomorrow morning here, in this place.' The king's son got good and right good treatment that night. Meat of each meat, drink of each drink, warm water to his feet and a soft bed for his limbs.

On the next day the raven gave him the same flight over six bens and six glens and six mountain moors. They saw a bothy far off, but, though far off, they were soon there. He got good treatment this night, as before – plenty of meat and drink, and warm water to his feet, and a soft bed to his limbs – and on the next day it was the same thing, over three bens and three glens and three mountain moors.

On the third morning, instead of seeing the raven as at the other times, who should meet him but the handsomest lad he ever saw, with gold rings in his ears and with a bundle in his hand. The king's son asked this lad if he had seen a big black raven.

Said the lad to him, 'You will never see the raven again, for I am that raven. I was put under a spell by a bad druid; it was meeting you that loosed me, and for that you shall get this bundle. Now,' said the lad, 'you must turn back on the self-same course, and lie a night in each house as before; but you must not loose the bundle which I gave you till you are in the place where you would most wish to dwell.'

The king's son turned his back to the lad, and his face to his father's house; and he got lodging from the raven's sisters, just as he got it when going forward. When he was nearing his father's house he was going through a thick wood. It seemed to him that the bundle was growing heavy, and he thought he would look what was in it.

When he loosed the bundle he was astonished. In a twinkling there appeared the very grandest place he ever saw. A great castle, and an orchard about the castle in which was every kind of fruit and herb. He stood full of wonder and regret for having loosed the bundle – for it was not in his power to put it back again now, though he would have wished this pretty place to be in the pretty little green hollow that was opposite his father's house; but he looked up and saw a great giant coming towards him.

'Bad's the place where you have built the house, king's son,' says the giant.

'Yes, but it is not here I would wish it to be, though it happens to be here by mishap,' says the king's son.

'What's the reward for putting it back in the bundle as it was before?'

'What's the reward you would ask?' enquired the king's son.

'That you will give me the first son you have when he is seven years of age,' says the giant.

'If I have a son you shall have him,' said the king's son.

In a twinkling the giant put garden, and orchard, and castle in the bundle as they were before.

'Now,' says the giant, 'take your own road, and I will take mine; but mind your promise, and if you forget I will remember.'

The king's son took to the road, and at the end of a few days he reached the place he was fondest of. He loosed the bundle, and the castle was just as it was before. And when he opened the castle door he sees the handsomest maiden he ever cast eye upon.

'Advance, king's son,' said the pretty maid; 'everything is in order for you, if you will marry me this very day.'

'It's I that am willing,' said the king's son. And on the same day they married.

But at the end of a day and seven years, who should be seen coming to the castle but the giant. The king's son was reminded of his promise to the giant, and till now he had not told his promise to the queen.

'Leave the matter between me and the giant,' says the queen.

'Turn out your son,' says the giant; 'mind your promise.'

'You shall have him,' says the king, 'when his mother puts him in order for his journey.'

The queen dressed up the cook's son, and she gave him to the giant by the hand. The giant went away with him; but he had not gone far when he put a rod in the hand of the little laddie and asked him, 'If your father had that rod what would he do with it?'

'If my father had that rod he would beat the dogs and the cats, so that they shouldn't be going near the king's meat,' said the little laddie.

'You are the cook's son,' said the giant and caught him by the two small ankles and knocked him against the stone that was beside him. The giant turned back to the castle in rage and madness, and he said that if they did not send out the king's son to him, the highest stone of the castle would be the lowest.

Said the queen to the king, 'We'll trick him yet; the butler's son is of the same age as our son.'

She dressed up the butler's son, and she gave him to the giant by the hand. The giant had not gone far before he put the rod in the child's hand.

'If your father had that rod,' says the giant, 'what would he do with it?'

'He would beat the dogs and the cats whenever they came near the king's bottles and glasses.'

'You are the son of the butler,' says the giant and dashed his brains out too. The giant returned in a very great rage and anger. The earth quaked under the soles of his feet, and the castle shook and all that was in it.

'*Out here with your son,*' says the giant, 'or in a twinkling the stone that is highest in the dwelling will be the lowest.' So they had to give their son to the giant.

When they were gone a little bit from the castle, the giant showed him the rod that was in his hand and said: 'What would your father do with this rod if he had it?'

The king's son said: 'My father has a braver rod than that.'

And the giant asked him, 'Where is your father when he has that brave rod?'

And the king's son said: 'He will be sitting in his kingly chair.'

Then the giant understood that he had the right one.

The giant took him to his own house, and he reared him as his own son. On a day of days when the giant was away from home, the lad heard the sweetest music he ever heard in a room at the top of the giant's house. At a glance he saw a maiden with the finest face he had ever seen. She beckoned to him to come a bit nearer to her, and she said her name was Auburn Mary; then she told him to go this time, but to be sure to be at the same place about that dead midnight.

And as he promised he did. The giant's daughter was at his side in a twinkling, and she said, 'Tomorrow you will get the choice of my two sisters to marry; but say that you will not take either, but me. My father wants me to marry the son of the King of the Green City, but I don't like him.' On the morrow the giant took out his three daughters, and he said: 'Now, son of the King of Tethertown, you have not lost by living with me so long. You will get to wife one of the two eldest of my daughters and have leave to go home with her the day after the wedding.'

'If you will give me this pretty little one,' says the king's son, 'I will take you at your word.'

The giant's wrath kindled, and he said: 'Before you get her you must do the three things that I ask you to do.'

'Say on,' says the king's son.

The giant took him to the byre.

'Now,' says the giant, 'a hundred cattle are stabled here, and it has not been cleansed for seven years. I am going to be away from home today, and if this byre is not cleaned before night comes, so clean that a golden apple will run from end to end of it, not only shall you not get my daughter, but 'tis only a drink of your fresh, goodly, beautiful blood that will quench my thirst this night.'

The lad began cleaning the byre, but he might just as well have been baling the great ocean. After midday when sweat was blinding him, the giant's youngest daughter came where he was, and she said to him: 'You are being punished, king's son.'

'I am that,' says the king's son.

'Come over,' says Auburn Mary, 'and lay down your weariness.'

'I will do that,' says he, 'there is but death awaiting me, at any rate.' He sat down near her. He was so tired that he fell asleep beside her. When he awoke, the giant's daughter was not to be seen, but the byre was so well cleaned that a golden apple would run from end to end of it and raise no stain. In comes the giant, and he said: 'Have you cleaned the byre, king's son?'

'I have cleaned it,' says he.

'Somebody cleaned it,' says the giant.

'You did not clean it, at all events,' said the king's son.

'Well, well!' says the giant, 'since you've been so active today, you will set to this time tomorrow to thatch this byre with birds' down, from birds with no two feathers of one colour.'

The king's son was on foot before the sun; he caught up his bow and his quiver of arrows to kill the birds. He took to the moors, but the birds were not so easy to take. He was running after them till the sweat was blinding him. About midday who should come but Auburn Mary.

'You are exhausting yourself, king's son,' says she.

'I am,' said he. 'There fell but these two blackbirds, and both of one colour.'

'Come over and lay down your weariness on this pretty hillock,' says the giant's daughter.

'It's I am willing,' said he.

He thought she would aid him this time, too, and he sat down near her, and he was not long there till he fell asleep.

When he awoke, Auburn Mary was gone. He thought he would go back to the house, and there he found the byre thatched with feathers. When the giant came home, he said: 'Have you thatched the byre, king's son?'

'I thatched it,' says he.

'Somebody thatched it,' says the giant.

'You did not thatch it,' says the king's son.

'Yes, yes!' says the giant. 'Now,' says the giant, 'there is a fir tree beside that loch down there, and there is a magpie's nest in its top. The eggs you will find in that nest I must have for my breakfast tomorrow. Not one must be burst or broken, and there are five in the nest.'

Early in the morning the king's son went to where the tree was, and that tree was not hard to hit upon. Its match was not in the whole wood. From the foot to the first branch was five hundred feet. The king's son was going all round the tree trying to find a foothold when she came who was always bringing help to him.

'You are losing the skin of your hands and feet.'

'Ach! I am,' said he. 'I am no sooner up than down.'

'This is no time for stopping,' says the giant's daughter. 'Now you must kill me, strip the flesh from my bones, take all those bones apart, and use them as steps for climbing the tree. When you are climbing the tree, they will stick to the bark as if they had grown out of it; but when you are coming down, and have put your foot on each one, they will drop into your hand when you touch them. Be sure and stand on each bone, leave none untouched; if you do, it will stay behind. Put all my flesh into this clean cloth by the side of the spring at the roots of the tree. When you come to the earth, arrange my bones together, put the flesh over them, sprinkle it with water from the spring, and I shall be alive before you. But don't forget a bone of me on the tree.'

'How could I kill you,' asked the king's son, 'after what you have done for me?'

'If you won't obey, you and I are done for,' said Auburn Mary. 'You must climb the tree, or we are lost; and to climb the tree you must do as I say.' The king's son obeyed. He killed Auburn Mary, cut the flesh from her body, and unjointed the bones, as she had told him.

As he went up, the king's son put the bones of Auburn Mary's body against the side of the tree, using them as steps, till he came under the nest and stood on the last bone.

Then he took the eggs, and coming down, put his foot on every bone, then took it with him, till he came to the last bone, which was so near the ground that he failed to touch it with his foot.

He now placed all the bones of Auburn Mary in order again at the side of the spring, put the flesh on them and sprinkled it with water from the spring.

She rose up before him, and said: 'Didn't I tell you not to leave a bone of my body without stepping on it? Now I am maimed for life! You left my little finger on the tree without touching it, and I have but nine fingers.'

The lad was mortified.

'Now,' says she, 'go home with the eggs quickly, and you will get me to marry tonight if you can know me. I and my two sisters will be arrayed in the same garments, and made like each other, but look at me when my father says, "Go to your wife, king's son," and you will see a hand without a little finger.'

He gave the eggs to the giant.

'Yes, yes!' says the giant, 'be making ready for your marriage.'

Then, indeed, there was a wedding, and it *was* a wedding! Giants and gentlemen, and the son of the King of the Green City was in the midst of them. They were married, and the dancing began, and that *was* a dance! The giant's house was shaking from top to bottom.

But bedtime came, and the giant said, 'It is time for you to go to rest, son of the King of Tethertown; choose your bride to take with you from amidst those.'

She put out the hand off which the little finger was, and he caught her by the hand.

'You have aimed well this time too; but there is no knowing but we may outwit you another way,' said the giant.

But to rest they went. 'Now,' says she, 'sleep not, or else you are a dead man. We must fly quick, quick, or for certain my father will kill you.'

Out they went, and on the blue-grey filly in the stable they mounted. 'Stop a while,' says she, 'and I will play a trick on the old hero.' She ran back, and cut an apple into nine shares, and she put two shares at the head of the bed, and two shares at the foot of the bed, and two shares at the door of the kitchen, and two shares at the big door, and one outside the house.

The giant awoke and called, 'Are you asleep?'

'Not yet,' said the apple that was at the head of the bed.

At the end of a while he called again.

'Not yet,' said the apple that was at the foot of the bed.

A while after this he called again: 'Are your asleep?'

'Not yet,' said the apple at the kitchen door.

The giant called again.

The apple that was at the big door answered.

'You are now going far from me,' says the giant.

'Not yet,' says the apple that was outside the house.

'You are flying,' says the giant. The giant jumped on his feet, and to the bed he went, but it was cold – empty.

'My own daughter's tricks are trying me,' said the giant. 'Here's after them,' says he.

At the mouth of day, the giant's daughter said that her father's breath was burning her back.

'Put your hand, quick,' said she, 'in the ear of the grey filly, and whatever you find in it, throw it behind us.'

'There is a twig of the sloe tree,' said he.

'Throw it behind us,' said she.

No sooner did he that, than there were twenty miles of blackthorn wood, so thick that scarce a weasel could go through it.

The giant came headlong and was soon head and neck in the thorns.

'My own daughter's tricks are here as before,' said the giant; 'but if I had my own big axe and wood knife here, I would not be long making a way through this.'

He went home for the big axe and the wood knife, and sure he was not long on his journey; and once he was behind the big axe, he was not long making a way through the blackthorn.

'I will leave the axe and the wood knife here till I return,' said he.

'If you leave 'em, leave 'em,' said a hooded crow that was in a tree, 'we'll steal 'em, steal 'em.'

'If you are going to do that,' says the giant, 'I must take them home.' He returned and left them at the house.

At the heat of day the giant's daughter felt her father's breath burning her back.

'Put your finger in the filly's ear, and throw behind whatever you find in it.'

He got a splinter of grey stone, and in a twinkling there were twenty miles, by breadth and height, of great grey rock behind them.

The giant came full pelt, but past the rock he could not go.

'The tricks of my own daughter are the hardest things that ever met me,' said the giant; 'but if I had my lever and my mighty mattock, I would not be long in making my way through this rock also.'

There was no help for it, but he must go home for them; once he had them, he was not long in making a road through the rock.

'I will leave the tools here, and I will return no more.'

'If you leave 'em, leave 'em,' says the hoodie, 'we will steal 'em, steal 'em.'

'Do that if you will; there is no time to go back.'

At the time of breaking the watch, the giant's daughter said that she felt her father's breath burning her back.

'Look in the filly's ear, king's son, or else we are lost.'

He did so, and it was a bladder of water that was in her ear this time. He threw it behind them and there was a freshwater loch, twenty miles in length and breadth, behind them.

The giant came on, and with the speed he had on him, he was in the middle of the loch before he could stop himself, and he went under, and he rose no more.

On the next day the young companions were come in sight of his father's house. 'Now,' said she, 'my father is drowned, and he won't trouble us any more; but before we go farther,' said she, 'go you to your father's house, and tell that you have me with you; but let neither man nor creature kiss you, for if you do, you will not remember that you have ever seen me.'

Every one he met gave him welcome and luck, and he charged his father and mother not to kiss him; but as mishap was to be, an old greyhound was indoors, and she knew him, and jumped up to his mouth, and after that he did not remember the giant's daughter.

She was sitting at the well's side as he left her, but the king's son was not coming. In the mouth of night she climbed up into a tree of oak that was beside the well, and she lay in the fork of that tree all night. A shoemaker had a house near the well, and about midday on the morrow, the shoemaker asked his wife to go for a drink for him out of the well. When the shoemaker's wife reached the well, she saw in the water the reflection of her that was in the tree, and thinking it was her own reflection – and she never thought till now that she was so handsome – she gave a cast to the dish that was in her hand, and it was broken on the ground, and she took herself to the house without vessel or water.

'Where is the water, wife?' said the shoemaker.

'You shambling, contemptible old carle, without grace, I have stayed too long your water and wood skivvy.'

'I think, wife, that you have gone crazy. Go you, daughter, quickly, and fetch a drink for your father.'

His daughter went, and in the same way so it happened to her. She never thought till now that she was so beautiful, and she took herself home.

'Where is my drink,' said her father.

'You homespun shoe-carle, do you think I am fit to be your skivvy?'

The poor shoemaker thought that they had both taken leave of their senses, and he went himself to the well. He saw the reflection of the maiden in the water, and he looked up into the tree, and there was the finest woman he ever saw.

'Your seat is precarious, but your face is fair,' said the shoemaker. 'Come down, for there is need of you for a short while at my house.'

The shoemaker realised that it was the sight of the maiden that had driven his womenfolk mad. The old man took her to his house, telling her that he had but a poor bothy, but that she should get a share of all that was in it.

One day a year later, the shoemaker had shoes ready, for on that very day the king's son was to be married. The shoemaker was going to the castle with the shoes of the young people, and the girl said to the shoemaker, 'I would like to get a sight of the king's son before he marries.'

'Come with me,' says the shoemaker. 'I am well acquainted with the servants at the castle, and you shall get a sight of the king's son and all the company.'

And when the gentles saw the pretty woman that was among them, they took her to the wedding-room, and they filled for her a glass of wine. When she was going to drink the wine, a flame went up out of the glass, and a golden pigeon and a silver pigeon sprang out of it. They were flying about when three grains of barley fell on the floor. The silver pigeon alighted, and ate them up.

Said the golden pigeon to him, 'If you remembered it was I that cleared the byre, you would not eat without giving me a share.'

Again there fell three other grains of barley, and the silver pigeon alighted, and ate them up as before.

'If you remembered it was I that thatched the byre, you would not eat without giving me a share,' said the golden pigeon.

Three other grains fell, and the silver pigeon alighted, and ate them up.

'If you remembered it was I that harried the magpie's nest, you would not eat without giving me a share,' said the golden pigeon; 'I lost my little finger bringing it down, and I am missing it still.'

The king's son heard these words, and he knew who it was that was before him.

'Well,' said the king's son to the guests at the feast, 'when I was a little younger than I am now, I lost the key of a casket that I had. I had a new key made, but after it was brought to me I found the old one. Now, I'll leave it to anyone here to tell me what I am to do. Which of the keys should I keep?'

'My advice to you,' said one of the guests, 'is to keep the old key, for it fits the lock better and you're more used to it.'

Then the king's son stood up and said: 'I thank you for wise advice and an honest word. This is my bride; she is the daughter of the giant and she saved my life at the risk of her own. I'll have her and no other woman.'

So the king's son married Auburn Mary and the wedding lasted long and all were happy. But all I got was butter on a live coal, porridge in a basket, and they sent me for water to the stream, and the paper shoes came to an end.

The Land of Green Mountains

Ronald Booe had rebelled against his chief but was defeated in battle. Then all his followers deserted him, and he found that he would have to flee from his native land. It chanced that he had heard tell of the wonderful Land of Green Mountains nigh to the world's end, a land in which there were great herds of wild animals, while fish could be caught in plenty round its shores and in its rivers. He made up his mind to go there and live happily and at ease. As he had no children, it was not difficult for him and his wife to depart in secret.

One fair morning, they launched a boat and set sail. Ronald's heart was made glad when he found himself far out on the wide blue sea. The broad grey sail swallowed the wind, and the creaking of the ropes was like sweet music in his ears. Ronald loved the shrill cry of the breeze that blew so steadily and tossed the sparkling brine-spray through the air in bright sunshine.

The whisperings and mutterings of the waves that went past the boat seemed to repeat over and over again the old song of the sea:

> Sweet to me, oh, sweet to me
> Is a life at sea, is a life at sea!

When the shore melted from sight Ronald's wife felt very lonely and sad. 'I wish,' she said, 'I could see the high brown hills of my own country.'

Said Ronald: 'There is no voyage so long that it will not come to an end. Speak not of brown hills, for we are voyaging to the wonderful Land of Green Mountains.

They sailed on and on for six days and six nights, and while the one slept the other sat at the helm. On the morning of the seventh day a storm arose. 'Alas,' the woman cried, 'the boat will be dashed to pieces and we shall perish!'

Said Ronald: 'Have no fear, Morag, daughter of Donald; am I not a skilled seaman? In storm and calm I am a king of the sea. My boat bounds over the waves like a spray-bright bird, and there is joy in my heart even in the midst of danger.'

The sky darkened, and the wind blew fiercer and louder, while the bounding waves gaped and bellowed like angry monsters seeking for their prey. Crouching low, the woman moaned and wept with fear, until at length Ronald called to her, saying: 'I see land ahead.'

His wife rose up and gazed towards the horizon. With glad eyes she saw before her the wonderful Land of Green Mountains. Thereupon she dried her tears and smiled.

It was not until late evening, however, that the boat drew nigh to the shore. Ronald tried to steer towards a safe landing-place, but, while yet some distance from it, the boat struck a hidden rock and began to sink. Ronald grasped an oar with one hand and his wife with the other, and leapt into the raging sea. He was a strong swimmer, and after a hard struggle, he managed to reach shallow water, and then wade ashore.

There was a cave near where he landed, and he carried his wife to it. Then he gathered dry sticks and withered grass and lit a fire by using flint and steel. Soon the flames were leaping high, and Ronald and his wife were able to dry their clothes. Then they lay down to sleep, and, although the sea roared all night long, they slept soundly.

Next morning Ronald found on the beach a keg of salt herring, a keg of meal and a pot which had been washed ashore from the boat. His wife cooked the herring and baked oatmeal cakes and after the two had eaten of these they felt quite happy.

A day or two went past, and then their store of food ran short. Ronald had no weapons with which to hunt game, and no hooks with which to catch fish, so he said to his wife: 'I will go inland and explore this strange Land of Green Mountains. Do not be anxious or afraid.'

'You may lose your way,' his wife said.

'There is no fear of that,' Ronald answered. 'I'll put marks on the trees as I go through forests, and set up stones on the plains I cross.'

Early next morning Ronald set out on his journey. As he passed through the wood he chipped the bark off trees, and on the plain he set up stones. After leaving the wood, he saw a high green mountain and walked towards it. 'When I reach the top,' he said to himself, 'I shall get a better view of this strange land.'

The sun was beginning to set when he found himself on the crest of the green mountain. He looked round about and could see many other green mountains but there was no sign of human beings, and his heart grew very sad. Although he was very tired and very hungry he did not despair however. 'I'll go down the other side of this green mountain,' he said to himself, 'and perhaps I shall have better luck.'

He began to descend in the dusk, and before long he saw a light. It came from a little house among trees on the lower slope of the mountain, and he walked towards it. Darkness was coming on when he reached the house, and as the door was open-he walked in.

To his surprise he found no one inside. A bright fire was burning, and near it stood a table and two chairs. The table was covered with a green cloth, and on it were two dishes of food.

'I am very hungry,' said Ronald, 'and must eat. I hope I shall not be found fault with for helping myself.'

He sat down and ate all the food that was on one of the plates. Then he felt happy and contented. Suddenly he heard the sound of footsteps, and, looking up, he saw an old grey-bearded man entering the house.

'Well, stranger,' this man said, 'who are you, and where have you come from?'

Ronald said: 'My boat was wrecked on the shore. I have been wandering about all day searching for food, and found naught until I came here. I hope you are not angry with me for eating without leave.'

Said the old man: 'You are welcome to my food. You can stay here tonight. I live all alone, and always keep enough food to give to any visitor who may come hither as you have done.'

Ronald thanked the old man for his kindness, and said: 'I shall tell you all about myself in the hope that you may help me with good advice.'

The old man sat down, and as he ate his meal, Ronald told the story of his life. When he had finished the other asked: 'Have you any children?'

'No,' Ronald said, 'I have no children.'

'That is a pity,' the old man sighed.

Next morning the old man wakened Ronald and said: 'Breakfast is ready. It is time you were on your way back to the cave, for your wife is anxious and afraid.'

When Ronald had eaten an excellent breakfast he said: 'I wish I had food to carry to my wife.'

Said the old man: 'What will you give me for this green tablecloth? When you want food all you have to do is to shake it three times and lay it down. As soon as you lay it down you will get all the food you need.'

Ronald was surprised to hear this. He longed for the green cloth, but, sighing, replied: 'Alas! I am very poor, having lost everything I possessed. I am not able to offer you anything for the green cloth.'

Said the old man: 'Will you promise to give me your eldest son for it?'

Having no son, Ronald promised readily.

'Very well,' the old man said; 'come back here in seven years, and bring your son with you.'

Ronald took the cloth, and bade goodbye to the old man. He climbed the green mountain and went down the other side of it. Then he crossed the plain, past the stones he had set up, and walked through the wood, guiding himself by the marks he had made on the trees. He had no difficulty in finding his way. The sun was beginning to set as he reached the shore and hastened towards the cave; there he found his wife sitting beside the fire moaning and weeping. She feared that her husband had been devoured by wild beasts.

'Here I am, Morag, daughter of Donald,' he said as he entered the cave.

His wife rose to her feet and kissed him joyfully.

'I have brought food for you,' said Ronald.

As he spoke he shook the green cloth three times, and laid it on the floor of the cave beside the fire. As soon as he did that, two dishes of hot, steaming food appeared before their wondering eyes.

They sat down and ate the food. 'Where did you find this wonderful green cloth?' asked Morag.

'It was given to me by an old grey-bearded man,' Ronald told her. 'Are we not in luck now? We shall never want for food as long as we live.'

Several days went past. Then Ronald and his wife thought they would go inland and explore the country. They felt lonely, and wished to find out where the people who inhabited it had their dwellings.

For six days they travelled inland, and on the morning of the seventh day they reached a village. The people were kindly and hospitable and invited them to stay. Ronald thought he might as well do so, and next morning began to build a house. He got every assistance from the villagers, and soon had a home of his own among his newly found friends. Before the year was out a baby boy was born, and Ronald and Morag's hearts were filled with joy. They called the baby Ian.

Years went past, and Ian grew up to be a handsome boy with curly golden hair, sea-grey eyes and red cheeks. Everyone in the village loved him, and he was very dear to his father and mother.

Ronald Booe remembered the promise he had made to the grey old man, but he never told Morag his wife about it until the seventh year was nearly at an end. Then one day he said: 'On the morrow I must go to the mountain house with Ian, because I promised the grey old man, when I was given the green cloth, to do so.'

Morag cried: 'Alas! alas!' and began to moan and weep. 'It was foolish and wicked of you,' she said, 'to make such a promise.'

Said Ronald: 'What can I do? My heart bleeds to part with our boy, but I must go, and he must go with me.'

Next morning he bade his wife goodbye, and she kissed Ian and wept over him. Father and son then set out on their journey, and in time they reached the dwelling of the grey old man, who spoke, saying: 'So you have come, as you said you would.'

'Yes,' Ronald answered sadly, 'I have come.'

'Do you find it hard to part with your boy?'

'Indeed, I do. My wife is heartbroken.'

Said the grey old man: 'You can take him home again if you promise me to come back when another seven years have gone past.'

Ronald thanked the grey old man, and, having promised, he returned home with Ian. His wife welcomed him with smiling face and bright eyes, and kissed her child, saying: 'If you had stayed away from me I should have died with sorrow.'

Ian grew and grew, and when he was twelve years old he was nearly as tall as his father and nearly as strong. He had great skill as a hunter and as a fisherman, and could work in the fields like a man.

When the second term of seven years was drawing to a close his father grew sadder and sadder, and one day he said to his wife: 'On the morrow I must go to the mountain house with Ian.'

'Alas! alas!' cried his wife; 'I cannot live without him.'

Said Ronald: 'You cannot have your son beside you always. To every youth comes the day when he must leave his parents.'

'Wait for a few years,' pleaded Morag. 'I have not long to live, and I would fain have him beside me until I die.'

Said Ronald: 'It cannot be as you wish.'

'Perhaps,' his wife sighed, 'the grey old man will send him back for another seven years.'

Said Ronald: 'He may, and he may not.'

Next morning father and son set out on foot towards the mountain house, and when they reached it the grey old man said: 'So you have come as you promised. It is well. Do you find it hard to part with the lad?'

Said Ronald: 'Indeed, I do. I find it harder now than I did seven years ago.'

'Has the boy been well taught?' asked the old man.

Said Ronald: 'He can fish, he can shoot, he can work in the fields. I have trained him myself.'

'You have trained his body, but I will train his mind,' the grey old man told Ronald. 'Knowledge is better than strength. You will be proud of Ian some day.'

The boy's father was stricken with sorrow when he found that the old man intended to keep Ian. He returned home alone. Morag wept bitterly when he entered the house, and all Ronald could say to comfort her was: 'The grey old man promised that we should be proud of Ian some day.'

Morag refused to be comforted, for she knew well that many years must pass before she would see her son again.

The grey old man was like a father to Ian. He spent six years in teaching the lad, and when the seventh came, he said: 'Now you have passed your twentieth year. You are strong, and you are well educated. It is time you began to work for yourself. Before you go to look for a situation, however, I shall take you on a long journey, so that you may meet friends who may help you in time of need. It is better to make friends than to make enemies.'

Said Ian: 'I am ready to do as you advise me.

'Well spoken!' the old man exclaimed. 'You have learned to obey. He who learns how to obey will rise to command. Come with me to the mountain-top. Behind the door hangs a silver bridle. Take it with you.'

Ian took the bridle, and followed the old man. On the mountain-top the old man said: 'If you will shake the bridle over me I shall become a grey horse. You can then jump on my back, and we shall go forward quickly.'

Ian shook the bridle as he was asked to do. The man changed at once into a grey horse, and as soon as Ian mounted, the horse galloped away at a rapid pace. Over hill and over moor went the horse. Nor did it pause until seven hours had passed. Then Ian heard the old man's voice, saying: 'Dismount and shake the bridle over me.'

Ian did as he was ordered, and the grey man at once returned to his own form again. He spoke, saying: 'Go and gather red moss, and fill your water-stoup at the well below yonder red rock.'

Ian gathered the moss, and filled his water-stoup, and returned to the old man, who said: 'Go now to the cave which opens behind the waterfall. Inside it you will find a wounded giant. Dress his wounds with the red moss, and give him three draughts from your water-stoup.'

Ian climbed down the side of the waterfall over slippery rocks, and when he entered the cave he saw the wounded giant. He put red moss on the giant's wounds, and bound them round with cords made of dried reeds. Then he gave the sufferer three draughts from his water-stoup. As soon as he did that, the giant sat up and cried out: 'I am feeling better now. Ere long I shall be well again.'

'Remember me and be my friend,' said Ian.

'Your friend I shall be,' the giant answered.

Ian then returned to the old man, who asked him at once: 'Have you done as I ordered you to do?'

'Yes,' Ian answered.

'It is well,' the old man told him. 'Shake your bridle over me again, and then leap on my back, so that we may go forward quickly.'

The old grey man in horse shape went galloping on and on, until a lonely shore was reached. Once more he called: 'Shake the bridle over me,' and when Ian had done so, the man appeared in his own form and said: 'Go down the ebb until you reach a flat brown stone. Behind that stone lies the King of Fish. Lift him up and put him into the sea, for this is a day of misfortune for him, and he is in need of help.'

Ian ran down the long dreary sands until he reached the flat brown stone. He found the fish lying gasping and twitching and helpless. Lifting him up, Ian put him into the sea and, as he did so, cried out: 'Remember me and be my friend.'

The fish answered him, saying: 'Your friend I shall be,' and then vanished.

Ian returned to the old man and once again changed him into a horse. They went onward together, and ere long reached a bronze castle on a lonely headland overlooking the sea. It was now late evening. The old man said: 'Enter the bronze castle, in which dwells a fair lady. You will see rooms full of silver and gold and flashing gems. Look on everything but touch nothing.'

Ian went through the castle. He wondered to see so much treasure, but although it seemed to be unprotected, for he did not see the fair lady even, he never touched a single piece of gold or silver. When, however, he was leaving the castle, his eyes fell on a heap of goose feathers. He pulled out a single feather and put it in his pocket, but he did not tell the old man that he had done so.

He mounted again and they returned to the grey old man's hut in the gathering darkness, and there the two rested for the night.

Next morning the old man became a horse again, and carried Ian to the capital of the country – a large and beautiful city in the midst of which the king's castle stood on a high rock.

Outside the city wall Ian shook the bridle over the horse, and the old man stood before him and said: 'Here we must part. You will go towards the castle, and ask for a situation. The king is in need of a scribe. If he offers to employ you, accept his offer.'

Ian then bade goodbye to the old man, who said: 'If ever you are in trouble, think of me and I shall come to you.'

They parted at the western gate of the city, and Ian walked towards the castle. He told the guards that he was looking for a situation, and after a time they took him before the chief scribe, who said: 'I am in need of an assistant. Will you enter the king's service?'

Ian accepted the offer, and next morning began to work. He thought of the goose feather he had taken from the bronze castle, and made a pen of it. When he began to use it, he found that it wrote beautifully, and he was delighted at his own fine pen-manship.

The head scribe was greatly surprised at the skill shown by the young man, and grew jealous of him. After a few days he asked Ian for the loan of his pen, and when he tried it he discovered that he could write just as well as Ian.

'This is a magic pen,' he said to himself. He then went before the king and told him about it, and the king tried the pen also. 'Bring this young scribe before me,' he commanded.

Ian was called for, and when he stood before the king he was asked: 'Where did you get this magic pen?'

Said Ian: 'I found it in a bronze castle.'

The king gazed at him in silence for a moment, and then spoke, saying: 'There is a beautiful lady in that castle, and she cannot leave it. Bring her here, for I wish her for my bride.'

Said Ian: 'Alas, sire! I am not able to obey your command. I do not know where the castle is, for I was taken to it at late evening, and returned home in the darkness.'

'If you fail to do as I command,' said the king, 'you shall be put to death.'

Ian went to his bedroom, and there wept tears of sorrow. He knew well that this trouble which had befallen him was due to his having disobeyed the old man, who had warned him not to touch anything he saw in the bronze castle. After a time he said aloud: 'I wish the grey old man were here now.' He heard a noise behind him, and, turning round, he saw the grey old man, who spoke, saying: 'What ails you, Ian?'

'Alas!' cried Ian, 'I have done wrong.' Then he told the old man how he had taken a goose feather from the bronze castle and made a quill of it, and that the king had discovered his secret, and ordered him to fetch the captive lady from the castle to be the king's bride.

'You should not have touched the feather,' the old man said. 'It is as wicked to steal a small thing as a great thing. Theft is dishonourable, even the theft of trifles. I placed my trust in you, and you promised to obey me. Because you have failed in that trust and done this thing, you now find yourself in trouble.'

'Alas!' Ian cried, 'I know I have done wrong, and am sorry for it.'

'Let this be a lesson to you,' the old man said. 'Because you are sorry for your wrongdoing, I shall help you once again. Let us go outside. I have the silver bridle with me. We shall visit the bronze castle once again.'

Ian walked with the old man to a solitary place outside the city wall. There he shook the bridle, and his friend became a grey horse. He mounted and rode away swiftly towards the seaside. Then he shook the bridle again, and his friend appeared in human form and spoke to him, saying: 'I have a magic rod. Take it and strike me with it. When you do so I shall become a ship. Enter the ship, and it will sail to the harbour below the bronze castle. Cast anchor there and wait until the lady looks out of a window and asks you whence you have come. Say: "I have come from a distant land." Then she will ask: "What cargo have you on board?" Say to her: "I have a cargo of fine silk." She will ask you to enter the castle with samples of the silk, but you will say: "Would it not be better if you came on board and examined the rolls of silk?" She will answer: "Very well," and come on board your vessel. Take her down to the cabin, and spread out the rolls of silk you will find lying there.'

Ian seized the magic rod and struck the grey old man, who at once became a large and noble ship, afloat beside the rock. Ian got on board the ship, cast off from the rock, and set sail. It had a crew of little men clad in green, with red peaked caps on their heads. The skipper who steered the vessel had a long grey beard and sharp beady eyes. He never spoke a word, but gave orders to the crew by making signs.

The ship sailed swiftly towards the bronze castle on the lonely headland. When the anchor was dropped in the little harbour, Ian walked up and down the deck until an upper window in the castle opened, and the beautiful lady looked out and spoke to him, saying: 'Where have you come from, my merry sailor man?'

'From a distant land,' Ian answered.

'What cargo have you on board?'

'A cargo of fine silk.'

'Come up into the castle and bring with you samples of your silk, and I perchance may buy a few rolls from you.'

Said Ian: 'I have so many kinds of silk that I cannot carry samples to you. Would it not be better if you came on board and examined the cargo, fair lady?'

Very well,' the lady answered, 'I shall do as you suggest.'

She came down from the castle and came on board the ship. Ian led her to the cabin, where he spread out before her the rolls of fine silk that he found there.

She examined them all carefully. Then, hearing the splashing of waves against the sides of the ship, she ran up the cabin ladder to the deck, and discovered that the vessel was far away from the bronze castle.

'Alas!' she cried, 'what is the meaning of this?'

Said Ian: 'The king, my master, has ordered me to bring you before him. It is his wish that you should become his queen.'

'It is your duty to obey your master, and I do not blame you,' the lady said. 'But I do not wish to be the king's bride. I should much rather have stayed yet a while in my bronze castle.'

As she spoke, she took a bundle of keys from her waist-belt and flung it into the sea.

'There go my keys!' she told Ian. 'No one else can now enter the bronze castle.'

The ship sailed back to the place from which it had started, and drew up alongside the rock, and Ian and the lady went ashore. Then Ian waved the magic rod three times. When he did so the ship vanished, and the grey old man appeared by his side and spoke, saying: 'Shake the silver bridle over me, so that I may become a horse. Mount me then, and take the lady with you.'

Ian shook the bridle, and his friend became a grey horse. He mounted the horse, and the lady mounted behind him. They rode away very swiftly, and when night was coming on they reached the city. Ian shook the bridle again, and the old man appeared by his side, and they bade one another goodbye. Ian led the lady to the castle and brought her to the king. His majesty thanked him for his service, and bade the lady welcome. He called for maidservants to attend to her, and she was taken to her room.

Next morning the king had the lady brought before him, and said: 'Most fair one, be my bride.'

Said the lady: 'I shall not be your bride until my bronze castle is brought here and placed beside yours.'

'No one can do that but Ian,' the king said. Then he called to a servant, saying: 'Bring Ian before me.'

Ian had returned to his place in the room of the chief scribe, and was busy at his work when he was ordered to appear before his majesty.

He obeyed the summons, and the king said to him: 'You must bring the bronze castle from the lonely headland, and have it placed beside my castle.'

'Alas!' Ian cried, 'I cannot do that.'

Said the king: 'If you fail to carry out my command you shall be put to death.'

Ian went to his room, and paced it up and down for a time, lamenting his fate. Then he cried out: 'I wish the grey old man were here.'

No sooner had he wished that wish than the grey old man appeared in the room and spoke to him, saying: 'What is wrong now, Ian?'

Said Ian: 'The king has set me an impossible task. He wants me to have the bronze castle carried here and placed beside his own castle.'

'Come with me,' the old man said.

Together they went outside the city wall. Ian shook the bridle over his friend, who at once became a grey horse. He mounted the horse, and rode away until he reached the waterfall behind which was the giant's cave. Then he shook the bridle again, and the old man appeared beside him and said: 'Enter the cave and speak to the giant whose wounds you helped to heal. Tell him you are in need of his aid, and ask him to carry away the bronze castle and place it beside the castle of your king.'

Ian went down the slippery rocks and entered the cave. He found the giant lying asleep on the floor, and walked towards him. As soon as he touched him the giant sat up and asked: 'Who are you, and what brings you here, little fellow?'

Ian was at first too terrified to speak, for the giant scowled at him. At length he said: 'I am he who dressed your wounds with red moss, and gave you three draughts of the healing water. I am now in need of your help.'

Said the giant: 'I remember you. I was in great pain, and you gave me healing. What do you wish me to do? Speak and I shall obey, even should you ask me to remove a mountain from its place and cast it into the sea.'

Ian laughed aloud, and the giant laughed also, but the giant's laugh was terrible to hear, for it sounded like thunder.

Ian then told the giant that the king wished to have the bronze castle carried from the lonely headland and placed beside his own castle on the rock in the midst of his capital.

Said the giant: 'The work shall be done tonight. I shall call all my strong men together. Begone! or it may not go well with you.'

Ian thanked the giant, and returned to the grey old man, who said: 'We must make haste. There is no time to be lost.'

As the grey horse, the old man travelled again swiftly until he reached the capital. Then he bade Ian goodbye.

That night as Ian lay in his bed a great thunderstorm arose and raged furiously. He could not sleep, and lay trembling with fear, for it seemed as if the whole world would be set on fire by the flashes of lightning. When the thunderstorm was at its height there came an earthquake. The rock beneath the castle trembled, and the castle swayed like a ship at sea. Ian was terrified, and he heard the shrieks of those who were even more afraid than he was. At length the storm died down, and he slept.

Next morning when Ian looked through the window of his room he saw the bronze castle beside the king's castle. Then he knew that the thunderstorm had been caused by the giants, and that the earth shook when they set down the castle upon the rock.

The king was greatly pleased, and spoke to the fair lady, saying: 'Your bronze castle has been brought hither. Now you will be my queen.'

Said the lady: 'I cannot marry until I am given the bundle of keys I threw into the sea. The castle cannot be opened without the keys.'

'Ian shall find the keys,' the king told her. Then he called for Ian and said to him: 'You must find the bundle of keys which this fair lady threw into the sea.'

'Alas!' Ian moaned, 'you set me a task I cannot fulfil.'

'If you do not bring the keys to me,' said the king, 'you shall be put to death.'

Ian turned away and went to his room. He felt sure that his end was near at hand because it did not seem possible that the keys could be found. 'I wish the old grey man were here,' he cried out.

The old grey man appeared in the room and asked softly: 'What does the king ask for now, Ian?'

Said Ian: 'He has ordered me to find the bundle of keys which the fair lady threw into the sea.'

'Come with me,' the old man said; 'we have a long journey ahead.'

Ian rode again on the grey horse until he reached the shore where he had found the King of Fish. He then shook the silver bridle and the old man appeared beside him. 'Go out on the ebb,' he advised Ian, 'and call for the King of Fish. When he comes, ask him to search for the keys and bring them to you.'

Ian walked down the sands and called for the King of Fish. Three times he called before the fish appeared. Then it rose and asked: 'Who are you that you should call upon me?'

Said Ian: 'I am the one who found you lying behind the flat brown stone on a day of misfortune when you were in need of help. I lifted you up and put you into the sea, and you promised to remember me and be my friend.'

'You speak truly,' the fish said. 'What is your wish? I am ready to grant it.'

Said Ian: 'Search for the keys which the fair lady of the bronze castle threw into the sea when I took her away in my ship. When you have found the keys, bring them to me.'

The fish vanished and returned soon afterwards.

'Have you found the keys?' he asked.

'I have,' answered the fish.

'Give them to me.'

'I will if you promise one thing.'

'What is that?'

'Promise that you will not call for me again.'

'I promise,' said Ian.

The fish then gave him the keys and vanished at once.

Ian was overjoyed. He ran up the beach towards the old man, who asked: 'Have you got the keys?'

'Oh, yes!'

'It is well. Shake the bridle over me and mount.'

Ian did so, and rode back to the capital on the back of the grey horse. Having bidden goodbye to his friend, he hastened before the king and handed the keys of the bronze castle to him.

'It is good for you that you found the keys,' the king said. 'Had you come back without them you would have been put to death.'

Ian bowed and turned away, hoping his troubles were at an end.

The king sent for the lady of the castle and said: 'Here are the keys of the bronze castle which my servant found for me.'

'He is a brave and noble lad,' the lady cried out.

'Now you will marry me,' said the king.

'I cannot promise to marry you, sire, until I get a stoup of water from the Healing Well.'

Said the king: 'I shall order Ian to bring the water without delay.'

He sent for Ian, and spoke to him harshly, saying: 'Bring hither without delay a stoup of water from the Healing Well.'

'Where is that well, your majesty?' asked Ian.

'I know not,' was the answer. 'But this I know: if you do not bring the water you will be put to death.'

Ian went to his room and wished for the grey old man, who appeared at once and asked: 'What ails you now, my poor lad?'

'Alas!' Ian exclaimed, 'the king has asked for a stoup of water from the Healing Well, but he does not know where it is.'

'We had better make haste and search for it.'

Away went Ian again on the back of the grey horse. All day long he rode over hill and dale, through forests and across bogs, over rivers and through lochs, until at length a lonely glen was reached.

'Shake the bridle,' called the horse.

Ian shook it, and the old man stood beside him and said: 'Strike me with the magic wand and I shall fall down dead.'

'I cannot do that,' Ian answered at once.

'You must do it. When I am dead three ravens will fly hither. Speak to them saying: "I shall kill you with my wand unless you take me to the Healing Well." They will then show you where it is. When you find it, fill two stoups and bring them to this spot. Sprinkle a few drops of the water in my mouth, in my eyes and in my ears. When you do so, I shall come to life again.'

Ian struck the old man with the magic wand and he fell down dead. He lay so still that the young man's heart was filled with sorrow, and he began to weep. 'Would that the ravens were here!' he cried out, as he looked round about. To his dismay he saw no sign of the ravens coming.